Contents

Level 3

3rd Edition

BTEC NATIONAL HEALTH AND SOCIAL CARE

Elizabeth ... and
Alison ...

Orders: please contact Bookpoint Ltd, 130 Park Drive, Milton Park, Abingdon, Oxon OX14 4SE. Telephone: (44) 01235 827720. Fax: (44) 01235 400454. Email education@bookpoint.co.uk Lines are open from 9 a.m. to 5 p.m., Monday to Saturday, with a 24-hour message answering service. You can also order through our website: www.hoddereducation.co.uk

ISBN: 978 1 471 87859 6

© Elizabeth Rasheed, Linda Wyatt and Alison Hetherington 2016

First edition published 2007

Second edition published 2010

This edition first published in 2016 by

Hodder Education,

An Hachette UK Company

Carmelite House

50 Victoria Embankment

London EC4Y 0DZ

www.hoddereducation.co.uk

Impression number 10 9 8 7 6 5 4 3 2 1

Year   2020 2019 2018 2017 2016

Cover photo © moodboard/Getty Images

Typeset in India

Printed in Slovenia

A catalogue record for this title is available from the British Library.

Acknowledgements

Every effort has been made to trace and acknowledge ownership of copyright. The publishers will be glad to make suitable arrangements with any copyright holders whom it has not been possible to contact. The authors and publishers would like to thank the following for permission to reproduce copyright illustrative material:

Fig 1.2a © TEMISTOCLE LUCARELLI – Fotolia; Fig 1.2b © Adam Borkowski – Fotolia; Fig 1.9 © deanm1974 – Fotolia; Fig 2.1 © Cathy Yeulet – 123rf; Fig 2.6 © JPC-PROD – Fotolia; Fig 3.1 © PHOTOTAKE Inc./Alamy; Fig 3.2 © PROF. P. MOTTA/DEPT. OF ANATOMY/UNIVERSITY 'LA SAPIENZA', ROME/SCIENCE PHOTO LIBRARY; Fig 3.4 © CNRI/SCIENCE PHOTO LIBRARY; Fig 3.7 © The Science Picture Company/Alamy Stock Photo; Fig 3.19 © Emine Donmaz/Getty Images; Fig 3.35 © Science Photo Library/Getty Images; Fig 5.5 © Vladimir Mucibabic – Fotolia Fig 7.2 © Alexander Raths – Fotolia; Fig 8.1 © George Whitelaw, Daily Herald (image courtesy of the British Cartoon Archive); Fig 9.1 © BSIP/Getty Images; Fig 9.2 © Dr. Kenneth Greer/Getty Images; Fig 9.3 © Scott Camazine/Alamy Stock Photo; Fig 9.4 © Dr. Kenneth Greer – Getty Images; Fig 9.5 © Peter Dazeley/Getty Images; Fig 9.6 © DR P. MARAZZI/SCIENCE PHOTO LIBRARY; Fig 9.7 © SUE FORD/SCIENCE PHOTO LIBRARY; Fig 12.1 © digitalskillet/Getty Images; Fig 14.3a © BSIP SA/Alamy Stock Photo; Fig 14.3b © Bubbles Photolibrary/Alamy Stock Photo; Fig 14.3c © Art Directors & TRIP/Alamy Stock Photo; Fig 14.4 © auremar – Fotolia; Fig 14.5 © Sven Bähren – Fotolia; Fig 14.6 © Phanie/Alamy Stock Photo, inset © microimages – Fotolia; Fig 14.8 © Jean-Marie Guyon – 123RF; Fig 17.2 © stocksolutions – Fotolia; Fig 19.3a © BIOPHOTO ASSOCIATES/SCIENCE PHOTO LIBRARY; Fig 17.3 © University College Cork; Fig 19.3b © US NATIONAL LIBRARY OF MEDICINE/SCIENCE PHOTO LIBRARY; Fig 19.6 © meteo021 – iStock/Thinkstock via Getty Images; Fig 19.9b and 19.9c © GASTROLAB/SCIENCE PHOTO LIBRARY; Fig 19.11 © Susan Chiang/Getty Images.

Crown copyright material is reproduced under Open Government Licence v3.0.

Walkthrough

This book contains all the units you need to master the skills and knowledge for the new BTEC National for Health and Social Care.

Key features of the book

About this unit

Health and Social Care Practitioners work with people of all ages. This unit explores physical, intellectual, emotional and social development across the human lifespan. You will explore patterns of growth and development and key factors that can affect health and development.

Learning aims

The aims of this unit are to understand:

A Human growth and development through the life stages.

B Factors affecting human growth and

About this unit: an introduction to the unit briefly explaining the topic, its importance and what will be covered in the unit. Including the learning aims and the ways in which you'll be assessed.

How will I be graded?

The table below shows the grading criteria for this unit. To achieve a pass grade you must meet all the P criteria; to achieve a merit grade you must achieve all the P and all the M criteria; to achieve a distinction grade you must achieve all the P, M and D criteria.

Pass	Merit	Distinction
Learners are able to explore familiar applications of physical, intellectual, emotional		Learners are able to articulate arguments and views concisely and professionally to justify

How will I be graded?: Feature showing the criteria that you need to achieve a Pass, Merit, Distinction.

Exam Practice

All questions relate to one family.

Benjamin is married to Andrea. Andrea was recently in a serious car crash that left her paralysed. They have two children. Anthony who is 15 years and Beth who is five years old. Benjamin has recently been promoted at work.

Anthony is friends with Daniel who has cystic fibrosis.

6 Outline what cystic fibrosis is and the impact upon Daniel's development. (4 marks)

7 Identify two health and social care professionals who can help Daniel and his family. (2 marks)

Exam practice: Enhance your understanding of the assessment criteria and test yourself with these exam-style questions.

Activity

Create a time line of the life stages to show the physical changes throughout. Illustrate with pictures to help memorise the main developments.

Activity: These appear throughout the chapter to support the learning of topics and to link them to the assessment criteria.

Distinction activity

Critically evaluate theories of language development. How useful are these for health and social care workers?

Distinction activity: Activity which is directly linked to Distinction criteria and which will help you to prepare for assignments.

Key terms

Anatomy The study of the body's structure and how each part relates to others.

Physiology The study of how the body works and functions within the organs and alongside other structures.

Key terms: To clarify any difficult terms, or to highlight any important terms relevant to the study of the unit. All key terms are listed in the glossary.

Check your understanding

1 Identify and describe four conditions that may occur in older age.
2 Identify two differences between the activity and disengagement theory.

Check your understanding: Test your knowledge of each unit.

Case scenario

Life events and their effect on health

Ahmed, who is 48 years old, has been married for 10 years and has a seven-year-old child. He was recently involved in a car accident in which his wife was killed. He was injured and

Case scenario and Think about it: See how concepts are applied in settings with real life scenarios and reflect on what you've learned.

Think about it

There is a lot of discussion in the news and health about the impact of an ageing population. Words such as demand, burden and challenge are often used.

What effect do you think words like this may

Further reading

ONS (2011) *Earning by Qualification, 2011.* Office for National Statistics, London

Useful websites

RNIB: www.rnib.org.uk/knowledge-and-research-hub/key-information-and-statistics

Macular degeneration: www.nhs.uk/conditions/macular-degeneration/Pages/Introduction.aspx

Further reading and Useful websites: Includes references to websites, books and other various sources for further reading and research

1 Human lifespan development

About this unit

Health and Social Care Practitioners work with people of all ages. This unit explores physical, intellectual, emotional and social development across the human lifespan. You will explore patterns of growth and development and key factors that can affect health and development. These factors could be inherited or the influence of the environment, social or financial factors. Throughout our lives, we experience a number of life events, these can be predictable or unpredictable, but both may have an impact on individuals. Theories exist to assist practitioners in understanding behaviour and some will be examined. Finally, this unit will explore the physical and psychological factors of the ageing process and the impact of confidence and self-esteem.

Learning aims

The aims of this unit are to understand:

A Human growth and development through the life stages.

B Factors affecting human growth and development.

C Effects of ageing.

How will I be assessed?

You will be assessed by a 90 minute externally set examination consisting of short- and long-answer questions. You will need to explore and relate to contexts and data presented, and show your understanding of growth and development through the human lifespan, the factors that affect them and the effects of ageing.

How will I be graded?

The table below shows the grading criteria for this unit. To achieve a pass grade you must meet all the P criteria; to achieve a merit grade you must achieve all the P and all the M criteria; to achieve a distinction grade you must achieve all the P, M and D criteria.

Pass	Merit	Distinction
Learners are able to explore familiar applications of physical, intellectual, emotional and social development across the human lifespan, factors affecting human growth and development and effects of ageing. Learners can use research with relevance to given situations related to human development theories/models and factors affecting human growth and development. They can select and organise information using appropriate knowledge and concepts about theories/models in relation to human development, factors affecting human growth and development and effects of ageing.		Learners are able to articulate arguments and views concisely and professionally to justify and evaluate physical, intellectual, emotional and social development across the human lifespan, factors affecting human growth and development and effects of ageing. They are able to use detailed analysis and research to make recommendations related to human development theories/models and factors affecting human growth and development. They can draw on knowledge and understanding of theories/models in relation to human development, factors affecting human growth and development and effects of ageing.

A Human growth and development through the life stages

Throughout our lives we continue to grow and develop. This can be physically, intellectually, emotional or socially. The life stages are shown in Figure 1.1 and explained below.

Physical development across the life stages

Growth and development are different concepts

Growth is measured as an increase in height or weight. The amount of growth varies between the different life stages, with rapid growth in infancy, early childhood and puberty. Growth also varies proportionately, for example in infancy, the head is proportionately larger and the legs shorter. This means that not all body parts grow by the same amount, or at the same time. Gross motor skills and fine motor skills develop. Gross motor skills are those that use the big muscle groups and fine motor skills are those that use smaller muscle groups. Growth is measured using height and weight.

Infancy (0–2 years)

When a child is born, it will have innate reflexes such as the grasp reflex or sucking reflex. In infancy (0–2 years), the child develops gross and fine motor skills. Table 1.1 illustrates some of the skills and milestones an infant will encounter.

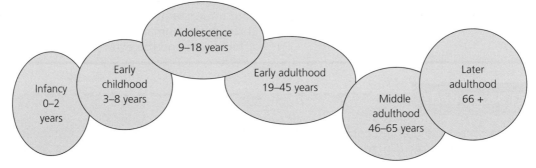

Figure 1.1 Life stages

Age	Gross motor skills developed	Fine motor skills developed
1 month	Can lift head slightly	Can grasp an adult's finger
3 months	Can lift head and chest	Can hold a rattle for a brief time
6 months	Has a straight back when held sitting or standing	Will reach and grab when a small toy is offered
9 months	Can maintain sitting position Stands, holding onto furniture Attempt to crawl	Can let go of objects or hand them to someone.
12 months	Can sit from lying down Stands alone for a few minutes 'Cruises' along using furniture for support	Picks up small objects with pincer movement Points with finger Builds a few bricks
1–2 years	Walking forwards (by about 13 months) Kneels without support By 18 months, can walk steadily and stop Squats to pick up a toy Walks up and down steps	Can put small objects into a bottle Points to known objects Uses a spoon to feed themselves

Table 1.1

Figure 1.2 Development of fine motor skills in infancy: from grasping a finger to holding a spoon

Development follows an orderly sequence and is the acquisition of skills and abilities. Milestones are significant stages in development. These are different in each age group, and when children reach these milestones will vary. However, it provides a general description and guide as to what a child should be able to do at each age.

Early childhood (3–8 years)
Within early childhood, gross and fine motor skills continue to develop. Many activities can help children develop these skills.

Age	Gross motor skills developed	Fine motor skills developed
3–4 years	Walk backwards and sideways. Ride a tricycle. Climb stairs with one foot on each step. Kick a ball.	Control a pencil using thumb and first two fingers. Can cut paper with scissors. Able to do buttons (and unbutton) on clothing, and turn pages of a paper book.
4–5 years	Can balance and walk along a line. Stand, walk and run on tiptoe. May be able to hop on one foot.	Hold and use pen in adult fashion. Thread beads on a lace.
5–6 years	Hop forward on each foot separately. Good co-ordination. Increased agility. Skip.	Good pencil control. Use a knife and fork competently. Learn cursive and joined up writing
6–7	Can confidently jump. Gaining in agility and running. Hop with balance. Ride a two-wheeled bike.	Write simple stories. Write their first and last names.
7–8	Hop on either leg. Walk on thin line. Control speed running and can swerve.	Competent in writing skills. Use a large needle to sew.

Table 1.2

Adolescence (9–18 years) and the role of hormones in sexual maturity

During this period there is acceleration in growth in both males and females.

Puberty is a stage of growth with physical, hormonal and sexual changes. Puberty starts due to the release of hormones which are chemical messengers. In females the pituitary gland, which controls growth and development in the body, sends a message to the ovaries to release a hormone, oestrogen. (Hormones are chemical substances that create an effect.) In males the messages are sent to the testicles to produce the hormone testosterone. Secondary sexual characteristics are traits that appear at sexual maturity and distinguish the two sexes. They are not directly part of the reproductive system.

	Changes in males	Changes in females
Primary sexual characteristics	Penis enlarges Testicles grow Sperm is produced	Sexual organs grow Ovulation and menstruation commence
Secondary sexual characteristics	Pubic hair grows Facial hair Voice deepens	Pubic hair grows Breasts develop Hips widen

Table 1.3 Development of primary and secondary sexual characteristics

Early adulthood (19–45 years)

Within this time frame, adults reach physical maturity. Many adults are considered to be at the peak of their physical strength. Females may become pregnant and the body changes during pregnancy. Pregnancy causes external and internal changes as the body adjusts to the needs of the foetus. In pregnancy preparation for lactation begins, this continues after birth and breasts will change in size and shape.

Towards the end of early adulthood, perimenopause often occurs. This is the stage before the menopause. The duration of this can vary from individual to individual. Woman in this life stage may have symptoms such as hot flushes, night sweats, mood swings and reduced libido due to the reduction in oestrogen levels. This causes the ovaries to stop producing an egg each month and the reduction in oestrogen levels causes physical and emotional symptoms. Hot flushes are one of the most frequent symptoms of menopause causing a quick feeling of heat, sometimes with an accompanying flushed face. If this occurs at night, it is called night sweats and can make it hard to sleep. A reduction in hormone levels can cause mood swings, irritability, sadness and difficulty in concentration. A woman may also experience vaginal dryness or a decrease in libido.

Middle adulthood (46–65 years)

In this life stage women will experience the menopause. This is when a woman stops having periods and therefore will no longer be able to get pregnant naturally. In the perimenopause stage the body is adjusting to reduced levels of oestrogen. The menopause is the date of the last menstrual period and signifies the end of a women's reproductive ability. There is continual decrease in the amount of oestrogen that is released and no longer a release of an egg each month. Similar symptoms to that of perimenopause may occur such as hot flushes, night sweats or mood changes.

Some women may try Hormone Replacement Therapy (HRT) where oestrogen is prescribed in order to replace the decline and relieve the symptoms.

As adults get older, they may begin to show physical signs of ageing such as greying hair or loss of muscles tone and strength. Some men may notice hair loss, and some may find that they gain weight more easily.

Later adulthood (65+ years)

In later adulthood, there are many effects of aging. Physical health as well as intellectual abilities may deteriorate. Examples of intellectual aging include forgetting names of people, misplacing items or forgetting to carry out an activity. Gross and motor skills may become more difficult and some people may experience the loss or deterioration of their senses (see section on ageing that starts on page 17). However, it is important not to stereotype, remember that not all older people will experience these symptoms.

Intellectual development across the life stages

Infancy and early childhood

Intellectual development is concerned with thinking, problem solving and language skills. There is rapid growth in this area in infancy and early childhood.

Piaget's theory
Piaget developed a theory of how children develop cognitively. Piaget believed that we adapt to our environment intrinsically. Piaget used the term 'schema' which was a pattern of learning which linked actions and behaviour and is used to make sense of the world. A child will recognise when schemas are unsuitable or inaccurate and adapt them. This is through two processes known as assimilation and accommodation. Assimilation is when new knowledge is added to the schema to help better understand it. Accommodation is when schemas are changed or new ones formed to fit the incoming information. If the new information does not fit the existing schema, it is a state of disequilibrium, motivating the child to develop or create schemas until a state of equilibrium is reached.

Piaget claimed that children pass through a series of stages in cognitive development. This model helps explain how children think and behave. Although the stages are often described with ages, Piaget did not claim that all children would reach a stage at a particular time. He did consider that the same sequence of development as described below is universal.

Age and stage	Children's thoughts and actions	Experiment
Sensorimotor 0–2 years	Children learn through using their senses and actions. Schemas are largely developed through reflexes, for example, grasping. Children learn about object permanence from 8 months (knowing that objects continue to exist when they cannot be observed).	**Blanket and Ball Study** (1963) A toy was hidden under a blanket while the child was watching. Searching for the toy would mean the child had object permanence.
Preoperational 2– 7 years	The child cannot use logic or combine or separate ideas. Experiences continue to be built. Children will focus on part of a situation at a time. Children are egocentric so thoughts are about themselves and children are unable to see a situation from another point of view.	**Three Mountains** (1956) Children were presented with a model of three different mountains. A doll was placed at different positions and the child asked to pick the view the doll could see from some cards. Younger children (4-year-olds) chose a picture that represented what they could see, 7 and 8 year olds chose the correct picture.
Concrete Operational 7–11 years	Children can think logically if the concepts are familiar and not abstract. Children can solve problems, but are not able to think abstractly.	**Conservation of Number** (1954) The children are shown two amounts that are the same for example liquid in a beaker. The liquid from the second beaker is poured into a tall thin glass and the child is asked if there is the same amount. A child unable to think this way will say yes. See Figure 1.3.
Formal Operational 11 years +	Children are able to think in an abstract manner and reason, imagining the outcome of particular actions.	**Pendulum Task** (1958) Piaget set children the task to finding out what determines how high a pendulum swings. At this stage children will be able to vary only one factor at a time to see its effect. Younger children will try factors at random or change two things at a time.

Table 1.4

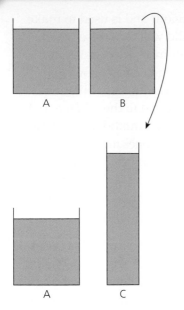

Figure 1.3 Beakers used to test conservation of number (see Table 1.4): when the liquid from container B is poured into container C, does the child recognise that A and C still contain the same amounts?

Chomsky's development of language

Chomsky (1965) proposed that language development is instinctive and we are all born with a capacity for language. Chomsky believed that every child has a 'language acquisition device' or LAD. This encodes grammar into the child's brain. This is essential for children to learn language and therefore this is a critical period of time. Chomsky thought this explained how children instinctively and rapidly gain language skills. Chomsky believed the evidence for this can be seen as adult speech is often broken up or grammatically incorrect. Furthermore children will often make mistakes in grammar and language such as saying 'mouses', 'sheeps' or 'I drawed'. They would not have learnt these terms from hearing adults. Children who learn two languages from birth will often be more fluent in both, rather than when learnt later on in adulthood. Chomsky also said that all children follow similar patterns in their development of language, which would be down to biological programming not the environment.

Early adulthood

During early adulthood our skills and abilities continue to increase. Our thinking becomes more logical, realistic and pragmatic, and adults will develop expert knowledge in areas relating to their job or life experiences. This enables judgements to be made from logical thought processes about important matters, and this may be seen as having wisdom. Many adults continue to learn and gain more qualifications.

The effects of age on the functions of memory

In later adulthood, some people may be less able to solve problems and experience loss of memory. There are different parts of memory for example procedural (how to ride a bike) or episodic (such as what I had for lunch). Episodic memory and remembering where and when events took place are the two types of memory which most commonly decline with age. Memory loss can happen as part of the ageing process, but some people may be concerned that they are developing dementia. Memory loss can have a number of physical causes which is important to be investigated.

Activity

Arrange to shadow or work in a Key Stage 1 nursery. See if you can observe children at each different stage of Piaget's cognitive development and compare the development of language.

Emotional development across the lifespan

Emotional development is about learning how to recognise emotions in others in addition to managing one's own emotions. It includes the development of self-esteem and self-concept and bonding and attachment with others. Emotional development begins in infancy and continues throughout the life span.

Attachment to care-giver in infancy and early childhood

Theories of attachment

There is much evidence to show the early years are vital, seen in childhood theories of attachment. Two examples are Bowlby and Ainsworth.

Bowlby (1958) linked the development of personality with a close and consistent relationship. The child was born with the need to attach to one main attachment figure which was usually the mother. The first two years of a child's life are critical for attachment, and

Type of attachment	Explanation	Implications for the child in later life
Secure	Distressed when caregiver leaves. Not comforted by stranger. Calms down when care-giver returns.	Able to make friends and meet new people. Adolescents can manage the transition more successfully throughout school.
Avoidant	Show no preference between caregivers and stranger.	Have difficulty maintaining relationships as have difficulty with emotions.
Ambivalent	Distress when care giver leaves. Avoids stranger. Child resists contact when caregiver returns.	May have difficulty trusting others in relationships.
Disorientated (added later)	Displays avoidant or unsure behaviour. May appear to be in a 'daze'.	May have trouble with attachments in later life.

Table 1.5

if this is broken or disrupted the child will suffer long-term consequences. These consequences could include delinquency, depression or aggression.

Ainsworth (1978) built on Bowlby's work. She devised an experiment using different situations for the child with a parent and then a stranger. The anxiety and reaction to the caregiver leaving and returning, as well as reaction to a stranger were observed. From this experiment four types of attachment were devised.

Activity

Carry out some research into theories of attachment. What are the strengths and weaknesses of the theories? How useful are they for health and social care?

The development and importance of self-concept

Self-concept is about our own knowledge of who we are. It includes self-esteem and self-image. This is important as it can help motivate an individual to achieve and feel confident in situations such as social situations. It can help an individual to lead an enjoyable life. Age, appearance, media, education, income and traumatic events such as abuse can influence self-concept.

Self-esteem is a measure of *how confident* a person feels about him or herself. A high self-esteem can

lead to greater optimism and a positive feeling about your abilities; whereas a low self-esteem can lead to a constant worry about what others may think or wanting to be like someone else. It is not fixed and can be positively or negatively influenced. Doing well in an exam, for example, can build self-esteem, whereas feeling left out or isolated can decrease self-esteem.

Self-image is how *you* see yourself, for example, you may consider your physical self, as tall, by a social role, for example, a student or a nurse, or a personality trait such as 'I worry a lot'. Factors such as the media can influence this, as individuals may compare themselves to media images or stereotypical ideals.

Factors that can affect self-concept include

- The reaction of others, whether people admire us, or seek our company.
- If we compare ourselves with others who appear more successful.
- Roles that carry a high level of prestige and some may have stigma attached to them.

Social development across the lifespan

The stages of play in infancy and early childhood.

Play is vital to all children's development. It can help build security, develop the imagination and teach relationship and social skills. Children progress through different stages of play.

Age	Type of play	Definition
0–2 years	Solitary	The child will play alone, focusing on one activity. Will explore and play with a range of toys and activities.
2–3 years	Parallel	Children will play alongside each other, but will not play together.
3–5 years	Simple co-operative	Children will join in different activities and begin to learn to share and take turns.
5 years +	Complex co-operative	Children may make up games, organise themselves and decide on their own rules.

Table 1.6

The importance of friends and friendship groups

Friends can come from different areas of life. This may be school, the work place or clubs and societies. Having friends has numerous benefits. It can help develop independence and self-concept. Many people will take part in exercise programmes with their friends benefiting their physical development. Friends can provide support through an emotional crisis and help with work or schoolwork. In some instances, individuals may find they are being pressured by the friends to act or behave in a certain way. This is known as peer pressure. It can be unhealthy activities such as smoking or drinking excessive alcohol. It can make individuals feel isolated and effect their social development if they do not take part in activities – peer pressure can be positive in encouraging an individual to complete some work or behave in a certain way.

The development of relationships with others

An ability to develop relationships with others is very important for well-being. Relationships require effective communication, valuing differences and mutual respect. This can be difficult at times and can be hard to learn to do. Relationships can offer emotional support and increase self-esteem.

The development of independence through the life stages

Independence develops throughout the life span, even in early childhood with children learning to do tasks for themselves such as getting dressed and cleaning their teeth. As the child gets older and enters adolescence, more freedom and independence is enjoyed which can sometimes cause friction in the family. Peer pressure may influence in both a negative and positive way. In adolescence and adulthood, many people gain employment which provides the financial means to become independent. It provides a source of income and an opportunity to make new friends. Skills such as time management, team work and meeting deadlines will be required. Most children will leave home which can be a mix of both a sense of excitement and anxiety. It can help develop skills such as money management by having to budget for bills and food, as well as social occasions. Taking responsibility for maintaining the property will help develop independence. Many people will have children and responsibility for a child can help build independence as you are responsible for another life. Some individuals may find it difficult to go out and do activities independently as they used to due to the extra responsibility.

Activity

Research some activities that can be carried out with children to develop their skills.

Distinction activity

Critically evaluate theories of language development. How useful are these for health and social care workers?

Check your understanding

1 Daisy and Alfred are 70-years-old. What life stage are they in? What changes may occur in their life stage?

2 Aaron is three years old. What life stage is he in? What type of play may he engage in and what are the benefits?

3 Bhavisa is 14-years-old. What changes will occur to her in this life stage?

4 Define 'self-concept' and outline two factors that can affect it.

B Factors affecting human growth and development

The nature—nurture debate related to factors

The nature—nurture debate explores whether genetic (nature) or the environment (nurture) is responsible for our behaviour and development. Genes are the blueprint for the development of the individual. They contain the code carried on chromosomes; we inherit 23 from each parent. If how we behave is down to our genes, then we have little control to change.

Development across the lifespan is a result of genetic or inherited factors – Gessel's maturation theory

Gessel developed a maturation theory of child development. Gessel considered that development is based on biology and genetic makeup. He believed there was a fixed prenatal sequence and after birth and although growth rates may vary the sequence of how children develop does not. Gessel (1925) formulated a cyclical spiral divided into stages repeated throughout life. Although Gessel acknowledged the environment can influence, he believed that this did not change the genetic makeup of a child, but provided stability for genetics to develop.

Development across the lifespan is a result of environmental factors – Bandura's social learning theory

Conversely nurture theorists believe that a child is born with a blank slate. The environment leads to the development of skills and behaviour. Bandura's (1961) social learning theory explored this theory. Bandura states that behaviour is learnt from the environment and carried out an experiment in a well-known study called the Bobo Doll. In this experiment children were shown into a room to play with toys. Some of the children then watched an adult behaving aggressively towards a doll, some watched an adult playing in a subdued manner and a control group were not exposed to anything. The children were then shown to a different room containing a range of toys, including the Bobo doll. Bandura found that those children that observed the aggression demonstrated more aggressive responses. Bandura therefore concluded that the environment plays a strong role in influencing behaviour.

Both genetic and environmental factors may play a part in development – the stress-diathesis model

In health and social care practice, it is unlikely that we would accept either of the above extreme positions. Instead of asking whether someone's personality is down to nature or nurture, how the nature and nurture interact is investigated. The stress-diathesis model combines these factors and can be used to explain some mental illness. Diathesis is the 'nature' or genetic function. Stress refers to an environmental stimulus that is generally unpleasant such as a traumatic event. The diathesis function increases the risk for developing a disorder, but the stress may actually trigger the onset.

Activity

Create a plan of how you could write an essay about the nature–nurture debate. Define key terms and list arguments for nature and arguments for nurture. You could explore how we develop language, mental illness and genetic conditions. Finally list how nature and nurture can be considered as an interaction with examples.

Genetic factors that affect development

Genetics is concerned with the genes that are passed on by parents to children. These can influence physical features and characteristics. The following table identifies some effects of genetic conditions.

A genetic predisposition is a genetic characteristic that increases the likelihood of developing conditions such as high cholesterol. However, this does not mean it is inevitable. It requires environmental or lifestyle factors (such as unhealthy diet in the case of cholesterol) to result in the condition.

Condition	Description	Effects on health and development	Treatment
Cystic fibrosis	Affects the gene which controls salt and water movement in and out of cells. The result is that the lungs and digestive system are clogged with mucus which makes it hard to breathe and digest food	Life limiting Breathing problems such as wheezing, shortness of breath Repeated chest infections Malnutrition Sinusitis Feelings of frustration Anxiety and insecurity Financial considerations	No cure, but treatments such as physiotherapy, exercise, mediation and nutrition can manage it.
Brittle bone disease	Results in fragile bones that break easily	Malformed bones Brittle teeth	Surgery Healthy life style Physiotherapy Pain medication
Phenylketonuria (PKU)	Body is unable to break down phenylalanine; high levels can damage the brain	Few symptoms if treated early	Low protein diet Dietary substitutes
Huntington's Disease	A disease that damages nerve cells in the brain	Huntington's disease affects movement Over time movements become more slow and muscles are rigid Fidgety movements Behavioural changes Psychiatric problems	No cure Medication can help with symptoms Speech and language and occupational therapy can help with activities of daily living.
Klenfelter's syndrome	A male baby is born with an extra X chromosome	Lower amounts of testosterone Babies may be born with undescended testicles Some physical features	Testosterone replacement therapy Emotional support
Down's syndrome	Causes some learning disability and characteristic physical features	Eyes that slant upwards and outwards Small mouth with protruding tongue Flat back of the head Some learning disability which is different for each individual Some have congenital heart defects, hearing or vision problems	Early intervention Medical and emotional support

Table 1.7

Condition	Description	Effects on health and development	Treatment
Colour blindness	People may find it difficult to distinguish between colours. Can vary in colours affected and severity	May have problems doing day to day activities such as understanding information or different colours at traffic lights	No cure Help with adapting and finding ways to manage
Duchenne Muscular Dystrophy	A progressive condition which causes the muscles to weaken. Usually affects boys Life limiting (most only live into their 20s or 30s)	Difficulty with gross motor skills such as jumping, climbing, walking or running. Learning difficulties	Mobility assistance Physiotherapy Surgery Emotional support
Susceptibility to disease such as cancer, high blood cholesterol and diabetes	May not be born with a disease, but have a high risk of acquiring it.	Dependent upon condition.	Healthy lifestyle to reduce risk.

Table 1.7

Biological factors

There are also **biological factors** that can affect development. Biological factors are factors that affect the development of a foetus. Exposure to different factors can cause long term or irreversible damage.

Foetal Alcohol Syndrome (FAS)

FAS is the name for a condition that occurs as the result of a mother drinking during pregnancy. The alcohol crosses the placenta to the foetus. The foetus is unable to break down the alcohol and affects the amount of oxygen and nutrients required for brain and organ development. It can cause characteristic facial features such as small or narrower eyes or a smaller head. A child with FAS may have learning disabilities, difficulties with language or problem with memory or attention.

Maternal infections

Some maternal infections can cause harm to a foetus. Rubella can affect sight and hearing, and brain and heart defects, chickenpox presents a small but major risk to the foetus resulting in brain damage or shortened limbs. Congenital defects are conditions that exist at birth. This could affect organs in the body such as congenital heart disease or affect the body such as cleft lip.

Lifestyle and diet can affect the foetus. It is important to eat a variety of different foods to ensure there is the right balance of nutrients. Some foods should be avoided in pregnancy such as soft blue cheese due to the risk of listeria which can cause miscarriage, stillbirth or severe illness. Smoking and alcohol have serious implications for the health of the foetus.

Activity

Consider one of the genetic conditions. What would be the impact upon the parents and sibling of the individual affected?

What support groups exist to help families?

Environmental factors that affect development

The environment is the world around us that we live in.

Pollution has been shown to have a number of effects on health. Physically, it can trigger respiratory (breathing) disorders from breathing in polluted air, either from an outside or indoor source by damaging the lungs. Children and those with weaker immune systems may be more at risk. Pollution can cause acute lower respiratory infections, pneumonia, chronic obstructive pulmonary disease and cancer (WHO, 2015). Pollutants impact upon the cardiovascular system (circulation of blood around the body) by being absorbed into the blood and transported to the heart. This was first observed after major smog in London in 1952. This can exacerbate existing heart conditions or trigger conditions in vulnerable people.

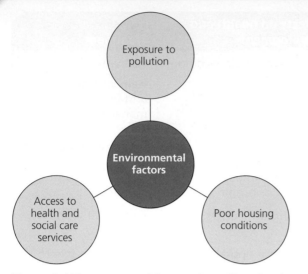

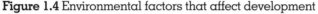

Figure 1.4 Environmental factors that affect development

This is thought to be because the particles that are absorbed into the blood will damage the blood vessels, causing inflammation and sensitise the heart to damage (BHF, 2012). The result can trigger hypertension, stroke and heart failure. Pollution can also trigger allergies causing the body to produce an immune response effect with sneezing, wheezing or skin rashes. Traffic related pollution and other air pollutants can trigger asthma attacks. Light pollution can make it difficult to rest, while noise pollution may make it difficult to concentrate on tasks. Pollution can also trigger allergic reactions and an increase in asthma.

Poor housing conditions can have a tremendous effect on development. Damp conditions can cause mould to develop releasing spores and triggering breathing problems such as asthma. Damp can also affect the cardiovascular system with a link to heart disease and therefore may have a long-term impact on health. Lack of heating can make people more vulnerable to illness and cause hypothermia. Hypothermia occurs when the body temperature drops below 35°C. It can be life threatening and build up over time (known as chronic hypothermia). Symptoms include consistent shivering, cold or pale skin, confusion and poor judgement. Lack of heat can increase pressure on the heart causing cardiovascular strain and damage. Overcrowding can cause anxiety or stress, leading to depression and may mean children do not have a place to complete their homework.

Access to health and social care services can sometimes cause constraints. This could be because of the times the service is open and

someone is unable to attend due to work or family commitments. Some more rural areas have fewer services than larger cities and so people may have to travel long distances to access care. This can have a negative impact on the development of a child. It is sometimes difficult to find information about the services available, and understand how they can assist. This may mean people aren't accessing the help they require, whether this be for physical or mental health or social care support. This can mean that needs will go unmet, and possibly worsening health. Some services may have very long waiting lists – with potential detrimental effects for the person while they are waiting.

Activity

Research health and social care services in your area.

Is there a wide variety? Would you have to travel a long way to receive specialist services?

Social factors that affect development

Social factors are factors that affect our day to day lives.

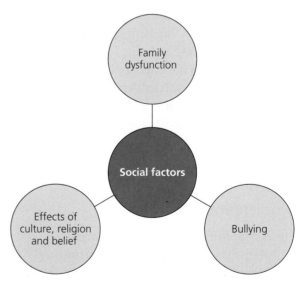

Figure 1.5 Social factors that affect development

Family dysfunction includes parental divorce or separation, sibling rivalry or parenting style. All of these can impact upon development. Divorce may create feelings of insecurity within children and a feeling of rejection. Some children may feel it was their fault that the marriage did not work. Very young children may get distressed when being left at nursery and may experience enuresis (wetting the bed). Older children may still feel insecure and this can impact upon educational performance.

Different parenting styles can have both short-term and long-term effects. Some parents may enforce adherence to rules, some may spend little time with their children, while others indulge their children with few rules or constraints. A combination of encouragement to be independent, along with limits and boundaries is thought to help a child be independent and develop social skills.

Bullying can affect everyone. There are links between bullying and all aspects of health. The effects of bullying can cause anxiety and depression which may impact sleep and eating. It can cause difficulty to make other friends, resulting in isolation and being able to concentrate at school which will affect achievement. Emotionally bullying can negatively affect self-esteem which may have long-term effects. Depression may also lead to self-harm and suicidal thoughts or behaviour.

Culture, religion and belief can influence a person's values and behaviour, what they eat and how they dress. Being with other people with the same values, beliefs or religion as yourself can create a feeling of acceptance and being valued. Sometimes, people are excluded or discriminated against because of their beliefs. Working in health and social care requires an understanding of your patient's or service user's beliefs. This can impact upon decisions they make about their care. Some Buddhists are strict vegetarians and this may also include some medications that are produced using animal products, Christian patients who are near death may ask for the Sacrament of the Sick (last rites). Some religions may prevent medical intervention – Jehovah's Witnesses are often against receiving blood (for example a blood transfusion), Jewish patients may observe strict rules about what they can and cannot do on the Sabbath and some Muslim patients will have spiritual and dietary needs as well as privacy and modesty concerns. It is important to not make assumptions about what a patient will or will not do based on their religion, but discuss this with the patient to make a care plan.

Activity

Create a table to collate information about religions. Include brief points about beliefs, food, rituals and medical intervention.

What would be the effect of not respecting and following somebody's beliefs?

Economic factors that affect development

Economic factors are those connected with money.

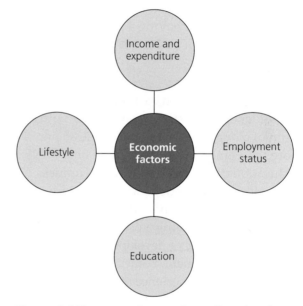

Figure 1.6 Economic factors that affect development

Income

Income is the amount of money a person receives on a regular basis, this could be wages from work, benefits or interest on money in a bank account. **Expenditure** is how much someone spends and may include mortgage or rent, food or lifestyle choices. A low income limits choices such as housing, food or leisure activities, impacting all areas of health. Financial pressures may be a source of stress and anxiety on both the individual and the family and negatively impacting relationships. This can affect all aspects of development.

Employment status

This means the type of work someone does, for example if the work is manual or non-manual is or full-time or part-time. Employment is a major source of income, so can impact on lifestyle and development. Being in work helps an individual develop skills and acquire knowledge promoting intellectual development and sometimes results in extra qualifications. This can in turn lead to promotions and higher income. Some jobs such as manual work can improve fitness. High-status jobs can increase self-esteem and emotional well-being and many individuals develop friendships through work promoting social development. Conversely, work can be very stressful and impact negatively upon an individual's health, and physical and emotional development. Work demands such as shift work may limit social opportunities. Unemployment and not having a job can cause anxiety, low self-esteem and low social status.

Education

Education can impact upon earnings and lifestyle choices. Evidence suggests that employees with a minimum of a degree earned on average 85 per cent more than employees with GCSEs only (ONS, 2011). Education can increase life opportunities, as well as encouraging independence, building an individual's own identity and creating lifelong friends and therefore having a positive impact upon emotional and social development as well as intellectual development. Some individuals may have a negative experience at school through bullying, feeling insecure or not achieving their desired qualifications. Individuals can complete education at any age with adult classes or online learning. Higher education can be expensive with tuition fees and living costs to pay.

Lifestyle

Lifestyle choices are choices that an individual chooses for themselves. This could include exercise, diet, smoking or alcohol. A poor lifestyle can have physical consequences with an increased risk of many diseases (such as smoking and cancer negatively impacting upon physical development). Obesity has numerous health implications. Some lifestyle choices such as a poor diet can reduce concentration and therefore affect educational performance, in adulthood a poor diet may lead to long-term illness reducing career prospects. This can all have emotional effects causing a negative self-image or self-esteem affecting emotional development and may impact on family or social relationships.

Activity

Working in groups, choose one lifestyle factor each. Research and then teach one another the impact of this factor on health and development.

Major life events that affect development

Life events are events that occur throughout the life span. For health and social care practitioners, it is important to understand the potential effect these events can have on the individual's well-being. This is part of treating someone holistically, that we understand the whole person. The events may have a positive or negative impact, may have short- or long-term effects, can impact upon any aspect of development, affects the individual's family and friends.

Predictable and unpredictable events

Life events can be predictable or unpredictable. Predictable life events are events that are expected to happen at a particular time. This does not mean that it will happen to everyone, but it is reasonable to think it would be expected. Unpredictable events are events that happen unexpectedly. They can often have serious effects on the individual. Although these life events may be expected, they may still have an effect on a person's health and well-being. This effect can be positive or negative or both. It can have both short and long-term effects.

Life events and their effects on health

Education

Education is compulsory for all children and young people in the UK. Most children will go to a school, with some being educated at home. Many children will also attend nursey which may be the first time a child has been without their parents. It can be daunting for the child, especially with so many new children and adults. This can be a source of anxiety for the child. However, children are generally keen to start and learn, absorbing new knowledge and developing new skills. They tend to feel very 'grown up' especially with a school uniform. This can raise their self-esteem. During this time, they will develop their own identity and form friendship groups.

Moving house

Moving house is often a stressful experience. Whether this is to a different house in the same area, or a new area there is much to organise. This is also a time of great excitement for new experiences and the opportunities or new start that this may give. There will be much to learn about the new area for example, where places are or finding your way around. It can take time to develop new friendships or relationships with people, and this can be a source of anxiety. An individual who moves may feel isolated as they do not know anyone in the area and may miss the friends they had. Leaving home is an opportunity for individuals to be more independent, and can promote emotional well-being. This can however be a stressful experience to start with as it involves managing finances and learning to cook healthy foods in order to maintain physical well-being.

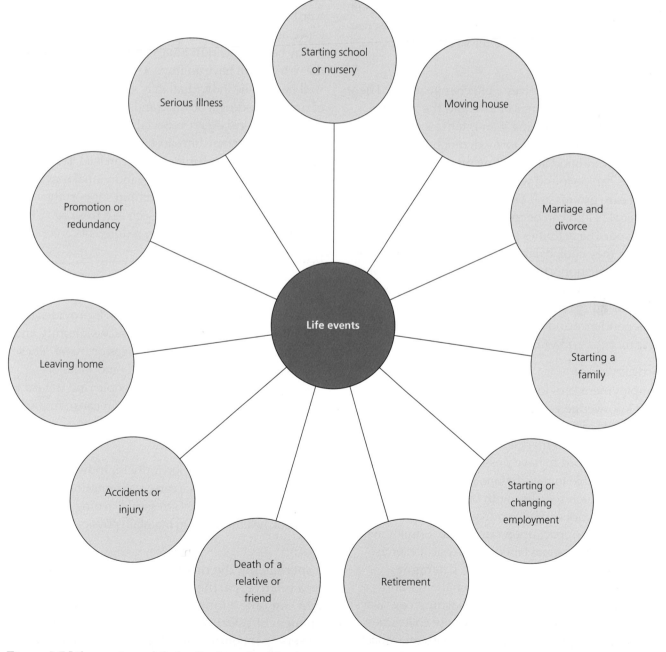

Figure 1.7 Life events and their effects on health

Marriage

Marriage is a big change that creates a strong feeling of security and contentment. Changes in how finances and day-to-day jobs are carried out may change which can be a source of anxiety and it can be difficult learning to live with another person. One individual may move locations or away from their family. Sometimes marriage results in **divorce**, a legal dissolution of a marriage. This can create a feeling of failure that the marriage did not work and a sense of loss and great sadness. Finances and custody of children along with assets such as possession and a house will have to be addressed. If marriage has been a stressful experience, then divorce can bring a sense of relief and the opportunity for a new start.

Starting a family

Starting a family involves a big change in life. There are often strong feelings of love and the need to protect the child making it an intense experience. Strong attachments are formed; much is learnt about parenthood and looking after a child. New friends can be found with other parents at pre-natal care groups and baby and toddler groups. Physical health can be improved as families may take sporting activities together or parents may ensure they cook balanced meals. This can provide a source of support for each parent. Children can make a parent feel anxious as they are a major responsibility and parents will experience loss of independence and tiredness, especially in the first few months and years of a child's life.

Employment

Employment provides opportunities to use skills and knowledge gained in school or training and new skills to be learnt. This can improve self-image and self-esteem. Financially, an individual may be able to afford to have possessions they may not have been able to have before. Friends can be made at work, which socialise with outside of work. However, work can be a source of much stress and anxiety, and impact upon family life. Employment that requires manual labour or physical exercise can improve physical well-being. Changing employment can present a new challenge and although it may be difficult, by learning new ways of working, and getting to know new colleagues, it can often be a positive experience with an impact on health and well-being. **Being promoted** is recognition of experience and skills and as such can positively impact on self-esteem. It can come with more responsibilities and an increase in wages impacting on life style. However, some people may struggle if they have been promoted over their friends and find this a difficult situation. The extra responsibilities may increase stress and anxiety felt.

Redundancy

Redundancy is when an employer no longer needs a particular job. As this job does not exist, the individual does not have any employment. This is often very stressful and can make the person feel worthless. The lack of income will have an effect, especially if it takes a long time to find another job. It may be that the individual cannot afford a healthy diet which will have an impact on physical health and well-being. The individual may spend a high volume of time on finding a new job and therefore not have time for physical exercise. Socially, they could become isolated as they may have lost work friends or have limited social opportunities. This can lead to lower self-esteem and depression. The individual may miss their way of life and the friends and support they had at work. Redundancy can be seen as a fresh start, the opportunity to re-train and try a different career.

Retirement

Retirement is a significant life event and involves major changes. If a job role has been very stressful, then this will change on retirement. It provides the person with more time to socialise, visit family and friends and take up new challenges or travel. These can improve physical health and emotional or social health well-being. Some people find it hard to adjust to a retired lifestyle and it can cause financial issues or loss of friends.

Leaving home

Leaving home is an opportunity for individuals to be more independent. This can create emotional well-being. It can be initially stressful learning to budget and cook healthy foods to maintain physical well-being.

Death

Experiencing the death of an individual (such as a relative, partner, or friend) is a major loss and can take a long time to adjust to this major change. Physical effects can include digestive upsets or insomnia or sleeping too much. As well as the sadness felt, individuals can experience anger or anxiety. Although if someone has been in a lot of pain or the illness has been long, an individual may feel relief which then may be followed by guilt.

Accidents or injury

Accidents or injury and serious illness can have a number of effects. Pain can impact emotionally and can affect concentration levels, as well as the physical experience. Time off work or school from being in hospital can affect intellectual development. If the accident or injury results in a life-altering event such as loss of a limb, then this adjustment may impact on self-image and will require support and new ways of carrying out daily tasks. It may result in financial loss if someone is unable to work for a prolonged period of time. It can demonstrate that someone has people to support them, raising self-esteem and making the individual feel stronger emotionally.

Holmes-Rahe

In 1967 Thomas Holmes and Richard Rahe carried out a study to explore whether stress had an impact on illness. They surveyed patients about life events in the previous two years. Each of these events had points attached to them. They found the higher the score of the points, the more likely the individual is to experience ill-health.

Case scenario

Life events and their effect on health

Ahmed, who is 48 years old, has been married for 10 years and has a seven-year-old child. He was recently involved in a car accident in which his wife was killed. He was injured and required a long period of time in hospital and rehabilitation. He started a new job last week. His total would be 189 (100 for death of spouse, 53 for personal injury or illness and 36 for change to a different line of work) and would therefore be at a moderate to high chance of becoming ill.

Activity

Create six revision cards, one for each of the different life stages. On each, write the life events that are most likely to occur within each life stage. Then bullet point the positive and negative effects that these life events may have. Using different colours or pictures may help.

Distinction activity

Evaluate three factors and the influence they can have on development. What connections are there between these different factors?

Check your understanding

1 Define nature and nurture and give one argument for and against.
2 Identify two genetic conditions that can affect development.
3 Describe two ways in which pollution can impact upon health.
4 What is an economic factor? How can it impact upon health?
5 Identify four life events and the effect that they have on the individual.
6 What is the Holmes-Rahe Social Readjustment Scale?

C The effects of ageing

The physical changes of ageing

As we get older, many physical changes occur. There are many changes to the body and some are discussed below. These will not happen to everyone.

Cardiovascular disease

Cardiovascular disease (CVD) is a broad term and covers any condition that is a disease of the heart or blood vessels. Examples of conditions include

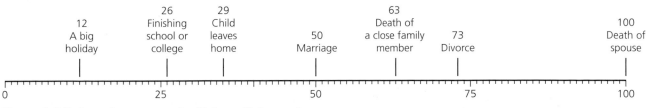

Figure 1.8 Selected events on the Holmes-Rahe scale

coronary heart disease, stroke, angina or arterial disease. In 2014 cardiovascular disease was the second most common cause of death, with coronary heart disease being the biggest single cause of death in the UK (British Heart Foundation). Age can increase the risk of cardiovascular disease along with genetic factors or lifestyle choices such as smoking or being physically inactive.

CVD occurs when the blood flow is blocked by a clot. This is known as a thrombosis, or if there is a build-up of fatty deposits in the wall of an artery this is known as atherosclerosis. These fatty deposits cause a narrowing of the artery and a restriction of the blood flow. The effect of this is a reduction in the amount of oxygen in the blood. If this occurs in the heart, then angina may result, causing pain and discomfort in the chest area. The fatty deposits (atheroma) may break causing a blood clot to form. In the heart, this may result in a heart attack, a very serious medical condition with symptoms including chest pain, shortness of breath and a feeling of anxiety. If the blood clot is in the artery leading to the brain, this can cause a stroke, resulting in damage or death to brain cells.

The degeneration of the nervous tissue

Degeneration of the nervous tissue can lead to conditions like Multiple Sclerosis (MS). This is a condition of the central nervous system in which the coating around the nerve fibres is damaged. Symptoms can vary, but MS can affect vision, balance and cause spasms and stiffness.

Osteoarthritis

Osteoarthritis is a condition that affects the movement of the joints in the body. All joints within the body can be affected, but it is more common in the knees, hips and hands. Osteoarthritis occurs when there is a deterioration of the cartilage that covers the bone ends. This causes pain and stiffness within the area and can impact upon the movement of the joint. The exact cause is not completely known, but there are a number of factors that can contribute with a higher incidence with age, joint injury and obesity. Treatment can include exercise, analgesics (painkillers) and anti-inflammatory drugs.

Degeneration of the sense organs

Sight

The risk of reduction in sight increases with age. By the time an individual is 75 years old, 1 in 5 will have sight loss. This increases to 1 in 2 by the age of 90 years old (RNIB, 2015). The reduction of sight loss can be caused by a number of conditions including macular degeneration and cataracts.

Macular degeneration results in loss of central vision and frequently in both eyes. The back of the eye is the retina and the macula, a tiny part of this, is affected. It is normally painless, but as it affects the central vision can impact upon reading and recognition of faces. It does not result in total blindness as the peripheral vision remains intact. It is more common as someone gets older, and other factors such as smoking can increase the risk.

Cataracts are very common and impact upon the lens of the eye which changes, becoming less transparent stopping light getting to the back of the eye. If this continues, then it will cause blurred or misty vision.

Hearing

Age related hearing loss develops gradually. Around 70 per cent of people aged over 70, and more than 90 per cent of people aged over 80, are living with hearing loss (Action on Hearing Loss 2013). This can mean the older person may experience communication difficulties, resulting in isolation with possible stress or anxiety. Hearing loss is caused because the sound signals are not reaching the brain. This may be due to inner ear damage impacting on the hair cells and auditory nerve or a blockage between the outer and inner ear, so sounds are unable to pass.

The reduced absorption of nutrients

The older population are more at risk from inadequate diet and malnutrition due to a decrease in the effectiveness of the body to absorption of nutrients from food (Brown 2006). Gastrointestinal changes can also mean that older people may not be able to taste food as well and brittle teeth can cause difficulty in eating. As nutrition is an important factor in preventing illness, there are consequences to this malnutrition. Nutritional screening commonly takes place on admission into hospital to help identify where people may need extra support.

Taste and sense of smell can also deteriorate in older age. The ability to identify different tastes diminishes which may mean that older people may find eating less enjoyable. As part of the ageing process, there tends to be a reduction in the ability to detect and identify odours.

Dementia

Dementia is a set of symptoms (known as a syndrome) that may include memory loss, thinking speed, language or understanding. The Alzheimer's Society says that there are 850,000 people with dementia in the UK, with 1 in 6 people over the age of 80 years having a diagnosis of dementia (Alzheimer's Society 2013). There are over 100 types of dementia. Some examples are Alzheimer's disease, Vascular Dementia and Dementia with Lewy Bodies.

1 Alzheimer's disease is the most common form of dementia. It is a progressive disease which means that it will get worse, the longer the person has the condition. Alzheimer's affects the brain and causes an abnormal amount of proteins to build. These are known as plaques and damage and destroy the neurons within the brain. The disease can then spread to other areas of the brain. One of the earliest signs is loss of memory. This could be the names of people or objects or not remembering conversations. Use of language, coordination and knowing the day or date may also be difficult. As the disease progresses there are symptoms of memory loss and the individual may experience difficulties with speech and swallowing.

2 Dementia with Lewy Bodies is a common form of dementia. If an individual has dementia with Lewy Bodies, they will also experience memory problems. In addition, the individual will have difficulty in concentration and visual perception which is about being able to understand the surrounding areas. There is no cure for dementia with Lewy Bodies, although physiotherapy or psychological therapies may be beneficial.

3 Vascular dementia occurs when the blood supply to the brain is reduced. This damages the brain cells, eventually causing them to die. Memory, thinking and reasoning are all affected. Early symptoms of vascular dementia include issues with attention, planning, language or behavioural changes. Treatments can help slow down the progression of the condition, but there is no overall cure or any way to reverse the damage to the blood vessels. See the unit 'Caring for individuals with dementia' for more information.

Effects of illnesses that are common in ageing

As we get older, our immune systems can become less efficient, leading to decreased defences against infections. Older people experience higher levels of mortality and morbidity as a result of infection. There are also cases where older people may have an infection, but not have a high temperature. Infections can give symptoms of drowsiness or confusion, which may be confused with dementia.

> **Activity**
>
> Create a fact sheet for one of the conditions more common in ageing. Include signs, symptoms, causes and treatments.

The psychological changes of ageing

Effects on confidence and self-esteem

The physical changes in ageing can negatively affect confidence and self-esteem as older adults see changes occur in their physical appearance and finding tasks more difficult. However, many older people find a secure sense of self that enables them to manage the physical changes.

Effects of social change

Social changes can occur within an individual's life. These can all have a serious impact upon the older adult's psychological well-being. Role changes such as retirement can have both a positive and negative impact. The individual may feel that they have less of a role in society with possible loss of self-esteem and confidence. It may also give the individual the chance to try new experiences or learn new skills.

The older person will experience loss or death of a partner or of a friend. The effect of this, especially for individuals who have been together for a long time, can be devastating. It can have long lasting physical and emotional effects and the older person will need to adjust to their new life without that person. An increase in leisure time can have both positive and negative effects. The individual may be able to take up new hobbies or learn new skills, but some could find it hard to occupy their time in comparison to being busy at work. Day centres, community outreach groups or befrienders can provide vital company to older people who are at risk of being isolated.

Financial concerns

Age UK state that there are 1.6 million pensioners living in poverty (2016). Some people have to make sacrifices to pay bills and take action to reduce heating costs. People are concerned about the economic climate and being able to manage their incomes in the future. The government provides winter fuel payments and state pensions, along with other benefits but a large amount of these remain unclaimed.

Effects of culture, religion and beliefs

Culture, religion and beliefs can provide a sense of belonging and support for older people. They may also support others in the community.

Theories of ageing

Theories of ageing are about exploring the ageing process, how we can live healthier and more fulfilling lives and how we can address the needs of the older population. Two theories are the social disengagement theory and the activity theory.

Social disengagement theory

Disengagement means to withdraw from being involved in something. Cumming and Henry (1961) consider that ageing is the process of individuals and structures within society withdrawing from each other. This is mutually agreed and inevitable. This disengagement is in preparation for the death of the individual. From this theory, many of the changes that occur within ageing link to this withdrawal. Retirement for example, means a change in role from employer to retired and with this a potentially reduced social role in society and contact with work colleagues. This theory has been criticised for suggesting that disengagement is both inevitable and required. Many older people continue to play an active role in their communities and therefore this is a generalised view point.

Activity theory

Havighurst's activity theory, developed in the 1960s, considers that older people need to remain active to prevent any segregation getting too far. This theory argues that successful ageing is dependent upon following similar activities from middle age. By doing this, happiness and satisfaction can follow. This has been criticised as being somewhat idealistic and there may be physical reasons which will prevent a similar level of activity in older age as middle adulthood.

Activity

Research provision for older people in your local area. Which theory of ageing do they reflect? How do they help older adults adjust to change?

The societal effects of an ageing population

A societal effect means something that has an impact upon the community that we live in.

Health and social care provision for the aged

There are numerous provisions for older people, for both medical and support needs. Some of these are listed below.

- Needs assessment focuses on care tasks or that an individual may need assistance. Examples could include shopping, cleaning, or washing.
- Winter assistance is provided by the government with a fuel payment.
- Meals on Wheels provide meals seven days a week for people unable to cook for themselves.
- Day centres provide a range of activities and services for older people. Activities could include arts, crafts, beauty, aromatherapy and quizzes.
- Residential services provide personal care and meals. A nursing home has a qualified nurse on site 24 hours a day and can provide nursing care for individuals with disability, illness or injury.

Figure 1.9 Care services can be provided at home, supporting someone elderly so that they can live independently

- Sheltered housing is for older people who wish to remain independent, but still be able to access help.

- Home care is support provided in the individual's own home. This could include personal care, domestic or social support.

- Telecare is about technology in an individual's own home. This means people with long-term conditions can live independently at home. Examples include personal alarms and health monitoring devices.

Economic effects of an ageing population

One of the successes of the NHS is an increase in life expectancy. Many people remain healthy, independent and active. However, as people age they are more likely to live with a range of conditions, increasing disability or frailty. Health and social care services are finding it difficult to keep up with the demand. The King's Fund (2013) consider this has both positive and negative effects. The annual costs of health and social care are greater for older people. Hospital admission for older people has increased and with the number of older people increasing this will lead to increased demands for care. However, an increasing number of older people continue to work past 65 years of age and continue in many other ways. For example, many older people volunteer in a range of capacities, provide informal care for neighbours, relatives or grandchildren and make donations to charity.

Activity

Falls

Falls cost the NHS £2 billion pounds each year. Research the reasons why people may fall and make links with some of the physiological changes explored earlier. How can falls be prevented in older people?

Distinction activity

Explain the evidence for the activity and disengagement theory in society. Evaluate each theory and draw a conclusion.

Check your understanding

1 Identify and describe four conditions that may occur in older age.
2 Identify two differences between the activity and disengagement theory.
3 Describe three effects of ageing on the psychology of older people.
4 Identify two implications of an ageing population.

Think about it

There is a lot of discussion in the news and health about the impact of an ageing population. Words such as demand, burden and challenge are often used.

What effect do you think words like this may have on older people reading the news? Are there other ways in which the issues could be discussed?

Further reading

ONS (2011) *Earning by Qualification, 2011.* Office for National Statistics, London

Useful websites

RNIB: www.rnib.org.uk/knowledge-and-research-hub/key-information-and-statistics

Macular degeneration: www.nhs.uk/conditions/macular-degeneration/Pages/Introduction.aspx

Osteoarthritis: www.arthritisresearchuk.org/arthritis-information/conditions/osteoarthritis/what-is-osteoarthritis.aspx

Osteoarthritis: www.nhs.uk/Conditions/Osteoarthritis/Pages/treatment.aspx

Cataracts: www.nhs.uk/Conditions/Cataracts-age-related/Pages/Introduction.aspx

Hearing impairment: www.nhs.uk/Conditions/Hearing-impairment/Pages/Introduction.aspx

Exam Practice

All questions relate to one family.

Benjamin is married to Andrea. Andrea was recently in a serious car crash that left her paralysed. They have two children. Anthony who is 15 years and Beth who is five years old. Benjamin has recently been promoted at work.

1 Describe two physical changes that will occur to Anthony in this life stage. (4 marks)
2 Identify the stage of play that Beth may engage in. (1 mark)
3 Explain the possible impact that the car crash may have had on Andrea. (6 marks)
4 To what extent might the recent events have affected Benjamin's well-being? (6 marks)

The family live in a polluted area.

5 Describe the possible impact that this may have on development. (4 marks)

Anthony is friends with Daniel who has cystic fibrosis.

6 Outline what cystic fibrosis is and the impact upon Daniel's development. (4 marks)
7 Identify two health and social care professionals who can help Daniel and his family. (2 marks)

Beth is about to move from her nursery into the reception class at the local primary school.

8 Evaluate how Gessel's Maturation Theory and Bandura's Social Learning Theory can both be used to describe Beth's development up until the age of 5. (10 marks)

Benjamin's parents have recently moved into sheltered accommodation.

9 Discuss and evaluate two theories of ageing. (10 marks)

2 Working in health and social care

The National Health Service (NHS) is one of the biggest employers in Britain. Social services also employ a large number of people. These services care for people from birth right through to the end of life, whether they need physical care, mental health care, or social care. If you want to work in these areas or if you use their services it is important to know something of what people working in health and social care do and how they do it. Knowing how workers and organisations in health and social care are scrutinised and controlled and how they work to principles of care will help you understand how the quality of what they do is maintained. Knowing how people in these organisations work together in different teams will help you understand how effectively they meet the needs of the wide range of people who use their services.

Learning aims

The aims of this unit are to understand:

A the roles and responsibilities of people who work in the health and social care sector.

B the roles of organisations in the health and social care sector.

C how to work with people with specific needs in the health and social care sector.

How will I be assessed?

You will be assessed by a 90 minute externally set examination consisting of short- and long-answer questions. There will be four sections to the paper. Each section will be based on a different scenario and relate to a different group of service users. There are 20 marks for each section (80 marks in total) and each section will have questions worth 2, 4, 6 and 8 marks.

How will I be graded?

Pass	Merit	Distinction
Learners demonstrate knowledge and understanding of the roles and responsibilities of the people who work in health and social care settings in context. They also understand how organisations in the wider context impact on employee practices. Learners understand the influence of codes of practice on how employees undertake activities, and how and why the work of people in health and social care settings needs to be monitored. Learners can make judgements on the effectiveness of practices on service users, and can propose and justify recommendations for delivering services in context, based on health and social care concepts and principles.		Learners demonstrate a thorough understanding of the roles and responsibilities of people who work in health and social care settings and the influence of organisations, in context. They can justify recommendations related to an employee's specific responsibilities, or multi-disciplinary activities, but understand the organisational context in which those employees and teams operate.

They can evaluate the impact and effectiveness of services in meeting the needs of different service users, and how monitoring and codes of practice impact on the work of employees within health and social care settings. Learners can analyse service user requirements in context and provide justified recommendations for service delivery for a variety of different service user groups underpinned by health and social care concepts and principles |

The support worker might be paid for from the personal budget the social worker organises for the individual.

Social workers, doctors and to some extent nurses should involve the individual and their families in assessing the person's needs and in making a person-centred plan that helps the individual to be as independent as possible. Families and carers may be able to help the person explain their needs. Families and carers can also say how much help they are able to give and for how long, so that social workers can plan how to fill the gaps in care.

Activity

Find three care agencies on the internet. What range of services do they offer?

Find your local social services website and make a list of what services they offer.

Now find the website for your local hospital and list what services they offer. Many hospitals no longer have accident and emergency departments. Does yours?

Specific responsibilities of people who work in health and social care settings

Applying care values and principles

People who work in health and social care settings have specific responsibilities that workers in other sectors may not have. Whatever they do, they must apply the care values and principles. These are:

1 to promote anti-discriminatory practice

2 to empower individuals

3 to ensure safety

4 to promote effective communication and ensure confidentiality

5 to be accountable to their professional bodies.

Promoting anti-discriminatory practice

Promoting anti-discriminatory practice means treating people with equality, dignity and respect. Workers do not favour one person or group of people over others and encourage other people to

behave in this way. People cannot be discriminated against because of age, disability, gender reassignment, marriage and civil partnership, pregnancy and maternity, race, religion and belief, sex, or sexual orientation. These are protected characteristics.

Nurses, midwives, doctors, social workers all have codes of conduct which tell them how to behave towards others. They also have equality and diversity policies or guidelines in their workplace. People who work in health and social care settings must use these codes and policies all the time. They must identify discrimination and favouritism and must not ignore it. They must challenge people who discriminate unfairly and who have favourites.

Here is an example.

Case scenario

Amina

Amina is a nurse. She was born in England but her parents are from Pakistan and she speaks English and Urdu. It is busy day in the outpatient's clinic and the doctor is late because he was called to an emergency. People are getting impatient. Benjy, a young man with learning disabilities has the first appointment but Mr C. who has the second appointment time is in a hurry. He is from Pakistan. He speaks in Urdu to Amina and asks her to get him in to see the doctor first because he says that Benjy will not know. Amina says she will not. It is not right to make Benjy wait. He has the first appointment. She will not favour someone from her own ethnic background over others. She treats people fairly.

People who work in health and social care settings must adapt what they do to suit the needs of different people who use the services. Later that day a patient comes to the clinic. The lady is visually impaired and cannot see. She uses a white stick. When it is her turn, Amina calls the lady's name but because the lady cannot see, Amina goes to her and offers to take her down the corridor to the correct room. Amina is adapting the way health and social care services are provided for this lady because of her needs.

Other people could read the sign on the door that says the doctor's name. This lady could not, so Amina helped her.

Empowering individuals

'Empowering' means 'giving power'. People who work in health and social care settings must treat people as individuals, put their needs first and plan care to suit the needs of the individual, just as Amina treated each of those people in outpatients as individuals. Amina adapted care to meet the needs of the individual, helping the visually impaired lady find the right room.

Case scenario

Carl

Benjy's support worker, Carl has come with him to hospital because Benjy gets nervous when he has to see the doctor. Carl has worked with Benjy for some time and knows that Benjy likes to be as independent as possible, counting out his money when he buys a cup of tea in the hospital cafe. Benjy likes to manage his own money and people in the queue are patient while he counts out the coins. Carl does not interfere – he supports Benjy's rights to dignity and independence. He helps Benjy when it comes to carrying hot drinks because Benjy is a little unsteady. Benjy likes bagels. They remind him of the ones his mother used to make when he lived at home, before he moved into supported accommodation. Carl helps Benjy choose a bagel to go with his cup of tea. Carl is providing active support consistent with Benjy's beliefs, cultures and preferences and is supporting Benjy to express his needs and preferences.

So far we have seen Amina promoting Benjy's rights, and Carl promoting Benjy's choices. Both of them are promoting his well-being. We have also seen Amina balancing individual rights to health and social care services with the rights of other service users. Amina dealt firmly with Mr C. who wanted to jump the queue to see the doctor and he accepted her decision but sometimes conflict can escalate.

Case scenario

Dr Day and Eric

Down at the local GP surgery, Dr Day is seeing patients. Eric is a recovering heroin addict who has come for his methadone prescription. The surgery is full and Eric is very edgy because he has run out of his prescribed medication. He starts shouting at the receptionist because he has to wait his turn and at one point he leans over the counter and tries to punch her. At that point Dr Day comes out of his room, takes Eric to one side and says very firmly that if Eric threatens staff, he will call the police and have him removed from the premises. Dr Day is balancing an individual's rights to health and social care services with the rights of the staff to work in a safe environment.

Conflict can happen on hospital wards too and staff must deal with it. Later that day Eric's behaviour became so disruptive that he had to be admitted as an emergency to a psychiatric unit. Staff there were trained in reducing conflict and aggression. They managed to calm him down by providing a calm environment and de-escalating the situation. It helped that he knew the staff on duty and they knew him, and the familiar routines of having a meal, and taking medication helped him relax.

Case scenario

Carl and the other support workers

Benjy meanwhile returned to the supported accommodation he shared with two other people. He was late getting back from the hospital and the others had already eaten. Carl, the support worker, helped Benjy cook some food, but meanwhile the others were watching football on television. Benjy wanted to watch a different programme and an argument broke out. Carl and the other support worker got everyone round the table to talk about how they could settle the conflict. The support workers asked each person what they wanted and helped them find a way through the problem. Benjy decided he would watch his programme at a later date on the computer and settled down with the others to watch the end of the match.

Case scenario

Dr Day and Alan Ford

Some of Dr Day's patients live in Oakwood residential care home. One of his patients there is Alan Ford, an elderly retired businessman who lived alone after his wife died. Before going into Oakwood, Mr Ford had domiciliary care which is care in his own home. A male carer, Gary, used to come every morning to help Mr Ford have a shower and get dressed. Sometimes Mr Ford did not want a wash and refused to eat anything. Gary found sour milk and mouldy bread in the house but no other food. Mr Ford did not flush the toilet and it got blocked so the house was smelly. When Gary tried to help Mr Ford wash, Mr Ford would sometimes hit him. Gary was concerned for Mr Ford's health and also for his own safety so he told the care manager what was happening and he wrote a report.

Mr Ford was admitted into Oakwood residential care a year ago. Recently his behaviour has become difficult. The staff say he swears at other residents and can at times try to hit them. Dr Day suspects Mr Ford may have dementia and may need a specialist care home where staff are trained in dementia care. He talks to Mr Ford and then to the staff who have kept a record of when Mr Ford gets upset and confused. Mr Ford's daughter comes to see him sometimes when she can spare time from her busy job. Mr Ford gets agitated when he needs the toilet so the staff decide to take Mr Ford to the toilet every two hours so that he doesn't wet himself. Dr Day asks the care manager to organise a case review and he also prescribes medication for Mr Ford's dementia.

Carl was putting the individual at the heart of service provision and promoting individualised care, promoting and supporting the individuals' rights to dignity and independence and providing active support consistent with beliefs, cultures and preferences of health and social care service users. He is supporting individuals who need health and social care services to express their needs and preferences and promoting the rights, choices and well-being of individuals who use health and social care services. He was dealing with conflict in a residential care situation for young adults but sometimes conflict occurs in residential care homes for the elderly and in domiciliary care settings.

Ensuring safety

People who work in health and social care ensure safety for individuals and staff through:

- use of risk assessments
- safeguarding and protecting individuals from abuse

- illness prevention measures, to include clean toilets, hand-washing facilities, safe drinking water
- control of substances harmful to health
- use of protective equipment and infection control
- reporting and recording accidents and incidents
- complaints procedures
- provision of first-aid facilities.

Risk assessment

When Mr Ford became agitated in Oakwood, the care manager Mrs Harris carried out a risk assessment. She made a list of the risks to staff, risks to other residents and risks to Mr Ford himself from his behaviour. Here is her list of a few of the risks, the likelihood of the risk happening and what staff could do to reduce the risk.

	Risk	How likely is it to happen?	How can we reduce the risk?
Risks to staff	Risk of being hit. Risk of being hurt when trying to help him when he is angry.	Very likely.	Try to find out what the problem is before he gets angry: Does he need the toilet? Is he thirsty?
Risks to other residents	Risk of being hit. Risk of being hurt when sitting near him.	Very likely.	Make sure there is plenty of room for others to get past Mr Ford. Take them into another room if Mr Ford is agitated.
Risks to Mr Ford	He might hurt himself when striking others.	Very likely.	Find out what the problem is before he gets angry. Take him to his own room where he has his own things around him to help him be less agitated. Ask for a review to see if he can have more appropriate care.

Table 2.1 Example of a risk assessment

You can see from this that she is safeguarding and protecting individuals from abuse. Risk assessments are carried out in all health and care settings and all staff should know how to carry them out.

In all health and care settings new members of staff should be inducted into their job role. All staff should follow illness prevention measures such as washing their hands before handling food and after going to the toilet and reporting sick if they have diarrhoea and vomiting. Managers must ensure there are clean toilets, hand-washing facilities and safe drinking water for staff and for patients.

Many health and care staff use substances that may be dangerous. *The Control of Substances Hazardous to Health Regulations* (COSHH, 2002) explain how to store harmful substances for example, medicines must be kept in a locked cupboard, bleach and other cleaning fluids also must be locked away when not in use.

Staff must use protective equipment such as aprons and gloves especially when dealing with body fluids such as blood and urine and when changing incontinence pads. Soiled material must be disposed of in the appropriate bags – usually bright yellow for clinical waste. **Infection control** involves stopping germs from spreading for example by using alcohol hand rub after handwashing, by not putting one person's pillow on another person's bed.

Accidents and incidents must be reported to the employer who will record them according to the Reporting of Injuries, Diseases and Dangerous Occurrences Regulations 2013 (RIDDOR). Accidents and injuries resulting in death, specific injuries such as amputations, crush injuries to the head or body, injuries that mean a person has to be off sick for seven days and dangerous occurrences are just some of the things that must be recorded.

All staff must be familiar with the complaints procedures so they can assist patients and relatives who wish to make a complaint. All staff should know where the nearest **first aid** box is kept and who their first aider is in case of emergency.

Information management and communication – ways of promoting effective communication and ensuring confidentiality

The Data Protection Act 1998 says how information about people must be stored. The data protection principles say that everyone using data must make sure the information is

- used fairly and lawfully
- used for limited, specifically stated purposes

- used in a way that is adequate, relevant and not excessive
- accurate
- kept for no longer than is absolutely necessary
- handled according to people's data protection rights
- kept safe and secure
- not transferred outside the European Economic Area without adequate protection.

There are even stricter rules when it comes to information about:

- ethnic background
- political opinions
- religious beliefs
- health
- sexual health
- criminal records.

The Information Commissioner's Office is the UK's independent authority that upholds information rights in the public interest, promoting openness by public bodies and data privacy for individuals. You can apply to them to find out what data is held about you.

In addition to the Data Protection Act there are legal and workplace requirements specified by codes of practice in certain health and social care settings. The Care Quality Commission (CQC) has a legal duty under the Mental Health Act to visit and interview detained patients, and to see records relating to their detention and treatment, to make sure people are not detained illegally. The CQC has a code of practice that says how it uses and stores this confidential information.

Skills for Care and Skills for Health publish a 'Code of Conduct for Healthcare Support Workers and Adult Social Care Workers in England'. Here is what it says:

'As a Healthcare Support Worker or Adult Social Care Worker in England you must:

1 Treat all information about people who use health and care services and their carers as confidential.

2 Only discuss or disclose information about people who use health and care services and their carers in accordance with legislation and agreed ways of working.

3 Always seek guidance from a senior member of staff regarding any information or issues that you are concerned about.

4 Always discuss issues of disclosure with a senior member of staff'

The Nursing and Midwifery Council (NMC) publishes the 'Code for nurses and midwives'. Here is what it says about respecting people's right to privacy and confidentiality:

'As a nurse or midwife, you owe a duty of confidentiality to all those who are receiving care. This includes making sure that they are informed about their care and that information about them is shared appropriately.'

To achieve this, you must:

'5.1 respect a person's right to privacy in all aspects of their care

5.2 make sure that people are informed about how and why information is used and shared by those who will be providing care

5.3 respect that a person's right to privacy and confidentiality continues after they have died

5.4 share necessary information with other healthcare professionals and agencies only when the interests of patient safety and public protection override the need for confidentiality, and

5.5 share with people, their families and their carers, as far as the law allows, the information they want or need to know about their health, care and ongoing treatment sensitively and in a way they can understand.'

Source: www.nmc.org.uk

The codes tell health and social care workers how recording, storage and retrieval of medical and personal information, including electronic methods, mobile phones, social media, written records, use of photographs must be kept confidential. Agreed ways of working may be local policies and procedures for confidentiality and for disclosure if a person tells that they have been harmed, are likely to be harmed or that they may harm someone else. In such situations a care worker must break confidentiality and tell their manager. This is legally required if a person is a risk to themselves or to others and they must follow their local organisation's procedure when doing so.

Being accountable to professional bodies

Accountability is to be responsible for the decisions you make and answerable for your actions.

Health and care employees are accountable to their professional bodies. They must follow the Code of professional conduct for their profession. We have already seen part of the Code for nurses and midwives, and the Code of Conduct for Healthcare Support Workers and Adult Social Care Workers in England. Both these codes stress that individuals are accountable for their actions and for their omissions, the things they fail to do which they ought to have done.

Social Workers in England are among 16 health care professions regulated by the Health and Care Professions Council (HCPC) which sets the standards of conduct, performance and ethics, of those professions. The HCPC Code says that

'As an accountable professional, you will be responsible for the decisions you make and you may also be asked to justify them'.

The NMC code says that a nurse or midwife must 'Be accountable for your decisions to delegate tasks and duties to other people'.

Health and social care professionals must be familiar with and use current codes of practice. These codes are revised from time to time so professionals must be familiar with the latest version of their code. It is their responsibility to make sure they follow any procedures needed

for revalidation. Although revalidation for social workers in England is still under discussion, nurses, midwives and doctors must prove they are competent in order to continue to practise. From April 2016 nurses and midwives will have to provide evidence of the following:

- 450 practice hours (or 900 practice hours if revalidating as both a nurse and midwife)
- 35 hours Continuous Professional Development including 20 hours participatory learning
- five pieces of practice related feedback
- five written reflective accounts
- reflective discussion
- health and character declaration
- professional indemnity arrangements
- confirmation usually by their line manager.

Source: www.nmc.org.uk

'Safeguarding means protecting people's health, well-being and human rights, and enabling them to live free from harm, abuse and neglect.'

Source: Care Quality Commission

It is essential in health and social care. Safeguarding regulations are part 5 of the Protection of Freedoms Act 2012. They include information about the Disclosure and Barring Service (DBS) which checks all people who work in health and social care to make sure they are safe to work with vulnerable children and vulnerable adults.

Accountability includes following procedures for raising concerns and for whistle-blowing. Every health and social care organisation has a procedure for raising concerns. Professionals who have concerns which are in the public interest must follow the procedures within their organisation first. Concerns might include fraud, abuse, or where someone's health and safety is in danger. The first stage is usually to raise concerns with their employer. If they have done that and no action was taken they can then raise their concern with the Care Quality Commission who regulate health and social care. The law protecting whistle-blowers is the Public Interest Disclosure Act 1998 (PIDA).

Multi-disciplinary working in the health and social care sector

'Partnership working' happens when different organisations and people work together to improve services. Partnerships can be formal or informal, between organisations or between individuals in organisations. In the case study earlier in this unit, Dr Day works with the care manager Mrs Harris and with Mr Ford's social worker to review what care Mr Ford requires. They include Mr Ford and his daughter in the discussions. This is one type of 'partnership working'.

In Northern Ireland where health, social services and public safety are all part of one government organisation, they work together to plan care, for example, for people living with long-term conditions in Northern Ireland. This is formal partnership working between different parts of an organisation.

Working in partnership

'The person, and the interests of the person, should be at the centre of all relationships. People, and where appropriate their carers, must be recognised as partners in the planning of services, which should be integrated and based on collaborative working across all sectors.'

Source: www.dhsspsni.gov.uk/index/long-term-condition

'Joined-up working' with other service providers is needed if we are to offer holistic care that meets all the needs of the individual. In England, where health care and social care are separate, care does not always meet the needs of the individual. When Mr Ford lived in his own home, a social worker arranged for a care worker to help him get ready for bed, but the care worker could only come at 8pm. Sometimes Mr Ford refused to go to bed. The care worker had to leave to go to their next visit, and so Mr Ford sat in a chair all night. Dr Day was unaware of the situation.

Since Mr Ford moved into residential care, things are a little better because health care and social care people meet together with him and his daughter to review his case every six months. This is partnership working for care reviews and care planning. It is one of the ways service users, carers and advocates, in this case Mr Ford's daughter, are involved in planning, decision making and support with other service providers. Everyone involved can share their views, and Mr Ford's daughter can help her father put forward his views about what he needs. This is a holistic approach that looks at his physical, social, emotional, cultural, intellectual and spiritual needs. At the review, Mrs Harris the care manager explained that they could no longer meet Mr Ford's needs and keep the other residents safe. She suggested he could be transferred to a specialist home where staff were trained in dementia care and could understand his needs. Mr Ford's daughter explained this to her father and although he seemed a little confused he agreed with the suggested change. The social worker organised an assessment to find out how much of his care would be funded by the NHS and then met with Mr Ford and his daughter to explain their options.

Partnership working is needed to provide care that meets all of the individual's identified needs. Partnership working avoids wasting money on unsuitable care – think of the carer who could not get Mr Ford to go to bed. It also helps health and care workers understand more of each other's roles in caring for an individual.

Partnerships can improve services in the voluntary or third sector too. Benjy, the young man with learning disabilities goes to a Gateway club that works in partnership with Mencap, the leading charity supporting people with learning disabilities. The leisure club provides health, leisure and social opportunities through sport, art, meaningful recreational activities and social opportunities. It helps Benjy develop independence.

Monitoring the work of people in health and social care settings

People who work in health and social care settings are monitored by their line managers. A social worker is monitored by their manager and so is a nurse. Care assistants are monitored by their managers. Managers are monitored by their line managers too right through to the top managers.

The NHS Trust Development Authority (NHS TDA) is responsible for overseeing the performance, management and governance of NHS Trusts.

There is also external inspection by relevant agencies. The Care Quality Commission (CQC) inspects and regulates different care services such as NHS Trusts, Adult Social care Services, Dental practices, for substance misuse services and some other services. They send inspectors into the organisation to check the quality of care given. They ask the same five questions of all the services they inspect. The questions are as follows.

- Are they safe?
- Are they effective?
- Are they caring?
- Are they responsive to people's needs?
- Are they well-led?

After each inspection, the CQC produces a report which usually includes ratings, showing the CQC's judgement of the quality of care. The judgements range from Outstanding, Good, Requires improvement and finally Inadequate. Organisations that require improvement are given a plan saying how they must improve. In organisations judged inadequate where the service is performing badly, the CQC takes action against the person or organisation that runs it.

When the CQC finds that an NHS foundation trust is failing to provide good quality care, Monitor, the regulator for NHS Foundation Trusts, can put the trust in special measures to ensure the problem is fixed.

The Human Fertilisation and Embryology Authority (HFEA) is the UK's independent regulator dedicated to licensing and monitoring fertility clinics and research involving human embryos, while the Human Tissue Authority (HTA) regulates organisations that remove, store and use human tissue and organs. The Medicines and Healthcare Products Regulatory Agency ensures that medicines and medical devices work and are safe.

The National Institute for Health and Care Excellence (NICE) provides national guidance and advice to improve health and social care. It regulates what drugs and treatments doctors can prescribe.

The Professional Standards Authority for Health and Social Care oversees statutory bodies that regulate health and social care professionals in the UK. It regulates these regulators:

1 General Chiropractic Council (GCC) which regulates the chiropractic profession.
2 General Dental Council (GDC) which protects patients and regulates dental teams.
3 General Medical Council (GMC) which regulates doctors.
4 General Optical Council (GOC) which regulates the optical professions in the UK.
5 General Osteopathic Council (GOsC) which regulates the practice of osteopathy in the UK.
6 General Pharmaceutical Council (GPhC) which regulates pharmacists, pharmacy technicians and pharmacy premises in Great Britain.
7 Health and Care Professions Council (HCPC) which regulates health, psychological and social work professionals.

8   Nursing and Midwifery Council (NMC) which regulates nurses and midwives in England, Wales, Scotland, Northern Ireland and the Islands.

9   Pharmaceutical Society of Northern Ireland (PSNI) which is the regulatory and professional body for pharmacists in Northern Ireland.

Whistle-blowing is reporting bad practice in the public interest. As we saw earlier, each organisation has a procedure for whistleblowing but the CQC is there if the organisation does not take action. The Care Council for Wales and the Care Inspectorate for Scotland are the prescribed bodies for reporting social care concerns in those areas. Concerns about registration and fitness to practise of health and care professionals should be reported to the Health and Care Professions Council.

The Public Interest Disclosure Act 1998 (PIDA) protects whistle blowers but life can be very uncomfortable for those who raise concerns. ACAS who provide help and advice for employers and employees have useful guidance on this.

Service user feedback is one of the best ways to monitor and improve services. It is the sign of a good organisation if they listen to people who use their services. Service user feedback is not always about complaints. Sometimes people want to say they had a good experience and say what worked well. Healthwatch makes sure that the health and social care system listens to people's views and experiences and acts on them. It works in partnership with the public, health and social care sectors and the voluntary and community sector to improve services. One example is where high patient numbers were causing long delays at Burton's Queen's Hospital A&E department, so the local commissioning group asked Healthwatch Staffordshire to find out why. They asked patients and as a result made suggestions that streamlined the service and reduced waiting times.

Some NHS providers have a Patient Advice and Liaison Service (PALS) to help patients and carers when making a complaint. Local Authorities also arrange advocacy services to support people who wish to complain about the NHS. Patients can take complaints about local authority services and services paid for by local authorities, to the Local Government Ombudsman. Anyone who feels their complaint has not been dealt with properly can take it to the Parliamentary and Health Service Ombudsman who make final decisions on complaints that have not been resolved by the NHS in England and UK government departments and other UK public organisations.

Criminal investigations are conducted by the police. Professionals are accountable for their actions. Sometimes they may be investigated for bad practice which is not a criminal offence. In this case if the complaint is proved, their professional body may caution them, impose conditions, suspend them or strike them off the professional register altogether so they cannot work in that profession. Sometimes the professional may have also committed a criminal act, for example, a nurse or doctor stealing drugs. In such a case the professional body may suspend the individual while the police investigate the criminal case. You can find the outcomes of investigations on the Nursing and Midwifery Council website and other profession's websites. Of course, everyone who works in health and social care must have an enhanced criminal records check under the Disclosure and Barring Service.

Activity

Look on the CQC's website and find a health or social care organisation near you. What rating does it have? If it requires improvement, what must it do to improve?

Distinction activity

Choose one health or social care profession.

Outline some of the things they might do in their work.

Give examples to show how they would apply each of the care values and principles.

Which other professional might they work with in partnership? Give examples.

Look at the regulatory body website for that profession. What standards are expected of someone in that profession? What sanctions might be used if they do not work to the standards expected?

Check your understanding

1 List five different roles on health and social care and say briefly what each role involves.

2 What are the care values and principles? Give examples for each.

3 What is partnership working? Give an example of it.

4 How is the work of people in health and social care settings monitored? Give examples.

B The roles of organisations in the health and social care sector

The roles of organisations in providing health and social care services

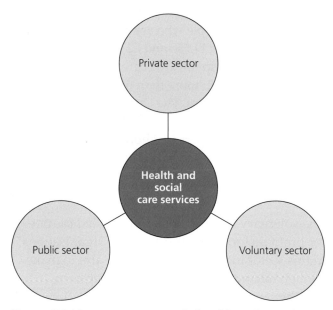

Figure 2.2 Three sectors provide health and social care

Health and social care services are provided by three sectors: the public or state sector, the voluntary sector and the private sector. The public sector provides care from cradle to grave, that is from ante-natal care, care during a person's lifetime right through to the end of life. Much of it is funded by the state from taxes and National Insurance contributions made by those in work. NHS care is free at the point where it is given, but social care is not. Commissioners plan what care is likely to be needed and then buy these services from any provider that meets NHS standards of care and prices. They may buy care services from the private sector or from the voluntary sector or from the public sector.

Clinical Commissioning Groups (CCGs) created following the Health and Social Care Act in 2012, replaced Primary Care Trusts on 1 April 2013. They enable GPs, working with other health professionals, to commission services for their local communities such as planned hospital care, rehabilitative care, urgent and emergency care (including out-of-hours and accident and emergency services), most community health services, maternity services, mental health and learning disability services. CCGs' governing bodies are made up of GP, nurse and secondary care representatives, and at least two 'lay' members who are not NHS professionals. All GP practices have to be a member of a clinical commissioning group. Local authorities and CCGs working through health and well-being boards use Joint Strategic Needs Assessments (JSNAs), and Joint Health and Well-being Strategies (JHWSs) to agree local priorities for local health and care commissioning.

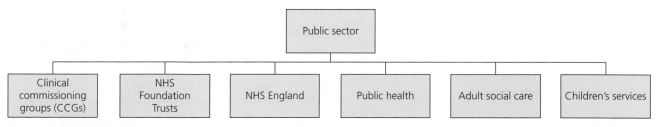

Figure 2.3 Public sector organisations

In NHS foundation trusts, the board of directors is directly accountable to the local population. The public, patients, service users, their families and carers and staff can become members. They then elect governors to represent them. This council of governors holds the directors accountable for the performance of the organisation.

National commissioning – NHS England commissions health care for:

- birth to five year olds
- for the armed services
- for prisoners, and
- for primary care including GP services.

It also commissions national immunisation programmes. NHS England is a single organisation, with 27 Area Teams across England. It also monitors how CCGs use their budgets and do what they are supposed to do.

Local authorities (or councils) are responsible for the health of their populations, for public health and for social care. They do this through health and well-being boards and encourage joined up working across the NHS, public health, social care, and other services. The health and well-being board includes the director of public health, director of adult social services, and director of children's services, representatives of all CCGs in the health and well-being board's area, someone from the local Healthwatch organisation and at least one elected local authority member. CCGs and local authorities can commission services together. Health and well-being boards assess health and social care needs of their local community through Joint Strategic Needs Assessments (JSNAs). They ask patient groups, voluntary organisations and the public for their views, then complete the JSNA. Health and well-being boards then jointly agreed priorities for local health and social care services in Joint Health and Well-being Strategies (JHWSs). Together, JSNAs and JHWSs form the basis of commissioning plans, across local health and care services, (including public health and children's services) for CCGs, NHS England and local authorities.

Public health – Local authorities are responsible for the planning and provision of public health services in their area, such as smoking cessation, and considering services, such as education, housing, social care and transport. Each local authority has a Director of Public Health. The main priorities for public health include stopping smoking, reducing alcohol consumption, eating more fruit and vegetables, and increasing physical activity levels. Public Health England (PHE), supports local authorities in improving public health and has national responsibility for protecting the public against major health risks.

Social Care – Local authorities commission social care for their local populations based on local need and national minimum standards. Social care includes services and support to help people maintain their independence and well-being, to protect vulnerable people and includes support for carers. The Adult Social Care Outcomes Framework sets priorities for the social care sector and is used to assess performance. State funded social care is means tested so people who are eligible for care and have between £14,250 and £23,250 in capital and savings get help towards care costs. Those eligible for care with more than this amount have to pay for it themselves. The Department of Health is responsible for national adult social care policy, and has introduced personal budgets for eligible individuals requiring social care. The Department for Education is responsible for national children's social care policy.

The voluntary sector is sometimes called the not-for-profit sector, or the third sector. Organisations in this sector include charities. They aim to make enough money to pay for their running costs and the services they offer. Most organisations in this sector rely on donations to survive. Age UK is a charity providing advice for older people. ChildLine is a service for children and young people provided by the NSPCC offering confidential advice and support online and by phone. The Prince's Trust supports 13 to 30 year olds who are unemployed and those struggling at school and at risk of exclusion. There are many more charities providing useful services alongside the public sector. Sometimes they work in partnership with the NHS and may supply services to CCGs, for example, Marie Curie nurses provide care and support in the individual's own home for people living with any terminal illness and their families. Marie Curie also have hospices where terminally ill people can be supported, have counselling and complementary therapies.

The private sector offers health and social care but aims to make a profit as they are businesses. BUPA care is a large business offering private health care in hospitals and for the workplace providing health checks for staff. Foster Care Associates is the UK's largest independent or private fostering agency. There are many private residential care homes and also many private care agencies offering domiciliary care in the individual's own home.

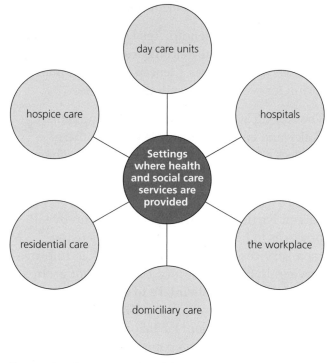

Figure 2.4 Settings for health and care

Issues that affect access to services

Access to services, how we get the service, depends on the type of service needed

Referral may be through professionals, for example, Benjy feels ill so he goes to see Dr Day his GP, who refers him to a hospital specialist. If Benjy fell down and hurt his arm he might go to the Accident and Emergency department of his local hospital. That would be categorised as 'self-referral'. Most voluntary and private sector organisations encourage people to approach them directly – through self-referral – but access to health care, which is generally free, is more tightly controlled as is access to social care.

Assessment – People are entitled to an assessment of their health needs. They go to their GP for this and he or she assesses their condition and whether they need treatment. Adults who find it difficult to cope can contact their local authority social services department and ask for an assessment. Carers too can ask for an assessment of their needs.

Eligibility criteria

Eligibility for adults with care and support needs depends on how their needs impact on their well-being. Adults are eligible if their needs arise from or are related to a physical or mental impairment or illness and make them unable to achieve two or more specified outcomes and as a result of not meeting these outcomes, there is a significant impact on the adult's well-being.

Outcomes include:

- being able to prepare and eat food and drink
- maintaining personal hygiene, being able to wash themselves and their clothes
- managing toilet needs
- being able to dress appropriately, for example during cold weather
- being able to move around the home safely, including accessing the home from outside

- keeping the home sufficiently clean and safe
- being able to develop and maintain family or other personal relationships, to avoid loneliness or isolation
- accessing and engaging in work, training, education or volunteering, including physical access
- being able to safely use necessary facilities or services in the local community including public transport and recreational facilities or services
- the ability to carry out any caring responsibilities, such as for a child.

Source: www.nhs.uk

Barriers prevent people using services. Barriers may be because of:

- Individual preferences – some people are proud and do not want to receive services. They may see it as a sign of getting old, and reject the idea they need help.
- Financial – some people have savings and a house over the limit, which make them ineligible for free services. Sometimes services are not free and people cannot afford them, for example, some infertility treatments not provided on the NHS may be available if they pay in the private sector.
- Geographical barriers to care occur when a person lives in a rural area. Their nearest hospital with accident and emergency services or maternity services may be a long way away.
- Social barriers occur when people do not think services are for them. Young males are less likely to visit the GP and men in general are less likely to seek help for health and for social care.
- Cultural barriers prevent some people accessing services. Information may be in a language they do not understand, or a care worker in the home may not understand their food requirements for example, if the person is vegetarian.

Activity

What services are available in your local area? Are there any services that people may have to travel a long way for? What barriers might prevent an older person in your community accessing these?

Look at health services; social services; voluntary services and private services.

Ways organisations represent interests of service users

We saw earlier in the unit how Healthwatch and PALS represent the views of people who use NHS services and we saw how good organisations improve by listening to feedback.

Charities such as Mencap, Age UK, Childline, and the Prince's Trust all welcome feedback from people who use their services. Mencap have an online forum for service users and their families.

The NSPCC website includes their complaints policy and encourages people who use their services and professionals to get in touch. The Prince's Trust has a feedback area on their website and a complaints policy.

Patient Participation Groups were set up by GP practices to hear the views of patients using their services and to use the feedback to improve services in the community. Some patient groups have worked with their GPs to streamline how appointments are made. The National Association for Patient Participation (NAPP) promotes and supports patient participation in primary care. NAPP is working in partnership with NHS England to support the Patient Online Programme to help general practices and patients with booking appointments online, ordering repeat prescriptions online and having online access to summary information held in patients' records.

Some organisations represent service users by offering advocacy, helping individuals make their views heard. Rethink, the charity supporting those with mental health issues, offers advocacy services. It also has a compliments, complaints and comments section on its website and uses feedback to improve services. VoiceAbility work across England with people who are vulnerable or marginalised to have their rights respected. They offer advocacy services.

As we saw earlier in the unit, whistleblowing policies require individuals who are disclosing matters in the public interest to follow their organisation's procedures and if this is not effective, they must approach the relevant regulatory body, usually this is either the CQC or the Local Government Ombudsman.

Activity

Choose one health or social care organisation from the public sector, one from the voluntary sector and one from the private sector. Compare the way they obtain feedback from service users and carers. Which organisation has the most open channels of communication?

Roles of organisations that regulate and inspect health and social care services

Regulation and inspection are two ways that the quality of services is maintained. We saw earlier in the unit how professions such as nurses and doctors regulate their members and we have seen how the CQC inspects and judges health and care provision, forcing improvements when services fall below expected standards.

There are some differences in each of the countries that make up the United Kingdom. Look at the section for the country you live in.

England

The Care Quality Commission (CQC) is the independent regulator of health and social care in England. CQC regulate and register people that provide services; use data, evidence and feedback from the public to help reach judgements. Inspections, announced and unannounced,

are carried out by experts who ask the same five questions in every setting. CQC publish information on judgements and in most cases publish a rating. They take action when services need to improve.

See section A5 for responses to regulation and inspection, changes in working practices required by regulation and inspection and how services are improved by regulation and inspection.

The Office for Standards in Education, Children's Services and Skills (Ofsted) inspect and regulate services that care for children and young people, and services providing education and skills for learners of all ages. They use a common inspection framework to gather evidence on the effectiveness of leadership, quality of teaching and learning, on the personal development, behaviour and welfare of children and learners, outcomes for children and learners. Ofsted inspect, form a judgment and publish a report with a rating grading provision on a four point scale:

Grade 1 outstanding

Grade 2 good

Grade 3 requires improvement

Grade 4 inadequate.

Ofsted has several powers. Some are non-statutory compliance actions such as issuing a simple caution, or a warning letter, making a recommendation or requirement at inspection. Other powers are stronger. These are statutory compliance actions which may be short-term or long term.

Short-term statutory compliance actions means that Ofsted can:

- Take emergency action to impose or vary conditions of registration
- Emergency suspension or cancellation of registration
- Serve a compliance notice
- Prosecute for an offence
- Restrict accommodation (children's homes, residential family centres and holiday schemes for disabled children)

Long term statutory compliance actions means that Ofsted can:

- Suspend, cancel or refuse registration
- Impose or vary conditions of registration
- Refuse to vary or remove conditions of registration
- Grant registration with conditions not previously agreed with the applicant.

Services are improved by regulation and inspection because they make sure only those service providers who are competent to do the job stay in practice. Those who are unfit are given a chance to improve but if they do not improve they are removed.

Wales

The Care and Social Services Inspectorate Wales (CSSIW) is responsible for reviewing the performance of local authority social services and for ensuring that regulated services comply with the relevant statutes, regulations and guidance. It can use its enforcement powers both civil and criminal to secure this in registered services. CSSIW regulates and inspects to improve care and social services for people in Wales from child minders and nurseries to homes for older people.

Inspections are unannounced with the exception of fostering services and adoption agencies. Most services have a baseline inspection six months after opening and focused and targeted inspections may follow. Provision is assessed against National Minimum Standards that set out the basic standards of care. A baseline inspection consists of tracking and triangulation across people's care experiences; staffing; leadership and clarity of purpose; quality assurance and health and safety; and also a systems check, sampling core policies, procedures and records. Enforcement powers are similar to those for the CQC in England. The Public Services Ombudsman for Wales has a similar role to that of the English Parliamentary and Health Service Ombudsman who makes final decisions on complaints that have not been resolved by government departments and other public organisations. Services are improved through regulation and inspection by ensuring only suitable people are care providers.

The Healthcare Inspectorate Wales (HIW) inspect NHS and independent healthcare organisations in Wales against a range of standards, policies, guidance and regulations. It regulates independent healthcare services and only registers a provider or manager if they can and will continue to meet the legal requirements and National Minimum Standards. Inspections take place regularly and often are unannounced. Where service providers fail to meet their legal obligations there is enhanced monitoring, targeted intervention and special measures may be introduced restricting the service. Enforcement action can include civil or criminal action and a range of sanctions.

HIW do not investigate individual complaints – NHS Wales Putting Things Right complaints process does that through Health Boards.

Her Majesty's Inspector of Education and Training in Wales (Estyn) is the equivalent of Ofsted in England. Estyn regulates and inspects schools, other education and training providers and local authorities after giving them notice. All inspections use the Common Inspection Framework and its three key questions about outcomes, quality of provision and effectiveness of leadership and management. Reports are published. Judgements range through Excellent, Good, and Adequate to Unsatisfactory. If a school or pupil referral unit requires significant improvement or is in special measures, they must produce a post-inspection action plan (PIAP). They have the same powers as Ofsted and work to improve services for children and young people.

Northern Ireland

The Regulation and Quality Improvement Authority (RQIA) is Northern Ireland's independent health and social care regulator. It improves the quality of health and social care services through inspections and reviews. Inspections are based on minimum care standards. RQIA regulates nursing, residential care and children's homes, day care settings, domiciliary care agencies, nursing agencies and independent health care services. It monitors the quality of services provided by the Health and Social Care (HSC) Board, HSC trusts and agencies and is responsible for ensuring the quality of services for people with a mental illness and those with a learning disability. It does this by registering, inspecting and encouraging improvement but has power to enforce decisions through a range of notices such as a Notice of Failure to Comply with Regulations, and notices to Cancel, Refuse, Vary, Remove or Impose Conditions on Registration. RQIA are the organisation for whistle-blowing in Northern Ireland.

The Education and Training Inspectorate (ETI) provides inspection services and information about the quality of education in Northern Ireland. This includes early years, primary and post primary schools, special education, further education and work-based learning, youth, initial teacher education, inspection of provision for the Department of Agriculture and Rural Development, Criminal Justice Inspection and the Department of Culture, Arts and Leisure as well as policy, planning and improvement work. Inspections focus on the quality of leadership and management; quality of provision and quality of achievements and standards and organisations are informed when they are about to be inspected. Judgements are either Outstanding, Very good, Good, Satisfactory, Inadequate or Unsatisfactory. Follow up plans and further inspections take place where provision requires improvement.

Health and social care regulatory organisations protect patients and the public. They register professionals, issue codes of practice and require members to keep up to date in their practice. Regulatory organisations investigate complaints against members and can suspend their registration or even strike them off the register. Recent changes require nurses and midwives to revalidate every three years proving that they practise safely and effectively. In the UK, and covering England, Wales and Northern Ireland, regulatory bodies include:

- The Nursing and Midwifery Council (NMC)
- The Health and Care Professions Council (HCPC)
- The General Medical Council (GMC).

In addition to the above, in Wales the Care Council for Wales (Social Care) and in Northern Ireland the Northern Ireland Social Care Council (NISCC) regulate social workers.

Non-regulatory bodies

The National Institute for Health and Care Excellence (NICE) – NICE's role is to improve outcomes for people using the NHS and other public health and social care services. They produce evidence-based guidance and advice for health, public health and social care practitioners; develop quality standards and performance measures for those providing and commissioning health, public health and social care services; provide informational services for commissioners, practitioners and managers across health and social care.

Public Health England protects the public's health from infectious diseases and other public health hazards; improves the public's health and well-being; improves population health through sustainable health and care services; builds the capacity and capability of the public health system. They do this through science, knowledge and intelligence, advocacy, partnerships and delivery of specialist public health services, such as managing vaccination programmes.

The Public Health Agency (PHA) in Northern Ireland is responsible for health and social well-being improvement; health protection; public health support to commissioning and policy development; and HSC research and development.

The Royal College of Nursing (RCN) is not a regulatory body. It represents nurses and nursing, promotes excellence in practice and shapes health policies but does not regulate the profession.

Activity

Check if your local GP practice has a patient panel to get feedback from patients. The minutes of meetings should be displayed in the clinic or surgery. Find out what changes have been made as a result of listening to patient feedback. If your GP does not have this in place, find out how they listen to the views of people who use their services.

Responsibilities of organisations towards people who work in health and social care settings

Organisations that provide health and social care services have a responsibility to ensure that employees understand how to implement the organisation's codes of practice, meet National Occupational Standards (NOS) and undertake continuing professional development (CPD). This protects patients.

Employers also have a responsibility towards their employees to make sure they are safeguarded through being able to:

- have internal/external complaints dealt with properly
- take part in whistleblowing
- have membership of trades unions/professional associations
- follow protocols of regulatory bodies.

Activity

Choose three health and social care professions. Find out which professional associations or trade unions represent their interests. Note – these are not regulatory bodies. Give an example of when there may be a difference between protocols of regulatory bodies and what an employer requests.

Distinction activity

Choose one of the following:

- How well does the structure of clinical commissioning groups and NHS trusts meet the needs of people using health services? Use examples to support your views.
- How well do social services meet the needs of the most vulnerable in society? Give examples to support your views.
- How useful are organisations that regulate and inspect health and social care? Give examples to support your views.

Check your understanding

1 Which three sectors provide health and social care?
2 What is the difference between them?
3 What is the role of clinical commissioning groups?
4 Outline the role of these: Ofsted, CQC, Nursing and Midwifery Council, the Health and Care Professions Council

C Working with people with specific needs in the health and social care sector

People with specific needs

Everyone uses health and social care services at some time in their life but some people have specific needs related to their particular condition or their age. Some specific needs may be related to the following.

- Ill-health, both physical and mental.
- Learning disabilities.
- Physical and sensory disabilities.
- Age categories such as early years or later adulthood.

Ill-health may be physical such as contracting an infectious disease like meningitis. Ill-health may be mental, for example, when someone is depressed or has an eating disorder. Their needs differ but both are health related. Learning disabilities covers a wide range of abilities. A high functioning autistic mathematician has different needs to someone who has limited ability. Physical disabilities covers a vast range of conditions. A person who was born without a hand has a physical disability, and so does someone who has lost both legs in a car accident. A deaf person has sensory disability but has different needs to someone who is blind. Children and older people have different health and social care requirements. Needs may be linked to cognition and learning, to physical and health requirements and to social and emotional aspects.

Activity

Choose one example of a person with specific needs. What support might they require in order to live a full life? Think of cognition and learning, physical and health requirements and social and emotional needs.

Working practices

Do you want to work in health and social care? Figure 2.5 shows some of the skills you will need. You will need:

- to understand and follow policies such as those for equality, confidentiality, health and safety and follow procedures such as safe storage of information
- to know how regulation affects people working in these areas.
- to know how working practices affect people who use the services.

You will also need to be familiar with recent examples of how poor working practices have been identified and addressed.

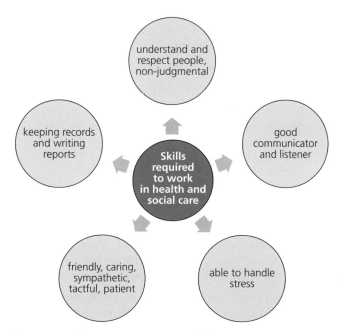

Figure 2.5 Skills for working in health and care

Figure 2.6 Health and social care workers need to have good communication skills

Activity

Choose one of these roles: children and families' social worker, social worker with adults, mental health nurse, general nurse, children's nurse, learning disabilities nurse.

For your chosen role outline three policies and procedures you might have to follow. Which organisations regulate the role? Give three examples of how working practices affect people who use the services (working practices may include whether they are involved in planning their care, how they are treated when receiving services, and whether they have an opportunity to give feedback on services)

Distinction activity

Find out what happened at Winterbourne View care home. Find out what happened in the Baby P case. What lessons have been learned from these cases?

Check your understanding

1 Give six examples of specific needs that individuals may have.

2 Give five skills needed by someone working in health and social care.

3 Give three examples of working practices in health and social care.

4 Give an example of poor practice. Say why it is poor practice and what could be done to avoid poor practice.

Case scenario

Benjy

Benjy is a young man with learning disabilities. He also has heart problems related to his condition of Down's syndrome. His support worker Carl is helping him to live independently, sharing a house with two other people with learning disabilities in supported accommodation. Which other health and social care professionals apart from Carl might Benjy encounter because of his health needs and his social needs? How could they best involve him in planning his care?

Exam Practice

Scenario 1 Ill-health

Ahmed who is a smoker and diabetic, developed chest pain. He went to see his GP, who referred him to a consultant at the local hospital. Ahmed had some investigations to check his heart. Following these investigations, the consultant surgeon recommended that Ahmed has a straightforward operation to improve the blood flow to his heart.

On admission to hospital, a nurse asked him questions about his health and well-being, checked his blood sugar level and recorded the information in his notes. The nurse checked that a risk assessment had been carried out.

Ahmed spent a week in hospital after his operation while medical staff checked his progress. Nurses

gave him medication and recorded his progress. Healthcare assistants helped him too.

When he went home, Ahmed's progress was monitored by a doctor at the hospital out-patient clinic.

1 (a) Identify two factors that a risk assessment might highlight when Ahmed is admitted to hospital. (2 marks)

(b) Describe two responsibilities of healthcare assistants when looking after patients on hospital wards. (4 marks)

(c) Explain how nurses are monitored to ensure that they maintain professional standards. (6 marks)

(d) Discuss ways that health and social care staff could empower Ahmed to improve his health when he goes home from hospital. (8 marks)

Think about it

The population of the UK is ageing. There is an increase in the average age of the population and the increase in the number and proportion of older people in the population. What impact might this have on the demand for health care? What impact might this have on the demand for social care?

Further reading

'Living with Long Term Conditions – A Policy Framework' April 2012, Department for Health, Social Services and Public Safety, Northern Ireland

'Blowing the whistle to a prescribed person', June 2015, Department for Business, Innovation and Skills.

Boyce T. and Hunter D. (2009) *Improving partnership working to reduce health inequalities*, The King's Fund.

'Guide to the Healthcare System in England', (2013), NHS

Useful websites

https://ico.org.uk

ACAS: www.acas.org.uk

Age UK: www.ageuk.org.uk

Childline: www.childline.org.uk

The CQC: www.cqc.org.uk

www.dhsspsni.gov.uk

Estyn: www.estyn.gov.wales

www.etini.gov.uk

Data protection: www.gov.uk/data-protection

Ofsted: www.gov.uk/government/organisations/ofsted

www.gov.uk/government/uploads/system/uploads/attachment_data/file/194002/9421-2900878-TSO-NHS_Guide_to_Healthcare_WEB.PDF

www.hcpc-uk.co.uk

Healthwatch: www.healthwatch.co.uk

www.hiw.org.uk

COSHH: www.hse.gov.uk/coshh

RIDDOR: www.hse.gov.uk/riddor

The King's Fund: www.kingsfund.org.uk

Marie Curie Cancer Care: www.mariecurie.org.uk

Mencap: www.mencap.org.uk

www.napp.org.uk

NICE: www.nice.org.uk

www.nmc.org.uk

www.ombudsman.org.uk

The Prince's Trust: www.princes-trust.org.uk

www.professionalstandards.org.uk

www.rethink.org

www.rqia.org.uk

www.skillsforcare.org.uk

VoiceAbility: www.voiceability.org

3 Anatomy and physiology for health and social care

About this unit

This unit provides an understanding of the anatomy and physiology of human body systems. It begins with cellular structure and function and builds to a more detailed knowledge of the body systems involved in energy metabolism. It provides knowledge of homeostatic mechanisms involved in regulating bodily systems to maintain health.

Anatomy is the structure or make-up of our body and physiology is the function of our body. The human body is made up of various levels of structures. This unit will start with the low-level structure, i.e. cells, then progress towards the complex workings of body systems.

Anatomy and physiology is an important topic to be studied as a health care worker so you can appreciate the body's normal conditions and so understand how systems work and recognise when they may not be fully functioning.

This process will be considered in this unit from conception through development, birth and the ageing process with links to genetics and disease patterns relating to each system.

Learning aims

The aims of this unit are to understand:

A   The structure and organisation of the human body.

B   The structure, function and disorder of body systems.

C   Medical research.

Assessment outcomes

AO1   Demonstrate knowledge of the structure, organisation and function of the human body.

AO2   Demonstrate understanding of the structure, organisation and function of the human body relevant to medical research.

AO3   Analyse and evaluate information related to anatomical and physiological systems and medical research related to disorders affecting these systems.

AO4   Make connections between common disorders and how they affect human anatomical and physiological systems.

How will I be assessed?

You will be externally assessed for this unit by the awarding body through a written examination paper. It will last for 1 hour and 30 minutes and you will be able to gain a maximum of 90 marks. There will be a range of multiple choice, short and long answers questions, you will demonstrate your knowledge and understanding about the structure and functions of Human anatomy and body systems.

Key terms

Anatomy The study of the body's structure and how each part relates to others.

Physiology The study of how the body works and functions within the organs and alongside other structures.

A The structure and organisation of the human body

How cells work

Part of cell	Function and structure
Cell membrane	This is the skin of the cell. It gives the cell its shape and allows the entry and exit of materials.
Nucleus	This is the control centre of the cell. It is surrounded by a porous membrane which allows for the exchange of proteins and nucleic acid. It is usually the largest part of the cell. Apart from red blood cells which do not have a nucleus, cells are unable to survive and reproduce without this structure.
Cytoplasm	This is a gel like fluid which contains a complex mixture of chemicals and nutrients which are the basic living materials for the cell.
Organelles	These are various parts of the cell with particular functions and are like miniature organs.
Mitochondria	These are sausage shaped bodies known as the 'power house' of the cell. In these structures, energy is released during cell respiration. Each mitochondria contain an inner membrane that is folded producing a ridge appearance known as cristae. Energy that has been released and is not yet required is stored in the mitochondria by a chemical called ATP (adenosine triphosphate). When energy is required ATP breaks down into ADP (adenosine diphosphate) releasing the energy.
Centrioles	Centrioles are tube like structures and are made up of protein strands called microtubules. Centrioles help to organise the cells during the process of mitosis (cell division) i.e. making the cell into two copies.
Endoplasmic reticulum	This is a series of membranous canals continuous with the cell membrane and assists with the exchange of materials inside and outside the cell. **Rough ER** – is dotted with black bodies called ribosomes and can produce protein and act as an extra storage area. **Smooth ER** – has no attached ribosomes and helps with the breakdown of fats.
Golgi Apparatus	These are flattened sacs, known as vesicles, which package proteins and deliver them to other organelles in the cell, they also produces Lysosomes.
Lysosomes	These are spherical bodies which store enzymes and then release them to destroy old or damaged organelles, they can be called the 'suicide bags'. They contain powerful chemicals which are responsible for the digesting of parts of the cells, bacteria and foreign materials which may enter a cell. They move around the cell freely.

Table 3.1 What is in a cell?

Characteristics of tissues

Cells which function together are called tissues; for example, the cells lining your digestive tract or your respiratory tract are all working together and form tissue.

There are four main tissue types found in our body, with special functions.

Epithelial tissue

The name of simple epithelial tissue tells us what shape they are:

● **Cuboidal** – shaped like their name implies, like little cubes. Found in glands and in the lining of the kidney tubules as well as in the ducts of the glands.

● **Columnar** cells are rectangular in shape. Simple columnar epithelium can be ciliated or non-ciliated. The nuclei are elongated and are usually located near the base of the cells.

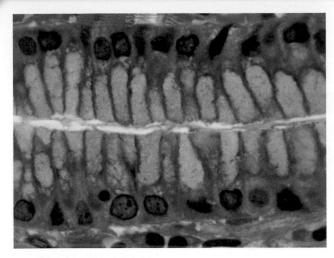

Figure 3.1 Epithelial tissue

Ciliated is found in the female reproductive tract. Non-ciliated is found in the uterus and digestive tract.

- **Squamous** – from the side they look something like a fried egg. Simple squamous epithelium is a common site for filtration. They are found in the lungs; walls of capillaries and inside of blood and lymphatic vessels. They form the lining of cavities such as the mouth, blood vessels, heart and lungs and make up the outer layers of the skin.

- **Ciliated** – these are simple columnar epithelial cells, but they have fine hair-like outgrowths, cilia on their free surfaces. These cilia wave in certain directions and are found in the air passages like the nose and in the uterus and fallopian tubes of females.

Compound epithelial tissue can be simple or keratinised. It is arranged in a single or multi-layered sheet and usually covers internal and external surfaces of the body.

Compound or stratified epitheliums are present in body linings where they have to withstand wear and tear. The top cells are flat and scaly and they may be keratinised, which means that the cells contain keratin. Skin is an example of dry, keratinised, stratified epithelium. The lining of the mouth cavity is an example of an un-keratinised, stratified epithelium

Connective tissue

Connective tissue is supporting; it has fibres in it which are tough and non-elastic, for example, cartilage, tendons, eyeball.

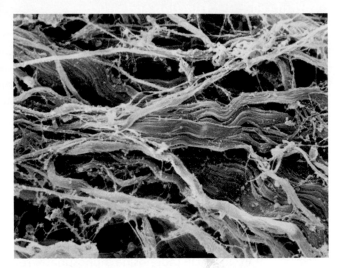

Figure 3.2 Connective tissue

- **Blood** is also considered a connective tissue. It basically consists of cells suspended in a matrix of fluid called plasma. It transports gasses such as oxygen and carbon dioxide and functions in clotting and immunity.

- **Cartilage** is rigid and strong so it can provide support and protection. It also forms a structural model for developing bones. Cartilage has no direct blood supply so nutrients must enter by diffusion. It gives strength, toughness; flexibility and slight cushioning when depressed. Found in symphysis pubis, inter-vertebral discs and the knee.

- **Bone** is the most rigid of connective tissues. Its hardness comes from mineral salts such as calcium phosphate and calcium carbonate. The primary cell of bone is the osteocyte. Bones of the skeleton consist of a solid outer layer, which appears like a honeycomb structure, allowing the bone marrow to produce blood and fat cells.

- **Areolar** – this is a loose moist tissue, irregular fibre arrangement and found in the dermis of the skin, superficial fascia, between muscles and around organs it provides strength, elasticity and support.

- **Adipose** connective tissue consists of cells containing lipid (fat) called adipocytes. The lipid is used to store energy to be used by the body if needed. Adipose tissue is also found around some organs and joints. It forms a cushion for shock absorption. Adipose tissue also insulates the body.

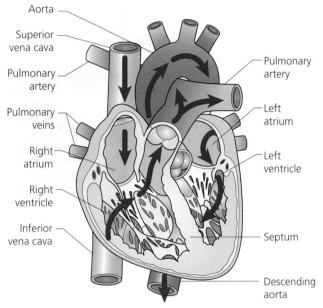

Figure 3.3 Blood flow through the heart

Muscle tissue

Muscle tissue: striated, non-striated, cardiac. Three main types – voluntary (striated) under control of the brain, e.g. muscles; involuntary (non-striated) under hormone and nervous control, e.g. muscles in the gut; cardiac – found in the heart.

- **Striated-skeletal** muscle is striated. The striations are caused by the density of overlapping protein filaments and it gives it a striped appearance. Skeletal muscle is usually under voluntary control.

- **Non-striated-smooth** muscle is not striated because the protein filaments are not as dense as in cardiac and skeletal muscle. Smooth muscle is found in organs such as in the gastrointestinal system and the arteries. Smooth muscle is usually under involuntary control.

- **Cardiac** muscle is also striated but has a unique structure called an intercalated disk. The disks are special intercellular junctions that allow electrochemical impulses to be conveyed across the tissue.

Nervous tissue

Nervous tissue consists of neurons to form the nervous system.

The function is to rapidly regulate and integrate the activities of the different parts of the body and can be found in the brain, spinal cord, and the nerves.

There are two kinds of cells:

- Nerve cells/neurons – the conducting units of the system
- Neuroglia – special connecting and supporting cells.

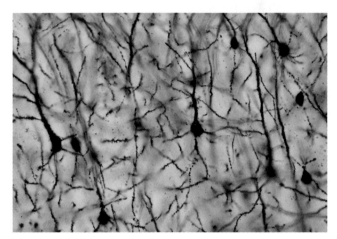

Figure 3.4 Nervous tissue

The structure and function of body organs

Tissues can also be grouped together to form larger structures called organs. So a group of tissues can all work together to carry out a particular function, for example, the eye, the heart and the liver. Organs have specific functions and distinctive shapes. For full details regarding the function of each organ see learning aim B.

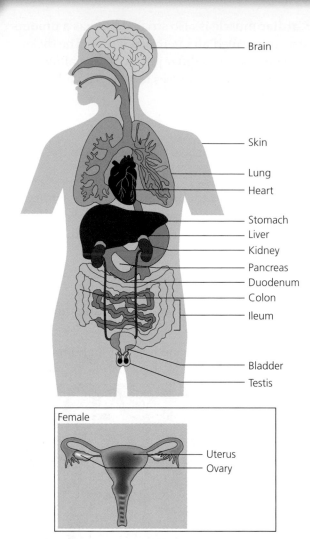

Figure 3.5 Organs of the human body

Energy in the body

Energy laws

Energy is required in order to perform things. Nothing happens without energy. To enable stored energy to do something useful it has to be transferred or changed into a different form. This process requires work and this also involves some wastage.

Energy is never created or destroyed; it is just transferred from one form to another. This is the 'principle of conservation of energy'. For example, a car engine uses chemical energy (the fuel) to make the car move – this is called kinetic energy. All physical processes are a result of energy being transferred from one form of energy to another.

There are many forms of energy:

- Magnetic
- Kinetic
- Electrical
- Heat
- Sound

- Light
- Gravitational
- Chemical
- Elastic potential
- Nuclear.

Metabolism

Energy is needed for our body to function. It is required for molecules to move in and out of the cells, for breaking down large molecules and also building new molecules.

The breakdown of large complex molecules to a simple form to release energy is called Catabolism and an example is when glucose is used in a cell to release energy.

The opposite reaction is called *anabolism* and is when energy is used to build complex structures from simple cells for example tissue growth and repair.

The energy comes from sugars and fats broken down. The cardiovascular, respiratory and digestive systems are all responsible for energy transfer.

Respiration is a set of reactions which allows the release of energy from glucose. Aerobic respiration is when this process uses oxygen.

GLUCOSE + OXYGEN $\longrightarrow$ CARBON DIOXIDE + WATER + ENERGY

During a period of exercise, oxygen may be in short supply so the release of energy is done without oxygen. This is called **anaerobic** respiration.

GLUCOSE $\longrightarrow$ LACTIC ACID + ENERGY

Metabolism is a continual process of chemical changes in cells which allows them to grow and function. It involves constant building of complex molecules (anabolism) and breaking them down (catabolism). These processes often release energy and the speed at which these reactions take place is called the *basal metabolic rate*.

Human genetics

The principles of Mendelian inheritance

In the nineteenth century, a monk called Gregor Mendel, conducted experiments using pea plants.

Some of them produced red flowers and some produced white flowers and had done so for generations. When he bred plants with different coloured flowers he noticed that the next generation of plants only ever had red flowers. He had discovered that red flowers in pea plants are a *dominant characteristic* and white flowers in pea plants are a *recessive characteristic.*

This principle of inheritance extends beyond pea plants and through to animal and human characteristics, like eye colour and the shape of your nose. Mendel's experiments were carried out before anyone had discovered genes. However, now we know that genes can have variations called alleles and the alleles can be dominant or recessive. Human beings normally have two alleles to determine a particular trait. For instance, there is an allele for brown eyes and allele for blue eyes. The brown eye allele is dominant and the blue eye allele is recessive, which means that if someone has one allele for brown eyes and one allele for blue eyes, their eyes will be brown. Because the blue eye allele is recessive, someone can only have blue eyes if they have two blue alleles.

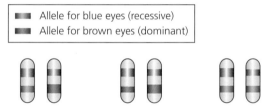

Figure 3.6 Alleles

People who are **homozygous** for a certain gene carry two copies of the same allele. People who are **heterozygous** for a certain gene carry two different alleles.

Children inherit one allele from each parent and the nature of characteristics that are genetic will depend on whether the alleles are dominant or recessive. For instance, cystic fibrosis (CF) is caused by a faulty recessive allele. If only one parent had this CF allele then none of their children could develop the condition, though they could carry the CF allele. If both parents carried the CF allele then there would be a 1 in 4 (or 25 per cent) chance that their child could develop CF; there would be a 1 in 2 (or 50 per cent) chance that their child would carry

the CF allele; and there would be a 1 in 4 (or 25 per cent) chance that their child would not carry the CF allele and therefore be completely unaffected.

Genetic mutation

A mutation is when an error is made in copying genetic information when a cell divides. Mutations are not necessarily a bad thing – in fact evolution by natural selection depends on the existence of small genetic differences caused by mutations. Mutations are responsible for the variations between alleles. Sometimes however these variations are responsible for disorders such as cystic fibrosis and sickle-cell anaemia.

> ### Key terms
>
> **Inherited disorder** A disorder which is passed on from a parent and is present in the genetic makeup.
>
> **Genetic disorder** A disorder which occurs when mutations are present in the DNA at conception (not always inherited).

Genetic variation

Down's syndrome

Down's syndrome is a type of genetic disorder that occurs as a result of an extra chromosome and in most cases is not inherited. There are three types of Down's syndrome – trisomy 21, translocation and mosaicism. Only translocation may be due to inherited factors. Down's syndrome is caused by changes in chromosomes during foetal development. Children with Down's syndrome have almond shaped eyes and have poor muscle tone. They may have heart conditions and problems with the digestive system, hearing and vision. With good healthcare, someone with Down's syndrome can live to around the age of 60.

Phenylketonuria (PKU)

PKU is a rare genetic condition that's present from birth (congenital). This is an inherited condition from a recessive gene and is caused by the absence of an enzyme which fails to break down the amino acid phenylalanine in causes to tyrosine. This then results in a build-up of phenylalanine and which causes brain pathways to be damaged and if undetected causes severe learning difficulties and growth problems. This condition is routinely tested for at birth with a blood test (heal prick). If detected a special diet can be given to avoid the disorder.

Sickle cell anaemia

This is an inherited disorder characterised by an abnormally shaped red blood cell (sickle or crescent shaped). Because the shape of the cell is smaller and lacks the surface area of a normal cell, its capacity to make haemoglobin stops the cell from living as long as normal. It is unable to carry sufficient amounts of oxygen so inhibiting the oxygen supply to the body. Because the cell is inefficient and has a short life span the result is anaemia (shortage of red blood cells).

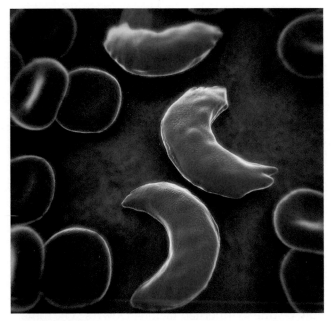

Figure 3.7 Abnormally shaped red blood cells in sickle cell anemia

Cystic fibrosis

This is an inherited condition where mucus, which is found normally in the digestive and respiratory tract, is thick and sticky. This leads to lung congestion and damage to the pancreas in the digestive system. Digestive juices which are secreted from the pancreas are unable to reach the digestive tract and so digest the food in the gut, this then leads to weight loss and malnutrition.

Huntington's disease

This is an inherited condition which causes damage to the nerve cells in the brain and so affects movement, thinking, reasoning and behaviour. This disease can manifest as early as the 30 to 50 age group and is a slow and progressive disorder that eventually leads to death. Because of the varied signs and symptoms it can be easily misdiagnosed and so mistreated.

It is caused by an allele that is dominant. This means that you only need one parent to carry the faulty allele for the child to have a 1 in 2 (or 50 per cent) chance of developing the condition. The diagram below shows what happens if the mother carries the allele.

H is the Huntington's allele

		Mother	
		H	h
Father	h	Hh	hh
	h	Hh	hh

Figure 3.8 Huntington's allele

Genetic testing in pregnancy

This type of testing is not routine and is only offered to women who are in a high-risk category such as:

- a previously affected pregnancy
- a family history
- an earlier antenatal screening which may indicate further testing.

Chorionic Villus Sampling (CVS)

CVS is done during the 11 to 14 week of pregnancy, cells from the placenta are removed for testing. Removal is done either vaginally or abdominally and results are available within three days.

Amniocentesis

Amniocentesis is done later in pregnancy at around 15 to 18 weeks. Fluid is taken from around the foetus and tests the cells which have been shed from the growing foetus. Rapid tests are available from about three days but full screening can take 2 to 3 weeks.

Complications and considerations

Both these procedures carry risks of miscarriage as the foetus is being disturbed. If the results of tests are positive then genetic counselling and advice is available. This advice may be support during and after a pregnancy to prepare for a child who has particular needs or advice about ending the pregnancy for therapeutic reasons.

B The structure, function and disorders of body systems

Homeostatic mechanism

Homeostasis is the mechanism in our bodies which regulates and maintains a stable and constant environment. The word homeostasis is taken from the Greek meaning *homoios* (same, like) and *stasis* (to stand still).

To help us understand homeostasis, imagine your body is your home and your homeostatic mechanism is your central heating system. Within the system is a thermostat, which regulates the heating system, similar to the hypothalamus in our brain, which regulates our internal environment. This is the control centre.

Hypothalamus

Our bodies are continuously making adjustments to regulate normal body functions; fortunately these adjustments are done automatically, otherwise we would be very busy people regulating our internal environment frequently. Homeostasis is controlled by the nervous system (autonomic) and the endocrine system (hormones).

Homeostasis is described as a 'negative feedback system'. This simply means that the system is able to take corrective action to maintain a constant environment. See Figure 3.10.

Negative feedback system

Homeostasis is responsible for maintaining the constant level of many body functions, for

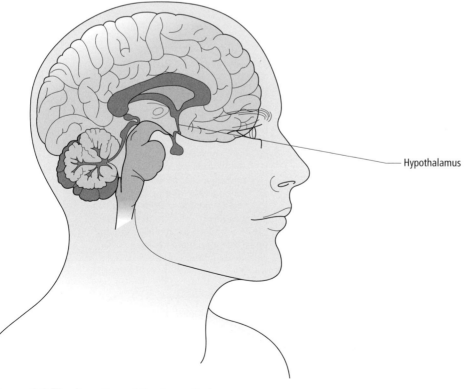

Figure 3.9 The location of the hypothalamus

Hypothalamus

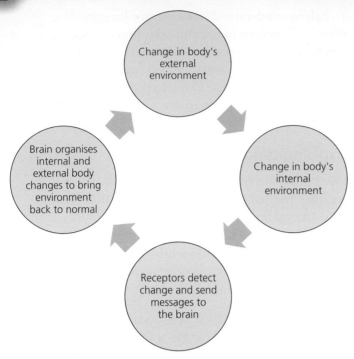

Figure 3.10 Negative feedback system

example **body temperature**. Monitoring of body temperature is called thermoregulation. The body's core temperature is held close to 37°C because this is the temperature at which chemical processes inside the body work most efficiently. Temperature detectors in the skin and internal organs monitor this and send messages to the hypothalamus in the brain to take corrective action when it rises or falls.

There are many ways in which we gain and lose heat:

- radiation
- convection
- conduction
- evaporation.

Homeostasis cannot take place without detectors and correctors. Look at Figure 3.11 which gives the corrective action the body takes to maintain a constant body temperature.

There are also behavioural actions that we take in response to a rise or fall in body temperature, for example:

- have warm or cold drinks
- put on or take off clothing
- take exercise
- switch on a fan.

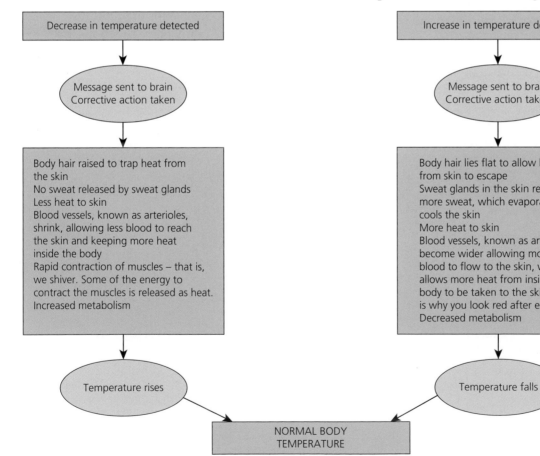

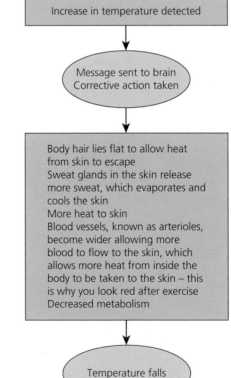

Figure 3.11 Homeostasis

In pairs, consider the corrective action the body has taken to get the temperature back to normal and with homeostasis in mind, explain why the corrective action has been taken. You may wish to put it in a table like the following examples.

Situation	Corrective action	Why?
Raised temperature	Raising the hairs	To trap a layer of warm air to insulate the body
Decrease in temperature	Shivering	Small muscle movements generate heat

The ratio of surface area to volume is an important factor for gaining or losing heat. For children and babies this ratio is a lot higher than for adults, and they will lose and gain temperature more rapidly.

A fever is normally caused by an infection. Your body tries to fight the infection by raising its temperature to kill the infection and this increase in body temperature causes various symptoms. Normal classification of a fever is a body temperature over 37.5 °C.

Blood glucose

The control of blood sugar or glucose levels in the blood flow is also based on a negative feedback loop. The pancreas monitors the concentration of glucose in the bloodstream and then releases hormones to ensure there is the correct balance. The pancreas releases the following hormones:

- insulin – this lowers blood sugar levels by instructing the liver to convert glucose in the blood into glycogen which is stored in the liver
- glucagon – this raises blood sugar levels by instructing the liver to convert some of its glycogen stores into glucose and release it into the blood.

Glycogen is a stored form of glucose.

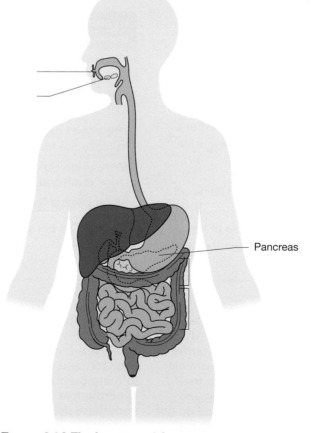

Pancreas

Figure 3.12 The location of the pancreas

Pancreas

Normal blood sugar level if measured is around 4–8 mmol/l (millimoles per litre). Study the table below to understand the body response:

- after a meal, i.e. high blood sugar level
- when hungry, i.e. low blood sugar level.

After eating	Hungry
Carbohydrates in food digested and changed to glucose	Low blood sugar level
Glucose high in blood	Pancreas produces the hormone glucagon
Pancreas produces insulin	Changes glycogen from the liver into glucose so it can be used in the body
Some glucose stored in liver as glycogen, some used by cells	Blood glucose level rises to normal
Blood sugar level decreases to normal	Pancreas stops producing glucagon

Table 3.2 The body's responses to changing blood sugar levels

Fluid balance

The kidneys are the organs which maintain the correct water balance in our bodies. Together with the pituitary gland and the anti-diuretic hormone (ADH), blood plasma is maintained at a stable concentration with the help of the negative feedback system.

As the kidneys act like sieves, they filter the blood and essential molecules like glucose, some salts and water is retained and recirculated for use in the body. Some elements like urea and molecular waste and some water is not required so allowed out of the kidneys, along the connecting ureters and to the bladder, and then excreted as urine. The kidneys, ureters, bladder and urethra are collectively known as the *renal system*.

So as our bodies exercise, sweat and drink fluids the blood plasma levels fluctuate, this is where ADH plays a part.

The diagram below will help you to understand the control of fluid balance in our bodies.

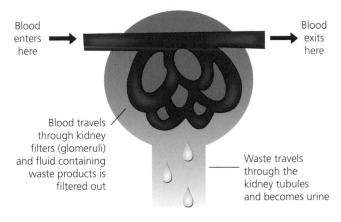

Blood enters here

Blood exits here

Blood travels through kidney filters (glomeruli) and fluid containing waste products is filtered out

Waste travels through the kidney tubules and becomes urine

Figure 3.13 Kidney filtration system

Hypothalamus in the brain monitors the blood plasma level	
Too high	**Too low**
The pituitary gland is alerted and levels of ADH is reduced	The pituitary gland is alerted and ADH is increased
This allows more water to leave the kidneys.	This causes the kidneys to absorb more water
More urine is produced. Urine is diluted	Less urine is produced. Urine is concentrated
Blood plasma levels return to normal	

Table 3.3 The body's responses to changing blood plasma levels

Think about it

Babies lose heat rapidly because they have a large body surface area in relation to the amount of circulating fluid. Their temperature control centre in the brain (hypothalamus) is immature so unable to work efficiently, therefore adults assist in their temperature control with sufficient clothing and bedding. Babies also are unable to shiver and do not have sufficient fat layers to insulate them properly.

Elderly people also find temperature control difficult. This could be due to being less mobile, eating less food and losing nerve sensations so that detectors and receptors work less efficiently. Failure to thermoregulate means the body may suffer **hyperthermia** (too hot) or **hypothermia** (too cold). Both these situations are life threatening and can cause major cell damage and death.

When the body has an infection, the core temperature can be raised abnormally, thus upsetting the homeostatic control temporarily. In this case the detectors now respond to 37°c being a low temperature, so corrective action such as shivering begins and the body temperature is raised. This condition is known as a rigor.

During *dehydration* the body water levels are low, these are detected and a message sent to the hypothalamus in the brain. Here ADH (anti-diuretic hormone) is secreted and causes the kidneys to keep water in the system and not allow it to be released in the form of urine. This process will then allow the body to rehydrate.

The structure, function and main disorders of the cardio-vascular system

The cardiovascular system is responsible for transporting oxygenated blood around the body to the cells and collecting de-oxygenated blood ready for excretion from the cells.

The cardiovascular system consists of the heart, blood and blood vessels.

The heart is located between the lungs, slightly to the left in the upper chest (thorax) area. This is the centre of the cardiovascular system and beats more than 100,000 times a day to pump blood through the vessels.

The wall of the heart is divided into:

- the epicardium – external thin layer
- the myocardium – middle layer; specialised cardiac muscle makes the heart contract
- the endocardium – inner layer; covers the valves and tendons.

The heart is divided into four chambers and is a double pump. Two upper chambers are called atriums. Two lower chambers are called ventricles. The right and left sides of the heart are separated by the septum, a solid wall which prevents the mix of venous and arterial blood.

The flow of de-oxygenated blood from the right ventricle to the lungs and return of oxygenated blood from the lungs to the left atrium is called pulmonary circulation (it goes to the lungs and back again).

The flow of oxygenated blood from the left ventricle via the aorta to the body and return of de-oxygenated blood to the right atrium is called systemic circulation (it goes to the organs and back again).

Stroke volume

Stroke volume is the amount of blood which can be pumped out of the heart (left ventricle) to the body per beat. The *cardiac output* is then said to measure this amount per minute. Therefore, the stroke volume and cardiac output determines how much oxygen rich blood reaches the body. An efficient heart muscle can produce a high cardiac output with strong efficient heart beats.

How blood flows through the heart

Oxygenated blood from the lungs returns to the heart via the pulmonary vein and enters the left atrium. Blood passes through the bicuspid valve into the ventricle. Blood is forced out of the aorta (main artery), which carries the oxygenated blood to the rest of the body.

De-oxygenated blood returns from the body to the right atrium via the largest veins of the body, the superior and inferior vena cava. The blood is then squeezed through the tricuspid valve into the right ventricle. Blood is forced through the pulmonary artery, which carries the de-oxygenated blood to the lungs.

Follow the arrows in Figure 3.14 and use these points as instructions to trace the path of oxygenated blood from the lungs, ending with the return of de-oxygenated blood from the body.

The cardiac cycle

Figure 3.14 illustrates arterial and venous circulation of oxygenated and de-oxygenated blood.

The following diagrams illustrate the flow of blood around the body.

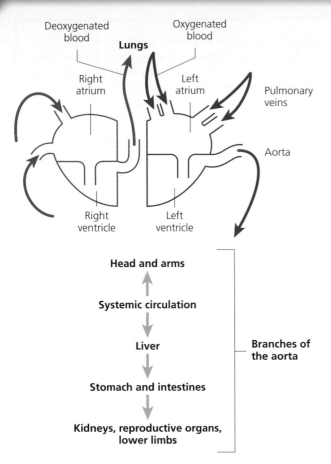

Figure 3.14 The cardiac cycle

Vessels

There are three types of vessels in the body:

- arteries
- veins
- capillaries.

Arteries

Arteries have the ability to contract and have to be elastic to expand under the high pressure that blood is delivered into them from the heart. They then recoil between the beats of the heart. Arteries divide like the branches of a tree to form **arterioles** and then further divide into capillaries. This allows the high pressure of the blood to decrease and be delivered effectively without damage to organs, tissues and cells. Arteries carry blood away from

the heart. In **veins** the blood is under less pressure so the walls are much thinner. Because the blood travels slower and usually against gravity (uphill), veins contain valves to prevent backflow. A collapsed valve is a varicose vein. Veins like arteries divide into smaller vessels called **venules** and then into capillaries. Veins carry blood towards the heart.

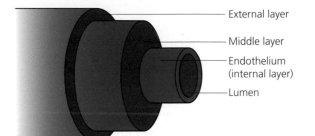

Figure 3.15 Arteries carry blood away from the heart

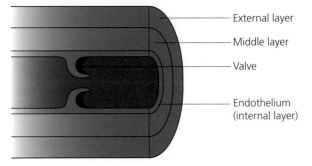

Figure 3.16 Veins carry blood towards the heart

Arteries	Veins
Carry blood away from the heart	Carry blood towards the heart
Carry oxygenated blood	Carry de-oxygenated blood
Blood flows rapidly	Blood flows slowly
Blood flows under high pressure	Blood flows under low pressure
Blood flows in pulses	Blood flows by squeezing action
Walls are thick	Walls are thin
Valves absent	Valves present
Internal diameter small	Internal diameter large
Cross-section round	Cross-section oval

Table 3.4 Differences between arteries and veins

Capillaries

Capillaries are thin-walled vessels which consist of a single layer of cells which are semi-permeable. This allows oxygen, vitamins, minerals and water to be exchanged into the tissues to nourish the cells. Carbon dioxide and water then pass out of the cells to be excreted. This is capillary exchange. Capillaries form a large network of blood vessels all over the body. The more metabolic activity in the tissue or organ, the more capillaries supply it.

Figure 3.17 Capillaries are the smallest vessels

Function and composition of blood

Tables 3.5 and 3.6 highlight what blood is composed of and the individual functions. Blood as a whole has many important functions:

- transport of nutrients, gases, hormones and antibodies
- defence and protection from disease and infection with clotting factors and antibodies
- temperature control with the homeostatic mechanism for control of body temperature.

Disorders of the cardiovascular system

Coronary heart disease

The arteries which supply the heart and cardiac muscle are called coronary arteries, when they are affected the result is coronary heart disease (CHD).

Element of the blood	Action
Formed elements/salts	
Erythrocytes Red blood cells	• Carry oxygen • Made in the bone marrow • Die after 4 months
Leucoytes White blood cells	• Fight infection • Made in the bone marrow • There is one white cell to every 600 red cells
Platelets	They help to clot the blood at wounds and so stop bleeding
Liquid element	
Plasma	

Table 3.5 The composition of blood

The heart requires oxygenated blood to function properly and this is supplied via the coronary arteries. If these are restricted by atherosclerosis or blocked by a clot (thrombosis), then angina or heart attack (acute myocardial infarction) can result.

Key terms

Thrombosis A blood clot that disrupts, slows or stops blood flow to major body areas.

Embolism This occurs when a part of the blood clot (thrombosis) breaks off and travels around the body colliding with small vessels, for example in the lungs, causing pain and difficulty in breathing.

Stroke

A stroke is an interruption to the blood supply in the brain. This can be caused when a blood vessel

Oxygen	The blood transports oxygen from the lungs to the cells of the body.
Carbon dioxide	The blood transports carbon dioxide from the cells of the body to the lung.
Waste products	The blood transports waste products from the cells to the kidneys, lungs, and sweat glands.
Digested food	The blood transports nutrients from the digestive organ to the cells.
Hormones	The blood transports hormones from the endocrine glands to the cells.
Heat	The blood helps to regulate body temperature.
Clotting	The blood contains platelets to help it clot.

Table 3.6 Functions of the blood

is blocked by a clot or the blood vessel bleeds so the brain tissue is not fully supplied with oxygen and nutrients.

Anaemia

Iron deficiency anaemia is the most common form of anaemia and occurs when the body has an insufficient supply of iron in order to produce an adequate amount of red blood cells. Iron is used to make the haemoglobin part of red blood cells which is responsible for the carriage of oxygen to all body cells.

Hypertension

This is high blood pressure. The heart has to work harder to pump blood around the body. This can weaken it and over time can lead to life threatening conditions, the increased pressure can damage the walls of arteries, which can result in a blockage or cause the artery to split (haemorrhage).

The structure, function and main disorders of the respiratory system

The respiratory system consists of the mouth, nose, larynx (voice box) trachea, bronchus (x2) bronchioles and alveoli.

The function of the respiratory system is to facilitate inspiration and expiration of air from the atmosphere into the lungs called pulmonary ventilation to exchange gases between the lungs and the blood, i.e. oxygen and carbon dioxide; this is called external respiration (breathing) and to exchange gases between blood and cells; this is called internal respiration (cell respiration or tissue respiration).

External respiration or ventilation

Let us follow the path of inhaled (breathed-in) air. Air is inhaled through the **nose** and mouth and flows down the trachea. The trachea is a muscular tube at the top of which is the larynx or voice box. The air is warmed and particles of dust and mucus are trapped by **ciliated epithelium** which lines the respiratory tract.

The trachea then divides into two, now called a bronchus or **bronchi** (plural). Then the tubes break into smaller tubes called **bronchioles** – this is similar to a tree trunk and its smaller branches. It is sometimes called the bronchial tree. At the end of these small tubes are grape-like structures which are one cell thick so as to allow oxygen to

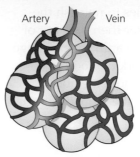

Figure 3.18 Alveoli

diffuse (cross over) into blood vessels which cover the outside of the **alveoli**. This is where external respiration or ventilation takes place.

The lungs are different sizes. The left side is smaller to accommodate the heart. Looking at the lungs from the outside, the right side has three lobes and the left has two lobes.

The grape-like structure gives a large surface area to allow maximum exchange of gases. Oxygen diffuses into the blood stream and then goes back to the heart to be circulated around the body. Carbon dioxide is exchanged from the blood circulation back into the alveoli and does a reverse journey through the respiratory system to be exhaled.

In the human lung there are approximately 300 million alveoli – this spaced out would cover a tennis court!

The breathing rate is mainly under involuntary (homeostatic) control, with our **diaphragm** and **intercostal muscles** assisting us with inspiration (breathing in) and expiration (breathing out).

Key term

External respiration Breathing in and breathing out is one respiration.

Disorders of the respiratory system

Asthma

This is a very common respiratory condition often found in children, if experienced long term (chronic) can be responsible for chronic obstructive pulmonary disease (COPD), particularly if not controlled. Asthma is an inflammatory disorder which affects the airways. It is triggered by infections, exercise, drug allergies, chemical and smoke fumes, emotions and animal allergies.

In asthma the muscle layer of the bronchi are irritated by the inflammation. This causes the muscle to tighten which causes narrowing of the bronchi and therefore difficulty in breathing, wheezing and coughing.

As asthma is an inflammatory condition it causes mucus to be produced which inhibits the gaseous exchange making breathing difficult.

Occasionally older adults may be told they have emphysema when in fact they may by suffering from asthma, or it could be genetically linked so therefore an inherited condition.

Chronic obstructive pulmonary disease (COPD)

This is a collective respiratory disorder which includes the conditions chronic bronchitis, emphysema and chronic asthma. It affects the respiratory systems, making breathing difficult.

As it is a 'chronic' or long-term disease, it usually affects people over the age of 40. It is responsible for over 30,000 deaths a year in England and Wales.

COPD is usually caused by smoking. Other causes can be occupational exposure to dusts, indoor pollutants, air pollutants or inherited causes, for example some people have an inherited form of emphysema where a lack of protein alpha-1-antitrypsin results in emphysema. This is also caused by lung damage caused by infection (chronic), smoke or pollutants and it damages the elastic structure supporting the air sacs (alveoli) in the lungs. Alveoli are grape-like structures where gaseous exchange takes place. This is reduced to a sac structure in emphysema; the result is reduced surface area, therefore reduced carbon dioxide exchange, so breathlessness occurs.

Pneumonia

This is inflammation of the lungs rising from an infection. The alveoli at the ends of the bronchial tree are inflamed, so filled with fluid which inhibits gas exchange, so breathing is difficult.

As the fluid is difficult to remove the infection can worsen causing coughing and expulsion of green or yellowish sputum. Anti-biotics need to be administered particularly in the elderly and young

as it can reduce circulating oxygen to such an extent that it may be fatal.

Smoking is a factor in either causing or exacerbating these conditions, as well as being directly linked to lung cancer.

The structure, function and main disorders of the skeletal system

The skeletal system consists of the bones of the skeleton.

- Humerus
- Radius
- Ulna
- Scapula
- Ilium
- Pubis
- Ischium
- Carpals
- Metacarpals
- Phalanges
- Femur
- Patella
- Tibia
- Fibula
- Tarsals
- Metatarsals
- Vertebral column
- Vertebrae.

The skeleton is made up of two parts: the *axial skeleton* which is the skull and spinal column, and *appendicular skeleton* which includes the limbs and girdles which attach to the axial skeleton. The function of the skeleton are:

1 Movement – they provide support for muscle attachment, this allows the bones to move freely.
2 Protection – they protect vital organs such as the brain and lungs.
3 Support – our Skeleton supports all of our organs and keeps them in place.
4 Production and storage – the bones provide a site for manufacture of red and white blood cells, and store such things as minerals.

Where two bones meet is called a joint and there are a variety of joints in our body which give different ranges of movement.

The classifications of joints

Structurally joints are classified as following:

1   **Fibrous joints** – the bones are held together by fibrous connective tissue that is rich in collagen fibres. No synovial cavity.
2   **Cartilaginous joints** – the bones are held together by cartilage. No synovial cavity.
3   **Synovial joints** – the bones forming the joint have a synovial cavity and are united by dense irregular connective tissue

Types of synovial joints

- **Planar joints** – the articulating surfaces are flat or slightly curved. Example are intercarpal joints in the hands.
- **Hinge joints** – the convex surface of one fits into the concave surface of another. E.g. Knee, elbow, ankle.
- **Pivot joints** – here the rounded or pointed surface of one bone articulates with a ring formed partly by another bone and partly by a ligament. An example of this can be seen in the wrist between the radius and the ulna.

Ball-and-socket joints

Examples of this joint are at the hip and shoulder where the end of the long bone has a rounded shape and the stable bone has an adjoining smooth socket to rotate within.

Types of movements in joints

- **Abduction**: this is the movement of a bone away from the midline.
- **Adduction**: this is the movement of bone toward the midline.
- **Circumduction**: this is the movement of the distal end of a body part in a circle.
- **Gliding**: this consists of side-to-side and back-and-forth movements.
- **Angular movements**: there is an increase or decrease in the angle between articulating movements. Includes flexion and extension.

Synovial joint structure

These have a space called a synovial cavity, between the articulating bones. The bones at the synovial joint are covered by cartilage. This capsule consists of two layers, an outer fibrous capsule and an inner synovial membrane. Synovial fluid is secreted inside the synovial membrane, this reduces friction by lubricating the joint. Supplies nutrients and removes metabolic wastes. Benefits of a 'warm up' before exercise is that it stimulates the production and secretion of synovial fluid and so avoiding injury.

Disorders of the skeletal system

Fractures

This is a term for a crack or a break in the bone and can be classified in many different ways.

Young bones may splinter or bend causing 'greenstick fracture'. Older bones may break easily from accidents or diseases.

Fractures can be:

- **Stable** – the broken ends of the bone do not move as they are forced together or they may not be completely broken. Example; wrist, hip, ankles, feet as in David Beckham's famous metatarsal injury.
- **Unstable** – bones can move out of line and could cause damage to tissues nerves and surrounding blood vessels.
- **Open** – one of the ends of the broken bone punctures the skin and can be seen externally.
- **Closed** – the skin is not broken but internal damage may still happen.
- **Direct** – this is when a fracture occurs from direct external force for e.g. a kick to the leg
- **Indirect** – this fracture occurs away from the site of impact. For example, if someone falls and puts out their hand to cushion the fall a fracture may occur in the shoulder or collar bone.

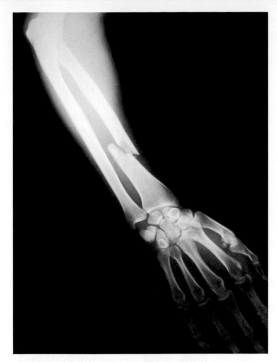

Figure 3.19 X-ray showing a fractured arm

Osteoarthritis

This is a degenerative joint disease, which is a gradual breakdown of cartilage in the joints. This chronic condition can cause pain and impair movement, especially in the elderly population. Many people consider osteoarthritis a natural part of ageing. It usually occurs in the knees, hips, back, hands and feet. It may be limited to one joint, but can affect several joints throughout the body.

Osteoporosis

This condition is more common in older people and affects bones causing weakness and fragility. Bones that are not continually repaired and nourished by protein and minerals will suffer over time. This condition may then be compounded as changes in hormone levels affect bone density, so as female oestrogen falls during the menopause bones can become thin and weak.

Rickets

This is a condition which leads to weak or soft bones, which can cause stunted growth and deformities of the skeleton. People with rickets may have bowed legs or curved spines. It is mainly caused by a lack of vitamin D, which is synthesised by the body during exposure to sunlight.

The structure, function and main disorders of the muscular system

A tendon is a tough, flexible band of fibrous connective tissue that connects **muscles** to **bones**.

Fascia is a flat band of tissue below the skin that covers underlying tissues and separates different layers of tissue. Fascia also encloses muscles.

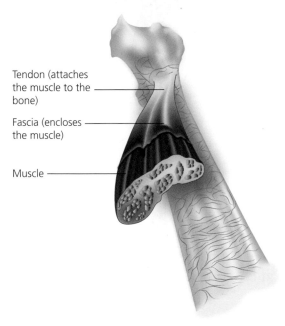

Tendon (attaches the muscle to the bone)

Fascia (encloses the muscle)

Muscle

Figure 3.20 The structure of striated muscle

Types of contraction

Isotonic contractions generate force by changing the length of the muscle and can be concentric contractions or eccentric contractions.

- A concentric contraction causes muscles to shorten, thereby generating force.
- Eccentric contractions cause muscles to elongate in response to a greater opposing force.
- Isometric contractions generate force without changing the length of the muscle.

Function of the muscular system

Muscles work in pairs to cause movement; a muscle always pulls in one direction, so an opposite muscle is required to return the muscles to the original position. This is called antagonistic pairs.

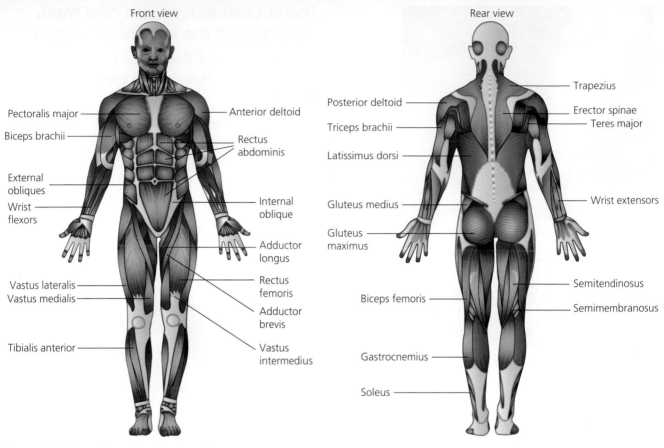

Figure 3.21 Location of major muscles

Muscle	Location	Action
Erector spinae	Up and down the spine	Extension of vertebrae
Rectus abdominus	Front of abdomen	Flexion of vertebrae
External oblique	Near the abdomen	Pulls the chest downwards and compresses abdominal cavity. It also has limited actions in both flexion and rotation of the vertebral column.
Internal oblique	Beneath the external abdominal oblique	Provides flexion and rotation for the trunk.
Biceps brachii	Front of upper arm	Flexion of elbow and shoulder, supination of forearm
Triceps brachii	Back of upper arm	Extension of elbow and shoulder
Deltoids	Shoulder	Abduction, flexion and extension of shoulder
Pectoralis major	Chest	Horizontal flexion and adduction of shoulder
Trapezius	Upper back	Elevation, retraction and depression of shoulder girdle
Latissimus dorsi	Lower back	Adduction and extension of shoulder
Gluteus maximus	Bottom	Extension of hip
Semimembranosus	Back of upper leg	Flexion of knee
Semitendinosus	Back of upper leg	Flexion of knee

Muscle	Location	Action
Biceps femoris	Back of upper leg	Flexion of knee
Adductors	Thigh	Adduction of the thigh
Rectus femoris	Front of upper leg	Extension of knee
Vastus lateralis	Front of upper leg	Extension of knee
Vastus medialis	Front of upper leg	Extension of knee
Vastus intermedius	Front of upper leg	Extension of knee
Tibalis anterior	Front of lower leg	Dorsiflexion of ankle
Gastrocnemius	Back of lower leg	Plantarflexion of ankle, knee flexion
Soleus	Back of lower leg	Plantarflexion of ankle

Table 3.7 The actions of the muscles

Disorders of the muscular system

Muscular dystrophy

This is an inherited condition which causes severe muscle wasting. The affected gene is predominantly carried by the female and mostly males are affected (affected females may have a milder form). Large muscle groups like the legs begin to waste and so mobility and balance can be seriously affected. As the disease progresses muscles like the heart, diaphragm and intercostal muscles are affected leading to cardiac and respiratory difficulties and eventually death.

The structure, function and main disorders of the digestive system

The digestive system consists of the mouth, salivary glands, pharynx, oesophagus, stomach, duodenum, ileum, colon, liver and pancreas.

The process of digestion starts at the mouth and completes at the anus. This is the digestive tract or alimentary canal. Digestion is the breakdown of food to enable the body to absorb it into the bloodstream and then into the cells for energy. The breakdown of food is:

- **mechanical** – by teeth, tongue and gums
- **chemical** – by digestive enzymes.

It is only after chemical breakdown that absorption takes place.

The functions of the digestive system are:

- ingestion – taking food into the body
- digestion – breaking down the food
- absorption – small molecules are taken into the blood stream
- assimilation – digested foods are used by the body
- egestion – removal of the undigested foods, waste products.

The process of digestion

Mouth

Your food starts its digestive journey in the mouth where mechanical breakdown of the food takes place. The food is chewed and broken into small pieces by the teeth and tongue. This is called mastication (chewing). The saliva causes the food to be mixed into a lump called a bolus.

The salivary glands secrete enzymes which chemically break down food. An enzyme called *amylase* begins to chemically break down the starches (in the carbohydrates).

The food then passes through a muscular tube called the pharynx, which leads to the **oesophagus**. It passes down this tube by swallowing. At the same time muscles in the larynx (see page 60 on respiration) contract and a flap of skin called the epiglottis snaps shut so that food does not enter the lungs.

The oesophagus is a muscular tube leading to the stomach and food moves along by means of peristaltic waves.

Follow this web link to see how peristalsis moves the food down the gut:

www.youtube.com/watch?v=KAfnIPYN0X0

> **Key term**
>
> **Peristalis** A muscular wave-like movement that moves the food through the digestive system. The gut muscles contract behind the bolus and relax in front of the bolus so that the food can move along the gut.

Stomach

The food then passes from the oesophagus through a muscular valve (cardiac valve) into the stomach. The stomach is the widest part of the alimentary canal and food can remain there for up to three hours. The stomach is a J-shaped organ and can be described as a strong muscular sac with many folds inside the lining called rugae. It is here where the food is churned around by large muscles and digestive enzymes are secreted from gastric glands. The food is now in a semi-liquid form called *chyme*. The enzymes here are called protease (pepsin) and hydrochloric acid. The high acidity level kills most bacteria. The content of the food depends on how long it stays in the stomach, for example:

- fats – approximately 6 hours
- protein – approximately 4 hours
- carbohydrates – approximately 2 hours
- water approximately – 15 minutes.

Alcohol is absorbed immediately into the bloodstream from the stomach so its effects are immediate. The chyme then leaves the stomach via the pyloric valve into the small intestine.

Duodenum

This is the first part of the small intestine. It is a long, convoluted tube split into two parts – the jejunum and the ileum. Two large organs help with the digestion of food here, the liver and the pancreas. The liver connects to the duodenum with the bile duct. One of the liver's jobs is to make bile which mainly digests fats. So as food containing fats enter the duodenum, bile is secreted (stored in the gall bladder under the liver) onto the food. This is the first point of fat digestion. Bile salts emulsify the fats – that is, make them into a form where they can be broken down further – they are now tiny fat globules.

Liver, gall bladder and pancreas

The pancreas is a large, slim gland and joins the duodenum via the pancreatic duct.

The pancreas pours pancreatic juices via the pancreatic ducts into the duodenum containing the enzymes, pancreatic amylase, trypsin and lipase which further break down proteins and fats. The pancreas is also responsible for the control of blood sugar with the hormone insulin (explained in homeostasis). This hormone is secreted directly into the blood stream, *not* the digestive tract.

As the chyme moves through the small intestine, many molecules are absorbed into the blood stream. The small intestine has a very efficient method to assist this process. It is in the small intestine that most of the absorption takes place. The small intestine has an excellent blood supply. The inside of the small intestine has finger-like projections called villi, which increase the surface area of the gut. Inside each villi are lacteals which are connected to the lymphatic system and they are responsible for the absorption of fats and eventually the digested fats pass back into the general blood circulation. The small intestine then leads to the large intestine through the *ileocaecal valve*.

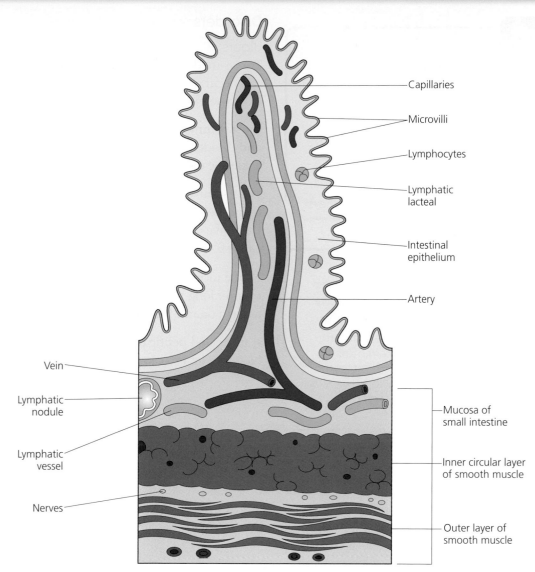

Capillaries

Microvilli

Lymphocytes

Lymphatic lacteal

Intestinal epithelium

Artery

Vein

Lymphatic nodule

Lymphatic vessel

Nerves

Mucosa of small intestine

Inner circular layer of smooth muscle

Outer layer of smooth muscle

Figure 3.22 The villi of the small intestine

The large intestine

The large intestine consists of the:

- Caecum
- Ascending colon
- Transverse colon
- Descending colon
- Sigmoid colon
- Rectum
- Anal canal.

It is wider than the small intestine and is approximately 1.5 metres long. It does not contain villi. The appendix is also contained in the large intestine but has no function in digestion.

The chyme continues into the large intestine and water absorption takes place, plus a little more absorption of nutrients. The large intestine secretes mucus that contains bacteria which ferment any remaining waste products which also causes a release of gases. The waste products (faeces) move through the large intestine (by peristalsis) towards the anal canal where they are expelled through the anus. This is under voluntary control in most adults.

Key words

- peptides and amino acids
- sugars
- glycerol and fatty acids
- roles in the body
- storage of excess fats and carbohydrates
- deamination of excess amino
- acids and the fate of end products
- the role of the liver and the role of the kidneys

Activity

Watch the digestive process following the web link below. Click on the names of the digestive system to find out more about their workings.

www.constipationadvice.co.uk/understanding-constipation/normal-digestive-system.html

Disorders

Ulcers

These are described as areas of inflammation that can occur anywhere along the alimentary canal so from the mouth to the anus.

Most common areas to be affected are the stomach and duodenum or small bowel, commonly known as peptic ulcers.

Ulcers cause pain and burning and can be associated with indigestion and heartburn. Ulcers that have developed over a long period of time can cause bleeding which can be seen in vomit or stools.

Peptic ulcers can appear from a bacterial infection or after long-term medication usage such as from aspirin or anti-inflammatory drugs.

If untreated peptic ulcers can cause perforation, bleeding or a blockage of the digestive system.

Major products of digestion

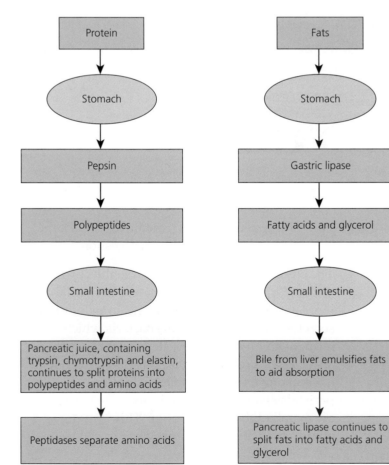
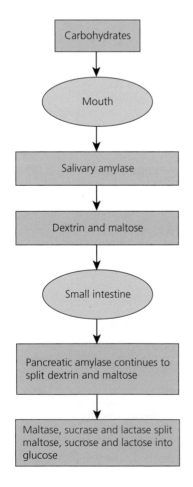

Figure 3.23 Major products of digestion

Hepatitis

This is inflammation of the liver and can be caused by infection or damage from harmful substances such as alcohol.

This can be repaired in some cases but it can also cause permanent damage of the liver which is called cirrhosis.

Symptoms for hepatitis can be flu-like, for example high temperature, headache, and sickness and occasionally jaundice. Long-term symptoms are tiredness, depression and jaundice. On many occasions these symptoms can go unnoticed.

Types of hepatitis:

1 **Hepatitis A** – usually acquired from poor hygiene or poor sanitation.
2 **Hepatitis B** – blood-borne virus and can be passed via body fluids such as semen and vaginal fluids so passed through unprotected sexual intercourse, sharing needles and from mother to baby.
3 **Hepatitis C** – most commonly occurring, also blood borne but rarely in other body fluids so can be passed through sharing needles.
4 **Alcohol hepatitis** – excessive amounts of alcohol will damage the liver and cause inflammation (cirrhosis) and eventually liver failure.

Key term

Jaundice A yellowing of the skin and whites of the eyes caused by a build up of something called bilirubin in the blood, or damage to the liver.

Coeliac disease

Coeliac disease is an autoimmune disease. Gluten, which is found in wheat, barley and rye, triggers an immune reaction in people with coeliac disease. This means that eating gluten damages the lining of the small intestine so absorption of food is incomplete resulting in weight loss, diarrhoea and vomiting. Other parts of the body may be affected. In babies, symptoms may only develop during the weaning process. Treatment will include adhering to a gluten-free diet.

The structure, function and main disorders of the nervous system

The nervous system consists of the peripheral nervous system and the central nervous system.

The **peripheral nervous system** includes sensory organs like the skin, ears, eyes, nose and tongue which receive messages from our environment, then the information is relayed to the **central nervous system** which is the spinal cord and brain, messages are interpreted and passed back to the peripheral nervous system where motor nerves carry information to muscles and glands to effect change within the body system.

The main function of the nervous system is *to receive* information from our external and internal environment *to interpret* (make sense of) this information and then *to take actions* accordingly.

The brain consists of billions of nerve cells. It is responding all the time to external and internal messages – those outside you and within you. For example, as you are reading this book your brain is interpreting information and allowing you to understand new ideas and perhaps make pictures. It will also be responding to external things. For example, are you feeling hot or cold? Your brain adjusts the internal environment to help you to feel comfortable, as well as creating feelings or emotions.

Spinal cord

This runs from the base of the brain to the lower part of the back (lumbar region). It is a bundle of nerve fibres, nerve cells and blood vessels. The spinal cord is protected by the spinal vertebrae in the spinal column, which acts as protection. The spinal cord is also protected by a tough outer membrane and between this and the spinal cord is a fluid that acts as a shock absorber called cerebro-spinal fluid. There are 43 pairs of **nerves** that make up the central nervous system. Twelve of these pairs are the cranial nerves, which supply the brain, and the other 31 pairs are spinal nerves, which supply the rest of the body.

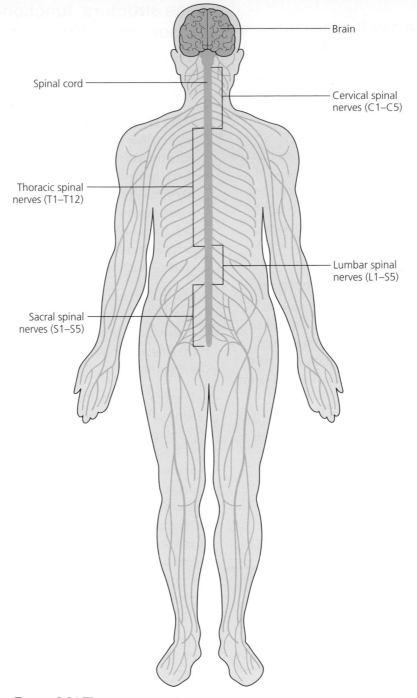

Figure 3.24 The nervous system

Nerves vary in thickness and consist of bundles of nerve cells or neurones. There are three basic kinds:

1   Sensory neurones – relay impulses from the sense organs to the central nervous system.
2   Motor neurones – relay the impulses from the central nervous system to the muscles or glands.

3   Relay neurones – transport impulses between nerves.

●   **Reflex actions** – these are movements that you do without thinking, such as blinking or your mouth watering. These actions are done in response to external stimuli, but you do not always have control over them. Have you ever tried not blinking for a few minutes?

- **Voluntary actions** – these are actions that we do have control over. You can decide to walk, run, sit down, read or write. These actions are under your control.

This part of the nervous system is not under our control and is called the autonomic nervous system. It has two parts, called the **sympathetic** and **parasympathetic** nervous systems (Figure 3.25), which together are responsible for maintaining vital organs and the stability of the body internally (homeostasis). This is discussed later in the unit.

The sympathetic nervous system prepares our bodies for fright, flight or fight situations, so this means our bodies will be prepared for immediate action.

One of its actions is to secrete the hormone adrenaline.

The parasympathetic nervous system has the opposite effect. It slows down the heart rate and allows the body to relax and recover.

Disorders

Parkinson's disease

Parkinson's disease is a disorder of the central nervous system that limits a person's ability to control some of his or her muscles. It's caused by a slow, gradual loss of certain cells in the brain. These cells make a chemical called dopamine. This chemical is needed for muscles to work normally.

Parkinson's disease causes movement and muscle problems. This may be a slight, uncontrolled shaking of the arms and legs, called tremor. Muscles feel stiff and rigid. The person may have difficulty moving his or her arms and legs, or may have shaky hands. Eventually, walking may become a process of taking small steps and slow movement, which is called a shuffling gait.

Multiple sclerosis

Multiple sclerosis is a condition of the central nervous system which controls the body's actions and activities, such as movement and balance.

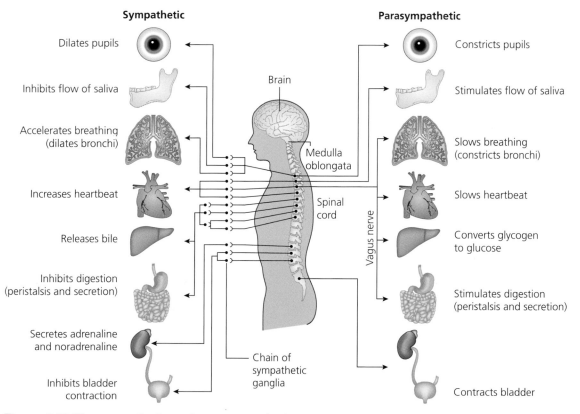

Figure 3.25 The sympathetic and parasympathetic nervous systems

Based on J. Hassett and M. White, *Psychology in Perspective*, second edition (1989) and www.drstandley.com

Each nerve fibre in the central nervous system is surrounded by a substance called myelin. Myelin helps the messages from the brain travel quickly and smoothly to the rest of the body. In multiple sclerosis, the myelin becomes damaged, interrupting the transfer of these messages.

Dementia
See Unit 17 'Caring for individuals with dementia', Learning aim A for a discussion of the types of dementia and their symptoms.

The structure, function and main disorders of the endocrine system

The endocrine system consists of a collection of ductless glands scattered all over the body that secrete hormones which controls how many internal organs work. The whole system is under control by the hypothalamus and the pituitary gland in the brain, together they regulate hormone levels in the blood. Some hormones act quickly like adrenaline while other hormones produce a slow response like growth hormones. See Table 3.8.

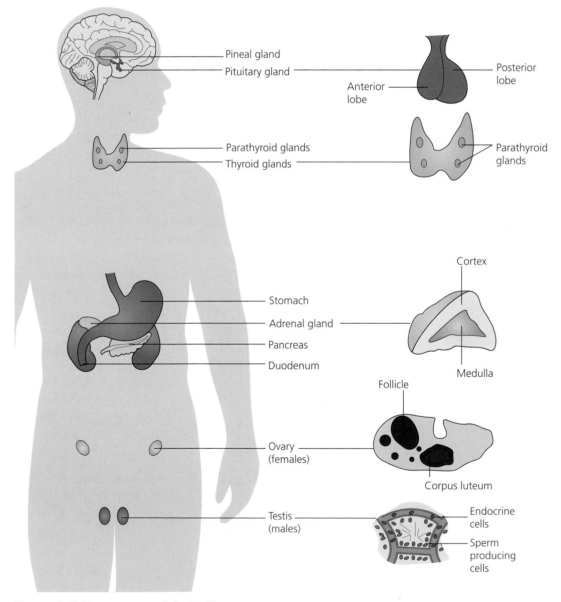

Figure 3.26 Hormones and their effects

Adrenal gland

The adrenal gland is found above the kidney and produces hormones that are vital to life. It helps with the production of cortisol which means it helps to regulate metabolism and helps your body respond to stress. It also helps the *aldosterone* which keeps control of blood pressure.

Gland/organ	Position	Hormone	Effect
Hypothalamus	Situated in the brain below the thalamus and above the brain stem, and is the size of an almond.	The hypothalamus is a collection of specialised cells that forms the link between the endocrine system and the nervous system.	This gland monitors and controls the eight major hormones released by the pituitary gland (listed below). It is also responsible for our sleep and waking cycles, known as circadian rhythms.
Pituitary (master gland)	Situated at the base of the brain close to the optic nerve, and comprising of two lobes: • Anterior lobe • Posterior lobe	Growth Hormone (GH)	
		Prolactin	Stimulates breast milk production
		Thyroid Stimulating Hormone (TSH)	Controls secretion of thyroxine
		Adrenocorticotropic Hormone (ACTH)	Controls secretion of adrenal glands
		Follicle Stimulating Hormone (FSH)	Controls production of eggs /sperm
		Luteinising Hormone (LH)	Controls secretion of sex hormones
		Oxytocin	Stimulates uterus to contract at end of pregnancy
		Anti-diuretic hormone (ADH)	Controls urine production and so water balance
Thyroid gland	In the neck	Thyroxine	Controls basal metabolic rate.
		Calcitonin	Regulates the uptake of calcium for bone development
Parathyroid gland	On the thyroid gland	Parathormone	Distributes the calcium in the body and regulates bone and muscle growth.
Adrenal glands	One on top of each kidney	Corticosteroids (cortisol and aldosterone)	Controls utilisation of major macronutrients and has anti-inflammatory properties. Controls the salt and water balance in the body.
		Adrenaline and noradrenaline	Prepares body for physical action 'fright, flight or fight situations' (see nervous system)

→

Gland/organ	Position	Hormone	Effect
Pancreas	Located behind the stomach and is a large pistol-shaped gland. The islets of Langerhans are the area responsible for the secretion of the hormones which control blood sugars.	Insulin	Lowers blood sugar levels by ensuring glucose is taken and used by the cells and any excess is stored in the liver as glycogen.
		Glucagon	Unlocks the stored glycogen and converts it to useable glucose when required thus raising blood sugar levels.
Testes	Two – situated in the scrotum of the male	Testosterone	Sperm production and development of the male sex organs.
			Secondary sex characteristics like body/pubic hair, voice changes and muscle development.
Ovaries	Two – situated at each end of the fallopian tubes in women	Oestrogen	Secondary sex characteristics like breast development, pubic hair, body shape. Production of ovum from the ovaries and preparation of the uterus lining.
		Progesterone	Prepares for and maintains pregnancy and prevents the release of further eggs during a pregnancy.

Table 3.8 The glands, the hormones and their effects

Disorders of the endocrine system

Diabetes insipidus

Diabetes insipidus isn't related to diabetes mellitus (but it does share some of the same signs and symptoms).

The two main symptoms of diabetes insipidus are:

● Thirst
● Passing large volumes of urine.

Diabetes insipidus is caused by problems with a hormone called *anti-diuretic hormone* (ADH), also known as vasopressin.

ADH plays a key role in regulating the amount of fluid in the body. It's produced by specialist nerve cells in a part of the brain known as the hypothalamus. ADH passes from the hypothalamus to the pituitary gland where it's stored until needed (also see page 53 on **homeostasis**).

In diabetes insipidus, the lack of production of ADH or, in rare cases, the kidney not responding to ADH, means the kidney can't make enough concentrated urine and too much water is passed from the body.

People feel thirsty as the body tries to compensate for the increased loss of water by increasing the amount of water taken in.

Diabetes mellitus is also known as Type 1 diabetes. Insulin, which controls blood glucose levels, is not produced by the pancreas. Too much glucose in the blood can lead to serious organ damage. Treatment is aimed at controlling the condition through regular insulin injections, in combination with awareness of diet and monitoring of blood sugar levels.

Around 10 per cent of all diabetes sufferers have Type 1 but it is the most common type diabetes for children.

Hypothyroidism

This is a disorder caused by an under active thyroid gland. This means that the hormone thyroxine is low or absent in the blood stream due to a damaged or inefficient thyroid gland. Thyroxine is responsible for the control of metabolic rates so this condition will make the service user feel tired, lethargic and they may gain weight for no particular reason. The gland can become swollen in this condition and this can be seen in the neck area and is called a goitre, which is a classic visual sign of hypothyroidism.

Structure, function and disorders of the lymphatic and immune system

These two systems are responsible for protection of the body.

The lymphatic system consists of lymphatic nodes, ducts and lymph. There are also organs which contain lymphatic tissues and also assist in the protection of the body when it is damaged or in times of infection. These are, tonsils, adenoids, thymus gland, spleen and appendix.

The main function of these two systems are to protect the body from infection, drain excess fluid from the tissues and transporting dietary fats to the blood via lacteals. When an infection is detected in the body an immune response takes place and lymphocytes and macrophages start to engulf and destroy the invaders or produce anti bodies to destroy the specific invader.

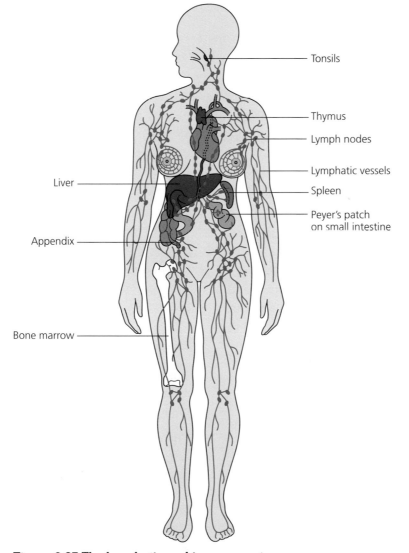

Figure 3.27 The lymphatic and immune systems

The lymphatic system is a network of *lymphatic vessels* similar to the circulatory system. The lymphatic vessels are responsible for the transport of the fluid lymph. *Lymph* is a clear fluid which contains white blood cells called lymphocytes which attack bacteria and viruses in the body which protect the body. *Lymph nodes* are found at various sites around the body. Bacteria and viruses are trapped and destroyed here. During infections lymph nodes may be swollen or tender.

The thymus gland is responsible for the development and production of T-cells, which destroy infections. B-cells mature and develop in the bone marrow. T-cells recognise, reproduce and destroy bacteria and viruses. B-cells remember the infection and quickly destroy it, particularly important if the infection invades for a second time. These specialised white cells are called Lymphocytes.

The spleen is on the left side of the body under the ribcage. Its function is to filter blood, it contains tissue called red and white pulp. The white pulp contains white blood cells and other pathogens, and the red pulp filters, destroys and remakes red blood cells, it also stores platelets.

Disorders of the lymphatic and immune system

Hodgkin's disease (Hodgkin's Lymphoma)

This is a type of cancer originating in the lymph glands and nodes and bone marrow. It is characterised by lumps in the armpits, groins and abdomen. Because the job of the lymph glands are to produce lymph and protect against infection the service user will be prone to infections and as the bone marrow produces new red blood cells they will suffer with anaemia.

Leukaemia

Leukaemia is the name for cancer of white blood cells. It can either be acute or chronic: acute leukaemia can appear quite suddenly, is aggressive and needs to be treated quickly. Chronic leukaemia develops at a slower rate.

Leukaemia can affect two different types of white blood cells and is given different names according to which type. In both cases, bone marrow – which

is responsible for the production of red blood cells, white blood cells and platelets – releases immature white blood cells, which are known as **blast cells**, into the blood before they have fully developed. Blast cells are not as good at fighting infections as fully grown white blood cells, and the large number of them can decrease the number of red blood cells and platelets in the blood. Fewer healthy white and fewer red blood cells and platelets leads to symptoms such as anaemia, pale skin, lethargy, vulnerability to infections and bleeding. If left untreated it can lead to life-threatening infections and/or serious bleeding.

Structure, function and disorders of the renal system

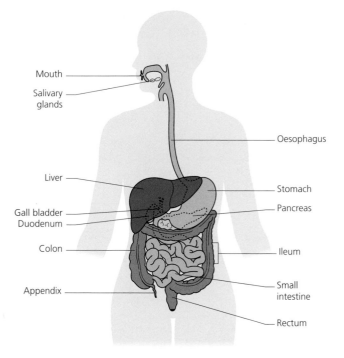

Mouth
Salivary glands
Oesophagus
Liver
Stomach
Gall bladder
Pancreas
Duodenum
Colon
Ileum
Appendix
Small intestine
Rectum

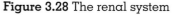

Figure 3.28 The renal system

The renal system, sometimes called the urinary system, consists of: two kidneys, two ureters, the bladder and urethra.

The main function of this system is regulation of salt and fluid balance in the body. The kidneys act as filters for the blood, ensuring important nutrients like protein and glucose remain in the blood stream and unwanted or excess products like urea, salt and water are excreted. This is a complex and selective process and is assisted by hormones which regulate salt and water levels so depending on the body's needs more or less urine is produced. (See homeostasis on page 53.)

After the blood is filtered in the kidneys the fluid travels down the ureters. These are muscular tubes, that are about 25 centimetres long. They are two vessels conveying urine from the kidneys to the bladder, their walls have three layers. The outer layer is composed of connective and adipose tissue. The middle layer has muscular fibres which contract to propel urine to the **bladder** in a **peristaltic** motion. The inner, mucosal layer, secretes mucus to prevent its cells coming into contact with urine. The bladder, where urine is stored, contains three indistinct layers of muscle fibre, jointly called detrusor muscle. This is situated in the pelvic cavity, a hollow muscular cavity, which can be described as an inverted pear. The normal capacity of the bladder is 300 to 1000mls. The bladder's main function is to store and release urine. Nerves in the bladder tell you when it is time to urinate (empty your bladder). As the bladder first fills with urine, you may notice a feeling that you need to urinate. The sensation to urinate becomes stronger as the bladder continues to fill and reaches its limit. At that point, nerves from the bladder send a message to the brain that the bladder is full and your urge to empty your bladder intensifies.

The urethra is a tube that connects urinary bladder to the outside. Its role is to excrete urine in both sexes and to pass the sperm in male. The male urethra is longer than a female's and this explains the increase in risk of infection of the bladder and the urinary tract for females. The female urethra is about 11.5 inches (4–5.1 cm) long and opens in the vulva. The male urethra is around 8 inches (20cm) and opens at the end of the penis. Both sexes have at least two areas of muscles: internal and external and they allow the control over urination.

Disorders of the renal system

Urinary tract infections
These are more common in women than in men. It is the inflammation of the urethra, the tube that leaves the bladder. Symptoms are a frequent need or sensation to pass urine with a pain or burning when passing urine which may cause bleeding in severe cases. Mild cases may pass in a few days and severe cases will need treatment from antibiotics to combat the bacteria which will have been isolated from a urine sample.

Renal failure
This condition can be acute, from an accident which damages the kidney or chronic which arises from conditions like raised blood pressure (hypertension) or diabetes.

Renal failure means the kidneys do not function properly so they fail to control body salts, water balance, and filtration of waste products. Small amounts of urine are produced which causes the body to become swollen. Conditions like anaemia and calcium deficiency can occur and in the long term the risk of cardiovascular disease will be increased.

Structure, function and disorders of the reproductive system

The female reproductive system

The female reproductive system consists of two ovaries, two fallopian tubes, a uterus, a vagina, a vulva, external genitals and two mammary glands.

An egg or ova is produced by the **ovary** and is pushed along the **fallopian** tube by the ciliated epithelium, it is here fertilisation can take place, once fertilised by a sperm the egg can now be called a zygote and will embed into the wall of the **uterus** and be nourished for 9 months. The uterus is also known as the womb. It is a hollow, muscular organ in which a fertilised egg, becomes embedded and in which the egg is nourished and allowed to develop until birth. The uterus lies in the pelvic cavity behind the bladder and in front of the bowel. The uterus is lined with tissues that thicken ready for pregnancy and is shed during the menstrual cycle. This layer is called the endometrium. During pregnancy, the uterus stretches from three to four inches in length to a size which will accommodate a growing baby. During this time, muscular walls increase from two to three ounces to about

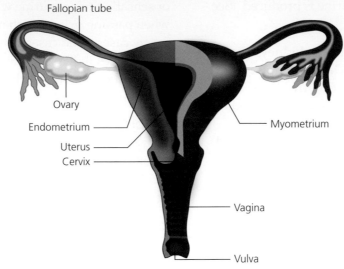

Figure 3.29 The female reproductive system

two pounds. During the birth, the unborn baby will be pushed out of the uterus via the cervix or cervical canal which is the entrance or neck of the uterus. The cervix allows sperm into the uterus and dilates during labour allowing the baby to be delivered. The last part of the internal reproductive anatomy is the vagina. This is a muscular canal which provides a lubricated entrance for the penis during sexual intercourse, and then the exit for the baby during labour. The female external genitalia is called the vulva. This area contains the labia majora, usually covered in pubic hair, labia minora (both are protective folds of skin), the clitoris and vaginal entrance, also here is the exit from the bladder, the urethra. Many of these processes are under hormonal control (see section on the endocrine system on page 72).

Disorders of the female reproductive system

Endometriosis

In this condition the inner lining of the uterus (endometrium) is found in different areas of the body for example, fallopian tubes, bladder and bowels. The tissue causes the uterus lining to thicken and so causes heavy painful bleeding during and between menstruation and after intercourse. It can also cause problems with fertility. As periods are heavy it causes tiredness, discomfort passing urine and faeces and can result in anaemia.

The cause is unknown and diagnosis is through a type of surgical procedure called a laparoscopy (or key hole surgery).

Polycystic ovary syndrome (PCOS)

This disorder causes cysts to develop in the ovaries and so inhibits the regular release of eggs (ovulation). High levels of the male hormone *androgens* are also detected in these cases.

Symptoms will include irregular or no menstruation, difficulty getting pregnant and male type features may appear, for example, hair on face, chest and back weight gain, hair loss from the head and oily skin.

Causes are unknown but have been linked with high levels of the hormone insulin. High levels of insulin cause the ovaries to produce too much testosterone, which interferes with the development of the follicles and prevents normal ovulation.

Insulin resistance can also lead to weight gain, which can make PCOS symptoms worse, because having excess fat causes the body to produce even more insulin.

The male reproductive system

The male reproductive system consists of two testicles, two vas deferens, a prostate gland and a penis.

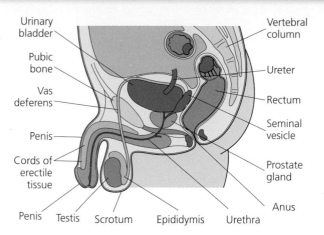

Figure labels (clockwise):
Urinary bladder
Pubic bone
Vas deferens
Penis
Cords of erectile tissue
Penis
Testis
Scrotum
Epididymis
Urethra
Anus
Prostate gland
Seminal vesicle
Rectum
Ureter
Vertebral column

Figure 3.30 The male reproductive system

The testes hang externally in the male body in a protective sac called the scrotum and they produce the male hormone testosterone and store sperm. The external position of the testes ensures that the sperm is kept below body temperature to keep it alive and healthy. Special muscles in the wall of the scrotum allow it to contract and relax, moving the testicles closer to the body for warmth and protection or further away from the body to cool the temperature.

The penis consists of erectile tissue which fills with blood during an erection and then the sperm travels along the vas deferens past the prostate gland and seminal vesicles where it receives nourishment and fluid to form semen. It then travels down the urethra to be ejaculated during sexual intercourse.

Disorders of the male reproductive system

Hydrocele
Hydroceles are swellings in the male scrotum caused by a build-up of fluid.

They often affect new-born babies, usually only causing a painless swelling of one or both testicles, although they can sometimes affect older boys or men, who may feel some discomfort in the scrotum.

In most cases affecting babies, the fluid is absorbed into the surrounding tissue during the child's first year or two of life and the hydrocele disappears.

Hydroceles that develop in men or older boys may be caused by inflammation of the scrotum resulting from problems such as an injury or infection.

Prostate cancer/BPH
The male prostate gland is enlarged in this condition and presses on surrounding structures like the urethra and bowel. This manifests with the need to pass frequent and small amounts of urine and sometimes a feeling of a full bowel. In order to confirm if the enlargement is due to a benign tumour or cancerous one it is necessary to take a blood test which will assess the level of prostate specific hormone (PSA). This, together with a rectal examination to assess the enlargement – and biopsy – will confirm the diagnosis. However, the PSA blood test is not specific just to prostate cancer. PSA can be raised due to a large non-cancerous growth of the prostate (BPH), a urinary tract infection or inflammation of the prostate, as well as prostate cancer.

The way in which natural conception occurs and patterns of pre-natal growth

Conception to birth

The cells from each parent that combine to form the **zygote** are called **gametes**. In humans, the male gamete is called sperm, and the female gamete is called an egg. When the gametes join they form a cell called a zygote; this is the first stage in the developing foetus.

The sperm cell contains 23 pairs of chromosomes and the egg cell contains the same number. The type of cell division that produces gametes with half the normal number of chromosomes (46 pairs) is called **meiosis**. It is used to produce cells for repair and asexual reproduction.

Meiosis is responsible for causing genetic variation. Gametes contain different genetic information to each other and to the parent cell.

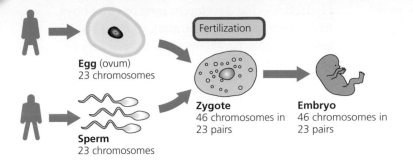

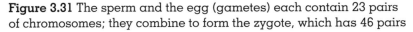

Figure 3.31 The sperm and the egg (gametes) each contain 23 pairs of chromosomes; they combine to form the zygote, which has 46 pairs

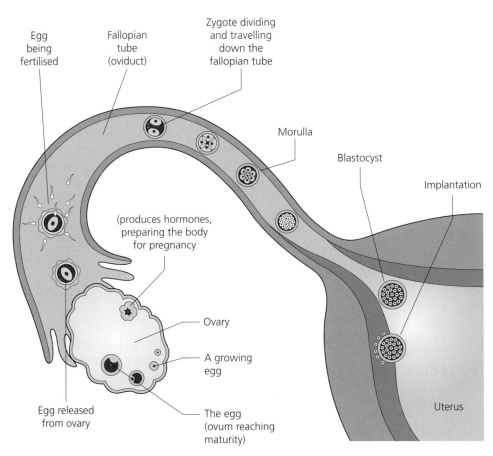

Figure 3.32 The process of fertilisation

Sperm cells travel from the penis to the egg cell via the vagina and cervix during sexual intercourse. The sperm have a tail to propel them, and many mitochondria to provide energy. The front of the sperm contains enzymes which digest the egg membrane and so penetrate it. The egg contains a large food store to support the developing zygote until it can feed from the placenta. The joining of the egg and sperm is called **fertilisation** and now the zygote will begin to develop with the correct

number of chromosomes (46) for the development of a new life

The period from conception to birth is a time of rapid development and growth. Once the ovum and sperm unite they become one cell – the zygote. The zygote continues to divide rapidly, some cells will form the placenta and some the embryo. After about 10 to 14 days when implanted into the wall of the uterus it becomes the **embryo**.

The stages of development during pregnancy are rapid and significant. They can be separated into three periods of time called trimesters – each trimester lasts around 12 to 14 weeks:

- **1st trimester** 1–13 weeks
- **2nd trimester** 13–27 weeks
- **3rd trimester** 28–37/42 weeks.

Trimester	Week	Stage of development
1	3	Foundation of the brain and nervous system is laid down
1	4	Length of embryo about 6.4mm
		Neural tube closes
1	5	Heart beat is detected

Table 3.9 Development during the first trimester

Mitosis

This type of cell division is for growth and repair and so exact copies of the cells are required. This means 46 chromosomes have to be duplicated. This process occurs and then the new chromosomes move to one half of the cell and the cell divides, producing two cells, each a copy of the other.

Birth

There are three stages of labour.

The first stage is the longest and it is confirmed when regular contractions gradually open up the neck of the uterus (cervix). This stage consists of early labour, active labour, and the transitional phase. As shown in Figure 3.34 the cervix shortens in diagram (a) and in diagram (b) and (c) it becomes thin and starts to open. Imagine the baby's head slipping through the neck of a roll neck sweater.

At the second stage (c) the cervix dilates (opens) to 10cms and the head is pushed out with the help of the very strong uterine contractions and the effort of the mother. The head travels down the vaginal canal and is delivered followed by the widest part of the baby (the shoulders) then the body.

The third stage is the delivery of the placenta.

Types of delivery

A vaginal or normal delivery is considered to be the most common method of child birth. On occasions this vaginal delivery may become prolonged or for medical reasons may need to be speeded up. This can be helped with methods such as:

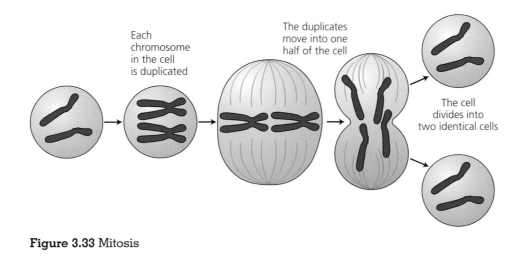

Each chromosome in the cell is duplicated

The duplicates move into one half of the cell

The cell divides into two identical cells

Figure 3.33 Mitosis

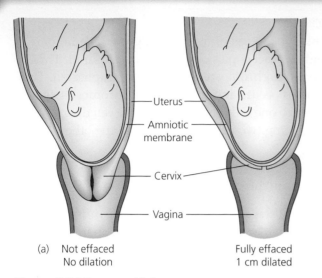
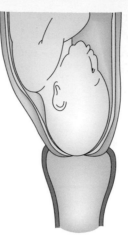
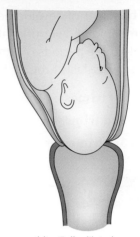

| Uterus |
| Amniotic membrane |
| Cervix |
| Vagina |

(a) Not effaced
No dilation

Fully effaced
1 cm dilated

(b) 5 cm dilated

(c) Fully dilated
(10 cm)

Figure 3.34 Stages of labour

- **Forceps** – large spoon-like instruments which are fitted around the baby's head and then gentle traction is applied by the midwife or obstetrician to deliver the baby.
- **Vacuum cup** – a cup-like appliance applied to the baby's head. With the aid of a suction machine air is drawn out of the tight fighting cap and a vacuum is created, the cup is now tightly fitted, pressure can be applied to guide and deliver the baby safely, by the midwife or obstetrician.

Caesarean section is an operation to deliver a baby and can be done using a general anaesthetic or a spinal anaesthetic. The baby is delivered through an abdominal incision which also opens up the uterus, and baby is delivered onto the abdomen.

This is not a routine method of delivery and is done for a few reasons:

- if the baby is breech
- if the baby has not made a descent into the pelvis so may be too large
- previous caesarean section
- in an emergency if the baby is in distress.

Factors affecting prenatal development

Different factors may affect the development and growth of a foetus in the womb. Some of these factors are listed below.

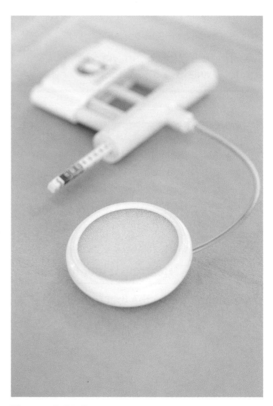

Figure 3.35 A vacuum cup

Genetics

Defects in genes are the cause of a number of illnesses and disorders. Such defects in the genes of a foetus can be passed on from either parent. For some conditions, the parent themselves may not have the disorder but may be a carrier of the defective gene. See pages 51 and 52 for details about inherited conditions.

Age

There is a greater risk for an adolescent mother to have a premature birth. First-time mothers over the age of 35 have an increased risk of having a baby with a chromosomal abnormality such as Down's syndrome – a woman in her 20s has a risk of one in several thousand of having an affected baby, but by the age of 40 this chance is about 1 in 110.

Diet

The food a pregnant woman eats during pregnancy is important. They should avoid foods that carry the risk of salmonella or listeria, such as soft cheese, as this can cause miscarriage or illness in a newborn baby. They need to have a diet rich in folic acid, which helps to develop the brain and spinal cord of the foetus.

Health

The general health of the mother can also have an effect. For instance, high blood pressure can increase the risk of a low birth weight, and conditions such as lupus or multiple sclerosis can increase the risk of a premature birth.

Smoking

During pregnancy, smoking reduces the amount of oxygen that reaches the foetus. Babies born to smokers are more likely to be born premature or to have a lower birth weight.

Alcohol consumption

Drinking alcohol during pregnancy increases the risk of miscarriage and foetal alcohol syndrome. Babies born with this condition may have stunted growth, facial deformities and learning disabilities.

Teratogens

Teratogens are drugs, chemicals or infections that can cause abnormal foetal development and birth defects. Most drugs taken by the mother, for example, will cross the placenta and enter the foetal circulation. These include prescription, non-prescription and illegal drugs. Babies born to parents who abuse illegal or recreational drugs may be born premature, have lower birth weight, and may have a variety of behavioural and cognitive problems. Substance abuse also increases the risk of miscarriage.

Congenital disorders

Congenital disorders are also known as birth defects and can be developed during the foetal stage, due to infection for example. They can also be passed on by the parents, or can occur as a result of injury to the foetus during birth.

Spina bifida

Spina bifida is the most common congenital disorder. This occurs when a baby's backbone or spine does not form normally. Babies with the disorder may experience mobility and cognitive difficulties as well as bladder and bowel problems. The exact cause of the disorder is unknown, but it can occur as a result of genetic and environmental factors. A lack of folic acid in the diet during pregnancy can lead to the baby developing spina bifida.

Cerebral palsy

Cerebral palsy results from damage to the child's developing brain before, during or after birth. This can be due to a number of factors including infection, and lack of oxygen to the brain. It affects the brain's ability to control the muscles and can also affect speech and language.

Effects of rubella

Rubella or German measles is a viral infection that is harmful to the developing foetus as it can cause miscarriage, stillbirth or congenital defects such as deafness, blindness and learning difficulties.

C Medical research

How data is collected and used

Clinical trials are important pieces of research which are carried out within the NHS to investigate, compare and improve medication, treatments and patient care.

Clinical trials may involve those who have an illness, for example, 'asthma' or those people who are 'healthy'.

All trials follow regulations called protocols and all those taking part in a trial will be fully informed and aware of the research they are taking part in and their part in it.

All the trials need to be fair so comparisons and results can be made with validity and reliability.

In doing so, they reduce bias and ensure a true finding. Those taking part in the trial and those delivering the trial may be unaware of what medication or treatment is being trialled, this is called a **double blind** trial.

A placebo

A placebo is when a 'dummy' treatment is substituted for a prescribed medication – without the recipient being aware. This is important, because it is the effect of the medication which are measured. For example, pain killers, if someone knows they are taking pain killers, the results need to be monitored carefully in order to assess if they are psychological or physical.

Epidemiological studies

Epidemiological studies are pieces of research which look at patterns of illness and disease in large groups of people. These studies often consider environmental factors with diseases, for example diet, exercise, smoking and their associated links with illnesses.

Mortality and morbidity statistics

Mortality and morbidity statistics is data which can be collected to inform us how the population suffers from illness and dies.

- Mortality rate is calculated as the number of deaths from a disease divided by the population.
- Morbidity is a definition for illness and should also be considered with the term prevalence which means the likelihood of a disease. This is said to be the total number of cases of a disease existing in a population.

Data analysis

Data analysis is a process where the gathered information is logically and reasonably examined. Data should be gathered, reviewed, analysed and then a conclusion or finding made under strict protocols to ensure reliability and avoid bias.

Exam Practice

SECTION A

Look at the diagram of the kidneys.

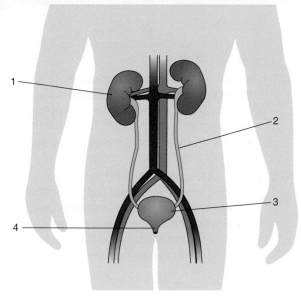

1   State the name of structure 2 and describe its role. (2 marks)

2   State the name of structure 4 and describe its role. (2 marks)

3   Explain how structure 3 is controlled. (3 marks)

The kidneys are labelled '1' in the diagram.

4   Describe the parts of the kidney. (2 marks)

5   Explain how the kidneys filter the blood. (4 marks)

6   Outline how a urinary tract infection can affect the workings of this system. (4 marks)

SECTION B

1   Outline the use of antibiotics in current medical practice today in light of resistant strains of bacteria becoming a growing problem in hospitals. (4 marks)

2   Explain the importance of homeostatic mechanism within the human body. (4 marks)

3   Compare and contrast the process of respiration and the release of energy with and without oxygen. (6 marks)

4   Atherosclerosis predisposes to coronary heart disease. To what extent could primary health care reduce the incidence of this disorder? (3 marks)

5   Occasionally genetic testing during early pregnancy has to be considered by the expectant parents. John and Meera are married. John's mother and father are both carriers of the Cystic Fibrosis (CF) allele.

a)   Deduce the chances that John has cystic fibrosis. (4 marks)

b)   John and Meera have a child, called Al. Meera is a carrier of the CF allele. Deduce the chance that Al is carrying the CF allele. (4 marks)

Further reading

'Fundamentals of Anatomy and Physiology for Student Nurses', Wiley-Blackwell; 1 Pap/Psc edition (4th March, 2011)

Norris, M. and Rae Siegfried, D. *Anatomy & Physiology For Dummies*, (2011), Wiley, New Jersey

Useful websites

www.diabetes.org.uk

Age UK: www.ageuk.org.uk

www.parkinsons.org.uk

http://alzheimers.org.uk/

www.nras.org.uk

National Osteoporosis Society: www.nos.org.uk

British Heart Foundation: www.bhf.org.uk

www.nhs.uk/conditions

www.babycentre.co.uk

https://ukctg.nihr.ac.uk/about-clinical-trials/

4 Enquiries into current research in health and social care

About this unit

The way we care for people has changed over time. We are shocked when children die from measles or starvation, yet once this was a common occurrence in Britain and still is in many countries today. Improvements in health and social care have happened because of research. Scientists researched the cause of tuberculosis, a major cause of death, and through research found a drug to treat it. In this unit you will learn why and how research is conducted and which organisations are involved in commissioning research. You will learn about some of the ethical issues involved in ensuring we can rely on research findings. The unit explains the difference between primary and secondary research and uses examples to analyse and evaluate current research.

Learning aims

The aims of this unit are to understand:

A Types of issues where research is carried out in the health and social care sector.

B Research methods in health and social care.

C Carrying out and reviewing relevant secondary research into a contemporary health and social care issue.

Assessment outcomes

AO1 Demonstrate knowledge and understanding of methods, skills and ethical issues related to carrying out research within the health and social care sector.

AO2 Apply knowledge and understanding of the methods, skills and ethical issues to current research in the health and social care sector.

AO3 Analyse information and data related to current research in health and social care, demonstrating the ability to interpret the potential impact and influence of the research on health and social care practice and service provision.

AO4 Evaluate current health and social care research to make informed judgements about the validity of the research methods used, further areas for research and the potential impact of the research on health and social care practice and service provision.

How will I be assessed?

This unit is assessed under supervised conditions. You will be provided with Part A of the assessment six weeks prior to the supervised assessment period. Part A will provide you with a choice of two articles for you to research. It is recommended that you spend 18 hours on the research over the six week period.

The supervised assessment period is a maximum of three hours. During the supervised assessment period, you will be given Part B of the assessment which will assess your understanding of research methods, the issues involved in planning research and the impact of the research findings on health or social care practice and/or provision.

The number of marks for the unit is 65.

The assessment availability is May to June each year. The first assessment availability is May to June 2018.

How will I be graded?

Pass	Merit	Distinction
Learners will demonstrate an understanding of the ways that current research is used in health and social care, and the appropriateness of different types of research related to specific issues and enquiries. They will apply secondary research techniques and review the success of techniques and skills in the context of current research into issues in health and social care, referencing validity and reliability. Learners will apply their knowledge and understanding from across their learning to explore feasible ethical solutions to further the research into key areas in the sector. They will demonstrate analytical and evaluative skills in order to judge the effectiveness of research in context, and recognise the implications for future practice/provision in the sector.		Learners will make critical rationalised judgements about the techniques and skills evidenced within the research around the issue/enquiry and its use in the health and social care sector. Their use of secondary research techniques and skills will demonstrate their understanding of the wider issue in context. They will evaluate the purpose, actions and results of the research against the principles of validity and reliability, and demonstrate a thorough understanding of how feasible ethical solutions to research can be planned and delivered in context. Learners will form conclusions linked to the implications of the research for future practice/provision in the sector. These conclusions, and any recommendations for adaptations, will be justified and articulated professionally.

A Types of issues where research is carried out in the health and social care sector

Purpose of research in the health and social care sector

The purpose of research is to:

- improve outcomes for people using services
- inform policy and practice
- extend knowledge and understanding
- identify gaps in provision.

Examples of research

Research has led to improvements in practice and policy. These include changes in treatment of health conditions and in practice in providing care and support. For example the Million Women Study uncovered links between hormone replacement therapy (HRT) and breast, ovarian and womb cancer, which resulted in changing the advice given to women about taking HRT. Research in immunotherapy has brought new treatments for lung cancer and advanced melanoma, a type of skin cancer, giving a longer life expectancy for patients. Research extended our understanding of the links between smoking and cancer and led to the policy of banning smoking in public places. Cancer Research UK scientists helped develop the drug Olaparib which extends the lives of women with ovarian cancer by an average of seven months compared to standard treatments. Researchers helped develop cisplatin, a drug which is used to treat cancer including testicular cancer in men. Thanks to this research nearly all men who are treated for testicular cancer recover.

Activity

Choose one piece of published research from the Million Women Study website. What was the purpose of your chosen piece of research?

Issues

Health conditions

Research tells us how effective certain types of treatment are, and can also highlight trends. For example research has shown that Cognitive Behavioural Therapy (CBT) can be as effective as medication in treating some mental health problems. Research highlights health trends in certain areas or among certain age groups and why this should be the case, for example, the Million Women Study found that in the United Kingdom breast cancer incidence is 15–20 per cent lower in South Asian and black women than in white women because they tended to have more children, tended to breast feed, and they were less likely to drink alcohol or to use HRT. Research can help. Reeves *et al* (2014) found that 1 in 8 female admissions to hospital was likely to be due to overweight or obesity and the conditions most strongly associated with a high BMI were diabetes, knee replacement, blood clots and gallbladder disease. This research links with the Change4Life strategy for avoiding obesity which was discussed in Unit 8 and is part of the strategy for preventing avoidable health conditions.

Lifestyle factors

According to 'Healthy Behaviours', a piece of research by the Kings Fund which highlights health differences across different ages, the rates of drinking, smoking and drug-taking in the young have fallen significantly over the past 10 years. Obesity rates in the young are also falling and levels of activity increasing. However, 80 per cent of children still have a poor diet. Adults are less healthy. 66 per cent do not reach recommended minimum levels of activity; 70 per cent eat less than the recommended amount of fruit and vegetables; 26 per cent are obese; 21 per cent smoke; and 27 per cent of men and 18 per cent of women drink more than the safe limits of alcohol. Older people develop conditions such as sight and hearing loss and dementia. Professional groups are improving their health faster than those in lower socio-economic groups.

Demand for services is expected to increase: by 2030 the number of older people with care needs is predicted to rise by 61 per cent and it is expected there will be 17 million people with arthritis and 3 million with cancer. People are living longer and developing multiple health problems. Such Long Term Conditions (LTCs) put an increased demand on services. By 2018 the number of people with three or more long-term conditions is predicted to rise from 1.9 million to 2.9 million. In addition to increased demand on services from those living longer, there will be more ill-health as bacteria develop resistance to antibiotics. A drug-resistant strain of gonorrhoea was detected in England in March 2015 and health experts predict that gonorrhoea may become untreatable, resulting in infertility, pelvic inflammatory disease and infection of the unborn child during pregnancy. In order to lessen the impact of such factors, population lifestyles need to change. People will need to take more responsibility for maintaining good health and reducing risky behaviours.

Social care and welfare needs

National spending is greatest on health, social care and welfare and the government looks at ways it can reduce this spending. One of the ways identified has been to cut out duplication of services and to personalise care so that care meets the needs of the individual. The Care Act 2014 made the personalisation of care mandatory. Individuals with specific needs such as mobility problems, or with learning difficulties or dementia are entitled to an assessment of needs. If they are eligible for help they then have a personal budget to meet those needs. They may let the local authority use the budget to provide services or may have a direct payment and employ people to provide the services they need. Here is an example: Mr Z had a stroke some years ago and needs help to get up, have a shower and get dressed. Before he had a personal budget he had services provided by the local authority and had a 30-minute slot when a carer arrived and rushed to do all this for him in the time allowed. Now he has a personal budget and employs a personal assistant, she arrives at the time he wants and she spends an hour helping him get ready. He is not rushed and has time for support to help him wash and dress himself, thus regaining some independence. By meeting identified needs and empowering people to manage their own care, individuals maintain independence, and have a greater sense of well-being.

Activity

Using the piece of research you found for the previous activity, decide whether the research relates predominantly to health conditions, lifestyle factors or social and welfare needs.

How does it relate to this? Which other needs may it relate to? Explain your answer.

Distinction activity

Did the research achieve its aim? Explain how it did or did not achieve the stated objectives.

Check your understanding

1 Give four reasons why research may be conducted.
2 Give an example for each purpose.
3 Give one example of how research can show which treatment is more effective.
4 How may lifestyle factors affect health?

B Research methods in health and social care

Research methodologies

Organisations involved in research

Health authorities such as NICE, Public Health and the NHS, gather data. NICE gathers data on the effectiveness of treatments. Public Health gathers data on the incidence of disease.

The Care Quality Commission gather information about the quality of services and publish their reports. Local Healthwatch organisations gather the views of local people regarding their needs for, and experiences of, local health authorities and social care services and publish these views. Charities such as Cancer Research and Alzheimer's Society, focus on funding research into specific disorders while other charities such as Age UK have a broader remit. Charities and community organisations often commission research and

university departments carry it out. The King's Fund, an independent charity working to improve health and health care in England, shapes policy and practice through research and analysis. It researched waiting times in Accident and Emergency departments to find out what was causing delays. The Office for National Statistics collects data and issues reports on a variety of issues including health. The National Institute for Health Research (NIHR) funded by the Department of Health commissions research. The NIHR School for Social Care Research, based at the London School of Economics, conducts and commissions research into adult social care practice in England and aims to improve adult social care practice.

Research methods

Research methods are determined by the type of research to be conducted and this is determined by the research question.

Questionnaires may be used in social research, where researchers want to get the views of a large number of people for quantitative analysis. They are quick and cheap to produce and distribute, especially if sent electronically. They are good for factual questions, can be completed anonymously and if carefully devised, ask questions whose responses can be measured on a scale, for example, how many units of alcohol the person drinks each week. If a large sample is used, as in the Million Women Study, results may be generalised to others with the same characteristics. In the case of the Million Women Study, results could be relevant for all middle aged women in the UK. The disadvantage of using questionnaires in this way are that they do not give scope to explore complex issues and are not suitable for getting information from very young children or from those who may not have capacity to understand the questions.

Interviews are good for getting detailed information from a small number of people. They use open questions such as 'Why?' and 'How?' and allow researchers to investigate complex issues. The advantages of interviews are that they produce a lot of information. Semi-structured interviews are sometimes used to keep the interview focused. The disadvantages are that they are time consuming to conduct as every response has to be recorded, categorised and then analysed. Results from small-scale research cannot be generalised to a wider population.

Case studies give detailed information on a few people. They have the same advantages and disadvantages as interviews. One key disadvantage of case studies is that they are not able to be generalised. Whatever is found for that person relates to them, but may not be true for everyone. If Mr A, when asked about diet, says he likes kippers for breakfast, we only know that he likes them. We do not know how many other people like them.

Scientific experiments are used in scientific research when developing new drugs and treatments or exploring the link between lifestyle factors and disease. The advantage of scientific research is that it can help millions of people. A treatment that reduces cancerous tumours or even gets rid of them, will help people around the world. There are disadvantages to this method. Scientific research is expensive, requires highly skilled scientists, takes a long time and researchers have to gain permission from the research council and ethics committee before they can start experiments. Drugs and treatments cannot be tried on humans until they have first undergone several trials on animals and even then things can go wrong.

In January 2016 one person died and others were disabled in a French drug trial. The drug had been successfully tested on animals and was in phase 1 of the human trial where a small dose of the drug was given. Volunteers were observed for side effects. Previous volunteers had taken lower doses in July, but those who took the increased dose in January became ill within days. Biotrial, the company conducting the experiment had followed correct procedures but even so unexpected side effects occurred.

Observation involves looking at and recording how people behave in particular situations in a structured way. Checklists are often used for observations. Scientists may use observation, for example, to observe the effects of a drug on a volunteer. Teachers in primary school have a list of what a child should be able to do and observe the child to see if they can do these tasks. Observation

can be participant observation, when the observer works alongside the person who is observed, or it can be non-participant observation where the observer stands aside and observes. Think of participant observation as a teacher observing while teaching, whereas an inspector sits at the back not participating, but just observing.

An advantage of observation is that it is great for finding out what actually happens, rather than what people say they do. There are disadvantages to observation. People modify their behaviour when they are being observed. This is known as the 'Hawthorne' effect. A social worker observing a child at risk of abuse may see a parent being kind to a child. When the social worker is not there, the parent may be abusive. The Hawthorne effect makes it difficult to know whether what is observed is really a true reflection of what a person normally does and can make findings from observation invalid.

Checklists are useful, for example when observing whether children have all reached a certain standard, or when observing a situation where a lot happens quickly, but checklists have limitations. They may not have space to record other information, for example if a child has an unusual ability that is not on the list.

All research requires those who take part to give informed consent, which means they fully understand the implications of what they are undertaking.

Analysis of data

Data compiled from local authorities and GP surgeries is used to identify whether methods of care and support, or treatment for health conditions are successful. The UK Clinical Trials Gateway collects information about current clinical trials and research. Public Health England and Public Health Wales, and the corresponding Public Health Agency in Ireland collect and analyse data such as that sent from local authorities and GP surgeries about notifiable diseases. They also identify trends such as a rise in cases of scarlet fever in the winter season. The Office of National Statistics (ONS) analyse data and publish information about health and care trends. NICE, the National Institute for Health and Care Excellence, analyses data and produces guidelines about the most effective methods of care.

Data from interviews is processed by content analysis which breaks down what is said into categories for example, students may be interviewed about their leisure time. Responses may be categorised into time with others, with sub categories for sport and socialising, or time alone for example reading, listening to music. Content analysis makes it easier to compare results. If results from 100 students in England show 90 per cent spend time listening to music, we can compare that with findings from a matched sample in another country. We may find that only 40 per cent spend time listening to music in Italy.

Data from large scale interviews is processed using the Statistical Package for the Social Sciences (SPSS) that produces tables and graphs to show results. It is not necessary to understand statistics as the computerised programme works out the formulae used.

The difference between qualitative and quantitative data

Data is information. Qualitative data concerns experiences and feelings and is subjective as it is based on personal views which may be biased. It comes from individual in-depth interviews, focus groups or questionnaires. Quantitative data is in the form of statistics that count and measure outcomes from a study. This data is usually more objective. Many participants are involved to ensure that the results are statistically significant.

Conducting effective literature searches

Literature searches or reviews involve searching for research studies already done on the topic you are interested in. It may be that the topic you are interested in has already been researched and you can then see whether your research would add anything new. It might be that the topic has never been researched and yours might be the first piece of research on the subject.

The advantages of conducting a thorough literature search at the start is that it may save time. You will not be duplicating work already done. It also gives a grounding in the subject. Disadvantages in doing

a literature search are that it is time consuming, and there may not be any research published on the subject. Research which is more than five years old may be out of date. A literature search is secondary research which is explained in more detail later in this unit.

Identifying, analysing and evaluating source material

Identifying source material is a matter of recognising whether it is relevant. Analysing means breaking it down and examining each section in detail. This is when to assess how valid and reliable it is. Evaluating means assessing how useful the research is, firstly as a piece of research. Is it valid and is it reliable? It may be both of these but how useful is it for the purposes you intend? You may identify a piece of research about measles, analyse it in detail but if you are trying to find out about tuberculosis, the research on measles may be of little value to you.

Source material must be reliable. It is a good idea to start with reliable collections of research that have been evaluated by professionals and academics in the area. The Cochrane Review gathers and summarises reliable research evidence for healthcare. The Campbell Collaboration is an international research network that produces systematic reviews of the effects of social interventions in Crime and Justice, Education, International Development, and Social Welfare.

> ## Activity
>
> Choose one piece of research.
>
> What was the aim of the research?
>
> What methods were used to gather data?
>
> Is it a qualitative study or a quantitative study?

Planning research

How to plan a piece of research

The more planning that goes into how to carry out a research project, the more successful it is likely to be. This is why it is important to conduct a literature search. There is no point in researching something that has already been well researched. It would be a waste of time to research whether smoking is linked to lung cancer, because that had already been shown to be the case in several pieces of research. It might however be useful to look at the effects of e-cigarettes on the body, as that area has not yet been studied in depth.

Rationale for the research

A rationale is a reason. It is essential to have a reason for conducting research, for example, to find out if a drug works or if the country requires to increase a stock of vaccines against a particular type of influenza.

Deciding on achievable objectives

Objectives must be achievable or the research will fail. It is no good deciding to research the diet of all 18-year-olds if the only 18-year-old you know is yourself. Such a study would require large numbers to be valid. It might be more realistic to conduct a small scale research with ten people of that age in your educational establishment with the aim of finding out about the diet of 18-year-olds in your class.

Selecting appropriate research methods

Research methods depend on the type of research to be conducted. Scientific research requires large scale studies, sometimes with experiments. Detailed observation and measurements will provide statistical data. Social research may be large scale using questionnaires to produce quantitative data, or smaller scale and use in-depth interviews and case studies to produce qualitative data.

Selecting target group and sample

The target group is usually determined by the research question. Dementia occurs more often in older people so older people are likely to be the target group from which to select the sample for dementia research. The sample is taken from the target group. Sample sizes are determined by the type of research undertaken. If it is a qualitative study, a smaller sample size may be required. If the objective is to find out how a large section of the population are affected, a larger sample may be required.

Samples are randomly selected, balanced for characteristics, so if the research is about 15-18 year old people's experience of binge drinking, the sample should include equal numbers of male and female and represent different sections of that target population.

Deciding realistic timescales

Research takes a lot of time. The literature search may take several weeks, and waiting for the return of questionnaires, processing the result and analysing data all take much longer than most people expect so it is important to have a timetable that has some flexibility built in. A small scale research might take a year. The Million Women Study, a national study of women's health, involving more than one million UK women aged 50 and over is in its twentieth year. Most research does not take so long, but it is important to set a realistic timescale for any research conducted. Running over time may mean research runs out of funding, or researchers move on to other programmes, and the project may not get finished.

Deciding how research will be monitored and modified

Research does not always go according to plan. Sometimes it stalls due to lack of funding or lack of participation. Participants may move away or decide not to continue in the study. Monitoring the research will help ensure progress is maintained. At times research has to be modified. Qualitative research may bring up issues the researcher had not considered. Allowing topics to emerge from the research process itself is referred to as 'grounded theory'. This is common in social research where patterns may emerge as people are interviewed, for example, interviewing people who have been in children's homes may bring out the finding that many have difficulty in coping when leaving care.

Deciding measures for success

The purpose of the study helps decide the measures of success. The Million Women study investigates potentially modifiable risk factors for a range of diseases of middle and old age in women. Several findings have already emerged, for example, that eating organic foods does not affect cancer risk, the risks of smoking and the benefits of giving up. In this study, measures of success occur frequently because of the large amount of data available from such a large sample size. Smaller studies may only have the findings at the end as their measure of success.

Considering ethical issues while carrying out research

All research must be approved by ethics committees in the relevant organisation. This can take several months. Major studies funded by the Medical Research Council must comply with their ethical standards. Informed consent must be obtained in writing from all participants as explained later in the unit.

Activity

As part of a larger study on lifestyle, a researcher wants to find out how people travel to work and why they use the means of transport they do. The researcher decides to focus on the staff of a local hospital as they assume that people working in health care are health conscious.

Which research methods might be used? Why?

What problems might the researcher meet when conducting the research? (Think of all the different types of jobs people do in hospitals, and the shift patterns they work.)

What limitations could be applied to any findings?

Ethical issues

Ethical principles in research include:

- confidentiality
- consent
- capacity to consent
- conduct of research
- conflicts of interest.

Confidentiality

Confidentiality is about privacy. Maintaining confidentiality of participants, and settings is essential if participants are to trust the researcher. In general the researcher should anonymise data taking out people's names and any other identifiable data. Locations should be anonymised.

There are however certain exceptions to this rule. Section 60 of the Health and Social Care Act 2001

updated by Section 251 of the NHS Act 2006 allows the Secretary of State for Health to set aside the common law duty of confidentiality for defined medical purposes. One such application from Guys and St Thomas NHS Foundation Trust set out to establish the relapse rate of infective endocarditis within one year in patients treated with heart valve surgery at the centre over a 10 year period. Some patients had died and contact was lost with other patients. Access to their data would help find out if antibiotics did help after heart surgery so the Confidentiality Advisory Group (CAG) part of the Health Research Authority gave approval for data disclosure under Section 251.

Consent

Consent must be obtained from anyone taking part in research. The Health Research Authority together with the Medical Research Council produced guidelines on obtaining consent for researchers. According to these guidelines for consent to be considered both legal and ethical it must be:

- given by a person with capacity
- voluntarily given, with no undue influence
- given by someone who has been adequately informed
- a fair choice.

The researcher should explain the research to the potential participant, answer any questions they may have and support this with an information sheet. For many studies consent can be written, oral or non-verbal but in Clinical Trials of Investigational Medicinal Products (CTIMP) consent must be in writing to be legal. Signing a consent form does not make consent valid. The person must agree with each statement on the consent form and either initial or tick or write yes, for each statement. The person who has explained the research and the participant must both sign the consent form.

Consent from those lacking capacity

Consent from those lacking capacity in England and Wales is governed by the Mental Capacity Act, and the Medicines for Human Use (Clinical Trials) Regulations which are applicable to Clinical Trials of Investigational Medicinal Products (CTIMP) research only. If an adult over the age of 16 lacks capacity, a legal representative in the case of Clinical Trials of Investigational Medicinal Products can be asked to give consent or a consultee (for other intrusive research) can be asked to give advice about the person's wishes. In each case the representative must act in the best interests of the individual.

If participants are under the age of 18, the law for obtaining consent is the same across the UK in CTIMP research. The Medicines for Human Use (Clinical Trials) Regulations forbid children under the age of 16 from giving consent to take part in a Clinical Trial of an Investigational Medicinal Product (CTIMP). Parents, or legal representatives if parents cannot be contacted, are able to give consent on behalf of children or young people, to take part in a CTIMP, in the UK. For non-CTIMP research common law presumes that young people aged between 16 and 18 are usually competent to give consent to treatment. For younger children the principle of 'Gillick competence' applies.

The Gillick competence is

'...whether or not a child is capable of giving the necessary consent will depend on the child's maturity and understanding and the nature of the consent required. The child must be capable of making a reasonable assessment of the advantages and disadvantages of the treatment proposed, so the consent, if given, can be properly and fairly described as true consent.' (Gillick v West Norfolk, 1984

Source: www.nspcc.org.uk/preventing-abuse/child-protection-system/legal-definition-child-rights-law/gillick-competency-fraser-guidelines/

In all cases, the wishes and views of the child must be considered. The Health Research Authority has extensive guidance on obtaining consent.

Research conduct

The Hawthorne effect where participants change their behaviour when they know they are being observed has already been mentioned. Keeping professional distance ensures bias is reduced as much as possible. The Research Council UK publishes Policy and Guidelines on Governance of Good Research Conduct. This outlines the process

for obtaining ethical approval and also what is unacceptable behaviour in research. Poor research practices such as poor documentation and record-keeping are less serious than fabricating or falsifying data or plagiarising. Misrepresenting findings by suppressing part of the data, misrepresenting the qualifications of staff and any interests they have which conflict or impact on the research are unacceptable. Failing to ensure the duty of care and failing to deal with misconduct are also unacceptable.

Data Protection Act 1998

Data protection legislation, policies and procedures, provide confidentiality under the Data Protection Act 1998. Researchers must follow the principles of Data Protection outlined in the Act.

Research must be used only for the stated purpose. As explained earlier, in certain situations Section 60 of the Health and Social Care Act 2001 as re-enacted by Section 251 of the NHS Act 2006 allows the Secretary of State for Health to set aside the common law duty of confidentiality for defined medical purposes in exceptional circumstances.

According to the Data Protection Act 1998:

- Personal data shall be processed fairly and lawfully and, in particular, shall not be processed unless

  (a) at least one of the conditions in Schedule 2 is met, and

  (b) in the case of sensitive personal data, at least one of the conditions in Schedule 3 is also met.

- Personal data shall be obtained only for one or more specified and lawful purposes, and shall not be further processed in any manner incompatible with that purpose or those purposes.

- Personal data shall be adequate, relevant and not excessive in relation to the purpose or purposes for which they are processed.

- Personal data shall be accurate and, where necessary, kept up to date.

- Personal data processed for any purpose or purposes shall not be kept for longer than is necessary for that purpose or those purposes.

- Personal data shall be processed in accordance with the rights of data subjects under this Act.

- Appropriate technical and organisational measures shall be taken against unauthorised or unlawful processing of personal data and against accidental loss or destruction of, or damage to, personal data.

- Personal data shall not be transferred to a country or territory outside the European Economic Area unless that country or territory ensures an adequate level of protection for the rights and freedoms of data subjects in relation to the processing of personal data.

Source: https://ico.org.uk/for-organisations/guide-to-data-protection/data-protection-principles

The conditions mentioned for processing personal data for schedule 2 are:

- The individual whom the personal data is about has consented to the processing.

- The processing is necessary: in relation to a contract which the individual has entered into; or because the individual has asked for something to be done so they can enter into a contract.

- The processing is necessary because of a legal obligation that applies to you (except an obligation imposed by a contract).

- The processing is necessary to protect the individual's 'vital interests'. This condition only applies in cases of life or death, such as where an individual's medical history is disclosed to a hospital's A&E department treating them after a serious road accident.

- The processing is necessary for administering justice, or for exercising statutory, governmental, or other public functions

- The processing is in accordance with the 'legitimate interests' condition.

Source: ico.org.uk

For sensitive personal data, at least one of the above conditions must be met and at least one of the following from schedule 3 must be met:

- The individual whom the sensitive personal data is about has given explicit consent to the processing.

- The processing is necessary so that you can comply with employment law.

- The processing is necessary to protect the vital interests of the individual (in a case where the individual's consent cannot be given or reasonably obtained), or another person (in a case where the individual's consent has been unreasonably withheld).

- The processing is carried out by a not-for-profit organisation and does not involve disclosing personal data to a third party, unless the individual consents. Extra limitations apply to this condition.

- The individual has deliberately made the information public.

- The processing is necessary in relation to legal proceedings; for obtaining legal advice; or otherwise for establishing, exercising or defending legal rights.

- The processing is necessary for administering justice, or for exercising statutory or governmental functions.

- The processing is necessary for medical purposes, and is undertaken by a health professional or by someone who is subject to an equivalent duty of confidentiality.

- The processing is necessary for monitoring equality of opportunity, and is carried out with appropriate safeguards for the rights of individuals.

Source: ico.org.uk

Human rights legislation, policies and procedures

Human rights legislation stems from the Universal Declaration of Human Rights which was adopted into European law and then into each member nation's law. The Human Rights Act 1998 made these human rights part of UK law.

'All human beings are born with equal and inalienable rights and fundamental freedoms'

Article 5 of the Universal Declaration of Human Rights 1948:

No one shall be subjected to torture or to cruel, inhuman or degrading treatment or punishment.

Human rights policies and procedures are included in the equality policies and procedures each organisation must hold.

If misconduct is detected the individual should first check the facts. If they are concerned they should follow the organisation's procedure for whistleblowing, which generally starts with raising concerns with their line manager. Whistle-blowing is explained in detail in Unit 2.

The use and misuse of results

The use and misuse of results is an important issue in research. Statistics inform practice, and treatment may be based on statistical data, for example a flu epidemic may be predicted on the basis of statistics, and vulnerable people vaccinated to protect them against the expected epidemic. The misuse of results is serious. Dr Andrew Wakefield published research in 1998 that claimed there was a link between the triple vaccine given to children to prevent Mumps, Measles and Rubella and autism and bowel disease. The impact of the study was that many parents refused to give their children the MMR vaccine and many children caught measles and mumps. Some children died from these diseases. In fact, the data did not show such a link but this was not found until later investigation. *The Lancet* journal which published the original research withdrew it and Dr Wakefield was struck off the medical register. It was later found that Dr Wakefield had an interest in a company manufacturing the single dose vaccines which many parents had bought privately as an alternative to the triple vaccine. The MMR research illustrates several examples of misconduct: falsifying data, conflict of interest and misrepresenting results.

Informed consent was introduced following the Second World War trials of doctors who had experimented on human beings held as prisoners. The 1947 Nuremberg Code set out ten points, the first of which was that researchers must obtain informed consent. The code said that participants can leave the experiment if they wish, doctors must stop the experiment if they realise it can harm the patient and no experiment can be made where the risks outweigh the benefits from it. Subsequently the World Medical Association (WMA) developed the 1975 Declaration of Helsinki: 'Ethical Principles for Medical Research Involving Human Subjects,' as a statement of ethical principles for medical research involving human subjects, putting the well-being of the patient before everything else.

Conflicts of interest

According to the British Medical Journal, a conflict of interests exists 'when professional judgment concerning a primary interest (such as patients' welfare or the validity of research) may be influenced by a secondary interest (such as financial gain or personal rivalry).'

Dr Wakefield was researching the link between the triple vaccine MMR and at the same time was involved with investing in a single vaccine so this was a direct conflict of interests. If his research found triple vaccines were linked with an increased likelihood of autism and bowel problems, no one would want the triple vaccine. Everyone would want the single vaccine and he would profit from that. This is why it was a conflict of interest.

Conflicts of interest can arise from other situations, for example, if a researcher was employed by a chocolate manufacturer to examine links between obesity and chocolate consumption, the researcher might experience pressure to hide results that showed people who ate chocolate every day put on weight. If the researcher had shares in a chocolate firm, they might also be tempted to suppress any results showing that too much chocolate makes people fat. Conflicts of interest should be disclosed at the start so they can be assessed to decide if they are likely to impact on the research. All reputable research has to be peer reviewed, which means it is read by others who are experts in the area. If they agree that the research is sound, based on appropriate methods and conducted correctly, the research is published. If they find a problem with conflict of interest they will reject the research and it will not be published.

Mentor arrangements in research, whether formal or informal, work best if the mentor is external or in a different department to the mentee to avoid a conflict of interest. Mentoring could be short term or longer term and might help the new researcher develop new research skills and network.

In the case of the MMR research conducted by Dr Wakefield, research misconduct was identified in adjusting the sample to make up the numbers.

There was insufficient professional distance between his business interests and the research. Concerns about research misconduct should be reported as should any disclosure of misconduct, but investigations will be conducted by the research ethics committee.

The role of organisations

The NHS Health Research Authority (HRA) is responsible for providing the National Research Ethics Service (NRES) which in turn provides an ethical review of all health research which involves patients in England. The HRA is responsible for Research Ethics Committees (RECs), the National Social Care Research Ethics Committee, Gene Therapy Advisory Committee and the Confidentiality Advisory Group, which advises on Section 251 of the NHS Act (2006). The diagram shows how the organisations fit into the structure of the NHS.

Source: www.gov.uk/government/publications/
the-health-and-care-system-explained/the-health-and-
care-system-explained

The National Social Care REC reviews adult social care research study proposals, intergenerational studies involving adults and children or families and some proposals for social science studies related to the NHS. NHS Research Ethics Committees have up to 18 members, a third of whom are not researchers and are not registered healthcare professionals. They safeguard the rights, safety, dignity and well-being of research participants. They review research applications, consider the proposed participant involvement and decide whether the research is ethical. RECs are independent of organisations conducting the research, funders and investigators so they put the interests of participants first. There are more than 80 RECs across the UK.

> ### Activity
>
> What ethical issues might a researcher have to consider when planning primary research?

Research skills

Research uses general life skills, academic skills and also specific research skills which have to be learned before starting research.

Time management and organisational skills

General skills include time management and organisational skills. If someone is bad at time keeping and poorly organised they will need to learn these general life skills before considering research.

Reading techniques, distinguishing between fact and opinion, identifying bias, and showing connections

Academic skills such as skimming and scanning reading techniques, making notes and keeping records from source material, distinguishing between objective fact and subjective opinion, and identifying bias are learned by the time students take GCSE. Showing connections between sources of information is part of essay writing technique. It is assumed that anyone conducting research would be competent in these skills.

Non-judgemental practice

Non-judgemental practice is a basic requirement for the health and social care sector. It is essential in research to avoid bias. An interviewer may introduce bias by asking a leading question such as 'What do you think about the overcrowded buses?' This is a leading question and should be avoided. The interviewer may feel buses are overcrowded but they must not express their own views if they are to get the real views of the person being interviewed. It would be better to ask 'What do you think about the buses?' Non-judgmental practice is needed when choosing the sample. A researcher who decided to include only their friends and exclude students from a certain ethnic group, or exclude students of a certain gender in a survey would be introducing bias in the sample.

Making notes, keeping records from source material and recognising sources of bias or error

Research skills build on a solid understanding of basic mathematics and English. Reading for the literature search requires the ability to skim and scan large amounts of material to select relevant ideas and then make notes. Refining the research question requires the ability to be objective, and be able to see when there is bias or error. Errors may

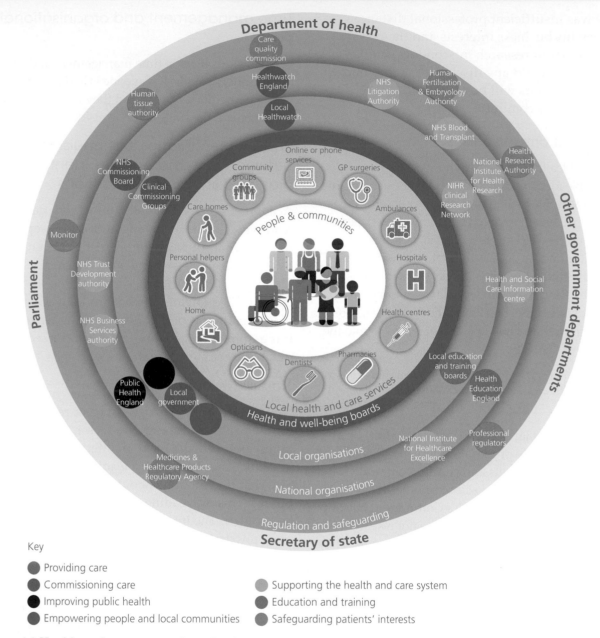

Figure 4.1 Health and care system from April 2013

occur in questionnaires, where questions are badly worded and where they may be open to different interpretations. Research planning requires time management and organisational skills if the research is to be completed within the allocated time. Once the research question has been refined and checked for bias, the appropriate methods are chosen for the type of research to be conducted.

Scientific research uses methods such as surveys, experiments and observation to discover facts which are quantifiable as numbers. The Health

and Social Care Information Centre (HSCIC) collect, analyse and present national health and social care data. Qualitative research would use smaller numbers of people and use interviews or questionnaires with open questions.

Analysis of results and selecting relevant numerical data

Analysis of results includes compilation of data, results and findings. Sometimes data has to be processed – interview notes may be transcribed, questionnaire answers compiled so that data can be put into tables, charts and diagrams as described earlier in the unit.

In the research report 'Smoking, drinking and drug use among young people in England in 2014', edited by Elizabeth Fuller, 6,173 pupils in England in years 7 to 11 (mostly aged 11 to 15) in 210 schools completed questionnaires in the autumn term of 2014. This is an annual survey, so results can be compared from year to year. The data was compiled for HSCIC by NatCen Social Research (NatCen) and the National Foundation for Educational Research (NFER).

We can see that large numbers are involved – therefore it is quantitative research. Appendix A 'Survey methods' describes how schools and then pupils were selected to ensure balanced representation. The authors recognise potential error and identify the possibility of sampling error which is the probability that any selected sample is not completely representative of the population from which it is drawn. The authors explain how questionnaires were administered to ensure confidentiality and obtain honest answers from pupils. The survey was taken under exam conditions to prevent pupils influencing each other and teachers did not see the responses so results were not influenced by pupils thinking their teacher would see what they wrote. Other sources of inaccuracy identified by the researchers include nonresponse bias, as well as over- and under-reporting.

Data was processed using SPSS (originally Statistical Package for the Social Sciences but now just called SPSS) a software programme for processing statistical data, the valid method for processing large amounts of data. This package gives graphs and tables. The authors presented raw data and selected relevant numerical data, for example, estimates for boys and girls aged 11 to 13 were not shown because of the very small base sizes when getting data about pupils who drank alcohol in the last week.

Results are presented as percentages. One result from the research is that the prevalence of drinking in the last week among 11 to 15 year olds fell from 22 per cent in 2005 to 8 per cent in 2014 (Fuller, p. 221). Using percentages enables comparisons, in this case comparing results in 2005 to 2014. Statistical averages are used. The number of smokers has fallen dramatically. Here, one of the key findings shows the use of statistical averages:

> Boys who were regular smokers consumed more cigarettes on average per week than girls who were regular smokers: the mean consumption in the last week for boys who were regular smokers was 34.6 cigarettes, compared with 29.0 cigarettes amongst girls who were regular smokers

(Fuller, p. 19)

In this extract from the report, the authors look at *average* cigarette consumption and *mean* consumption. Averages can be mean, median or mode.

'Triangulation' is not mentioned in this research, but it means that in some types of research two methods are used, such as surveys *and* interviews. If the results are the same from each, the researcher can be more confident that the findings are accurate, for example, if a survey of 20 pupils shows that most pupils like the food in the school canteen, and separate interviews of other pupils give the same result after compiling and analysing data, then the researcher can be confident that canteen food is popular.

Methods of analysis and drawing conclusions

Analysis is about looking at the information and drawing conclusions. It is easier to see patterns in data if we use graphs and charts. In Figure 4.2 taken from the report, we can see that Year 7 pupils recalled fewer lessons and the lesson they best recall is about smoking. Years 9, 10 and 11 recall lessons about drug use more than they do about smoking or alcohol.

Interpreting graphs and tables produced by others can give a lot of information, especially if they are examined during a literature search.

Conventions for presenting bibliography and reference lists vary between institutions.

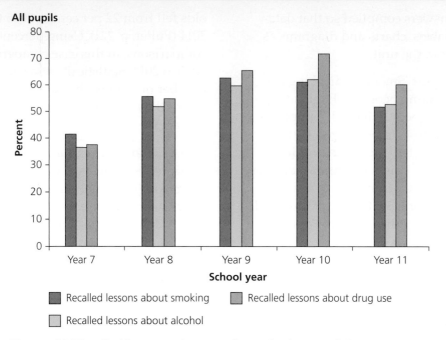

All pupils

Figure 4.2 Recalled lessons about smoking, drinking and drug use

A bibliography is a list of all the materials read as background to the research. A reference list is a list of what has been referred to in the report. Often these two are combined. In the report 'Smoking, drinking and drug use among young people in England in 2014' the authors have a section headed 'Notes and references' and include websites and government reports they have used or referred to and explanatory notes which are numbered in the text and given in full at the end.

The Harvard referencing system is a popular way of listing references and a bibliography. The reference list for 'Ethnic differences in breast cancer incidence in the UK are explained by differences in known risk factors' (Gathani *et al* 2014) uses the Harvard system, listing references alphabetically with the author name, initial, date of publication, title of the article, the journal in which it was published and the volume and page numbers. The web link is also given as shown in the first title in the reference list is:

Ali R, Barnes I, Kan SW, Beral V (2010) Cancer Incidence in British Indians and British whites in Leicester, 2001-2006. Br J Cancer 103: 143–148.
| Article | PubMed | ISI |

If something from Ali's work on page 144 of the article is mentioned in the study, there will be an in-text reference such as (Ali, 2010 p.144). Each institution has guidelines for the presentation of references. Some organisations want the title in italics, others want the title to be underlined, while others want the title of the article in the same form as the rest of the reference.

Activity

How might a researcher process the data from interviews?

How might a researcher process the data from questionnaires?

Activity

What factors might make someone's research invalid?

What factors might make someone's research unreliable?

Check your understanding

1 How may bias be introduced into research? Show three ways this can be done.

2 Which research methods might be suitable for finding out if a drug works?

3 Which research method is likely to contain larger numbers in the sample – qualitative or quantitative?

4 Express 25 out of 100 as a percentage then show it in a pie chart.

5 What is triangulation? How might you triangulate the findings in a study?

6 What ethical considerations might you think about in designing research?

7 Why is it important to keep notes during research?

8 What are the advantages of using tables and graphs to present data?

C Carrying out and reviewing relevant secondary research into a contemporary health and social care issue

Secondary research is commonly used to find out about a topic and involves reading research that others have done. (Primary research means collecting the information for yourself by carrying out surveys or interviews or using other research methods.) A researcher who does a literature review is doing secondary research, finding out about the topic. A student who has to write an essay about health and disease may read articles and reports. They are conducting secondary research.

Selecting appropriate secondary sources

Selecting sources of reliable secondary research

Professional journals, professional bodies, up to date textbooks, periodicals, websites, and research organisations can be useful sources of secondary research but must be used with caution. It is important to check that sources are up to date. One major issue in health and social care is the frequent change in laws and policies. The Care Act 2014 which came into force in 2015 brought many changes, creating new bodies and amalgamating others, for example in Public Health. This may mean that sources of research change and new sources emerge as new public bodies are created.

Professional journals are published online and in hard copy. The British Journal of Social Work, published by Oxford Journals is the leading academic social work journal in the UK and publishes research. Community Care, available online, is less academic but often summarises published research in an understandable way and is a good starting point before reading more academic research articles. The Royal College of Nursing provides online access to e-journals and also lends nursing related books to members. The Social Care Institute for Excellence has online articles.

Conducting electronic searches using academic search engines

Serious researchers use academic search engines such as CINAHL (Cumulative Index to Nursing and Allied Health Literature) which is an index of 'English language' and selected 'other language' journal articles about nursing, allied health, biomedicine and healthcare. The Cochrane Review mentioned earlier in this unit gathers and summarises reliable research evidence for healthcare and the Campbell Collaboration produces systematic reviews in Crime and Justice and Social Welfare. A common place to start looking for information is a search engine such as Google. It is important to use the right key word when searching. A search for 'zika virus' on Google brings up 71.5 million results which is far too many to look through. Refining the search to 'zika virus transmission' brings that down to 2.4 million, but that is still too many. Adding the term 'research' to the phrase brings 146,000 results. If we want to find out reliable information about whether there is a link between Zika virus and microcephaly we could then look on the World Health Organisation and the Pan American Health Organisation websites as many of the articles refer to these sites as their source of evidence.

Consideration of the suitability of the sources

Reliable and reputable sources will have already considered ethical principles, confidentiality,

101

conflicts of interest, and fair representation of people using services. Samples are drawn randomly from representative groups to avoid bias. In scientific research where double blind trials are held, people may be assigned to either the control group or the trial group. Peer reviewed articles will already be screened for these issues. See page 92 on Ethical issues and principles of research.

We have covered selected relevant numerical data, to include graphs, tables and statistics, and examined and interpreted graphs and tables produced by others below under 'Recognising bias in graphs, tables and statistics'.

Recognising bias in graphs, tables and statistics

Recognising bias in graphs, tables and statistics will only be required if the sources are not reputable and in such cases they should not be used. For example, Jo only read two books but Robin read nine. If Jo wants to impress the history teacher they need to read more history books. An obvious way that bias may be introduced in graphs is to start the base line from a point higher or lower than zero. Another way to misrepresent data is to change the scale on the left side, the vertical axis, so it increases in tens and the difference between Jo's rate of reading and the other students will be less obvious. (See Figures 4.3 and 4.4.)

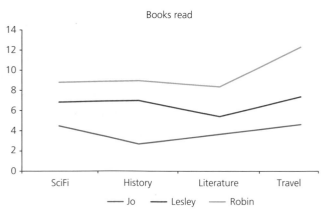

Figure 4.3 The original data

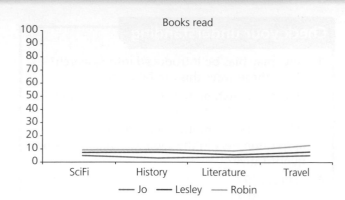

Figure 4.4 The same data using a different scale

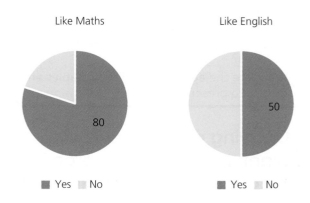

Figure 4.5

Statistics can be misrepresented. Ravi did a survey and found that 80 per cent of pupils like Maths and 50 per cent of pupils like English. Ravi concluded that 130 per cent of pupils like English and Maths. Can you spot the flaws in Ravi's reasoning? (Hint: 100 per cent is the most you can have.)

Here is another example: Chanelle, who is 18 years old, surveyed her classmates and found that 1 in 5 of them were taking driving lessons. She concluded that 1 in 5 of all 18-year-olds take driving lessons. This is a misuse of statistics. She has only small numbers, not enough to ensure that all 18-year-olds are represented. If she had done the study in a country area, more people might be taking driving lessons because of public transport difficulties. In a large city with excellent public transport and expensive parking fees, fewer students might be taking driving lessons. Results might be different if the survey was done in winter, rather than in summer. Generalising from a small sample is not valid.

Activity

Search online for the article 'SACN's sugars and health recommendations: why 5 per cent?'

Public Health England published the Scientific Advisory Committee on Nutrition's recommendations about sugars and health. Read the executive summary. Which type of studies did the SACN consider the most reliable?

Evaluation of research

Examining content of secondary materials

An introduction, main body and conclusion is not the usual way to present research, however this may be used if someone is reporting on a piece of research they have read about.

Secondary research is when you read someone else's research to get an understanding of a topic, for example if you are thinking of doing some research on the topic yourself and want to find out if another person has researched it (a literature review). Most research is presented in a standard way and begins with a summary or abstract. Here is an example: 'Moderate Alcohol Intake and Cancer Incidence in Women', published in 2009 by Allen *et al* as part of the Million Women Study, which presents an abstract with an overview of background, methods, results and conclusions. The full text is available free of charge at http://jnci.oxfordjournals.org/content/101/5/296.short

Always ask these questions as you read research.

1   Who published it?
2   Where was it published? Is it in an authoritative journal or the local free paper? Is it published in this country or another country? Are the results applicable to this country?
3   When was it published? Is it up to date or out of date?
4   Why did they do this? Was there funding from a sponsor and could this influence the research?
5   What are they trying to find out? Did they have any problems? What possible bias is there?

What are the conclusions and what are the recommendations?

6   How did they do the research? Is it quantitative or qualitative? What methods did they use such as observation, questionnaires and interviews? Do they include sample questionnaires so you can check whether they used open or closed questions? How did they process the data? Do the chosen research methods match the type of research? Do the findings relate to what they set out to find?

Academic reading includes critically surveying the structure of source materials

Academic reading requires practice to understand the technical terms so it is always a good idea to read the 'abstract' first. In the research report on Moderate Alcohol Intake and Cancer Incidence in Women, the full article starts by reviewing what research has already been done, then sets out the aims of the current study. This is followed by a detailed section on participants and methods and then a section on statistical analysis explaining how data was processed. The next section presents results and this is followed by a discussion of what the results mean and how these relate to findings from previous research. The concluding paragraph states that 'regular consumption of low to moderate amounts of alcohol by women increases the risk of cancers of the upper aerodigestive tract, rectum, liver, and breast' (Allen, 2009 p.309)

Advantages and limitations of research sources and methodologies

Allen's study was part of the Million Women Study which is tracking the health of women aged 50 and over and has more than one million UK women in the study. This meant access to a sample was relatively easy and the methodology used, questionnaires, were appropriate for such a large sample size in this quantitative study. A further source was information on incidence of specific cancers obtained from a national registry. When evaluating the research, learners need to consider the validity of these methods.

Limitations of the study were identified. The study could not explore the risk created by heavy sustained drinking due to the composition of the cohort. Researchers were unable to assess the cancer risk for never drinkers and former drinkers separately because the recruitment questionnaire did not discriminate between lifelong non-drinkers and those who had stopped drinking. They were not able to assess the impact of changes in lifetime alcohol consumption.

Validity and reliability of results

Validity means that the research tests what it set out to test, or that conclusions are based on the findings. Research that set out to test the fitness of 50-year-olds but included some 20-year-olds would not be valid. A study that finds alcohol consumption causes liver damage cannot be used to conclude that sugary drinks also cause liver damage.

Reliability refers to methods used. If a study of a sample of 100 first-year students finds that 70 per cent oversleep for lectures, a repeat of that study using the same sample and same methods should get the same findings. If it does not, the methods are unreliable.

Possible bias error, where the researcher may assume information and offer their own interpretation on a situation, can be minimised and adjustments made to counteract any missing data. Researchers excluded 42,408 women who had a cancer and 9,721 who had missing information on alcohol intake, leaving 1 280 296 for the main analyses. Statistical sampling methods were explained in detail. Ethical principles (see page 92) were followed. All participants gave written informed consent to take part in the study. The research was approved by the Oxford and Anglia Multi-Centre Research and Ethics Committee. Generalisability, where conclusions can be applied to a wider population, from a large sample such as this is valid. The sample included 1 280 296 middle-aged women, the largest study yet conducted so we can have confidence that the findings can be applied to the population of women. Such research can have implications for practice, especially for health promotion.

Recommendations

No specific recommendations for policy change are made in this research but based on these

findings and other research which investigated the link between alcohol and health, government guidelines were changed to say that there is no safe alcohol limit.

Potential areas for further development of the research

The research mentions that a few studies report that alcohol drinking appears to be associated with a reduced risk of other cancers and suggests further investigations of the possibility that alcohol reduces the risk of thyroid cancer, non–Hodgkin lymphoma, and renal cell carcinoma.

Potential for development of working practice and provision of services

The findings of Allen's study show that regular consumption of low to moderate amounts of alcohol by women increases the risk of cancers of the upper aerodigestive tract, rectum, liver, and breast, although no statistically significant increases were found between increasing alcohol intake and other cancers. Findings from this and other studies led to a change in advice. The Committee on Carcinogenicity of Chemicals in Food, Consumer Products and the Environment which advises the Department of Health stated that 'Drinking alcohol has been shown to increase the risk (or chance) of getting some types of cancer.' The value of such research may be helpful in directing health promotion campaigns.

Activity

Search online for McGuinness B, Craig D, Bullock R, Passmore P. Statins for the prevention of dementia. Cochrane Database of Systematic Reviews 2016, Issue 1. Art. No.: CD003160. DOI: 10.1002/14651858.CD003160.pub3.

This is a report of research conducted to find out whether statin drugs can prevent dementia.

Read the abstract and make notes on the background, objectives or purpose of the study, an outline of methods and data collection, and a summary of results. Evaluate the research in terms of validity and reliability.

Wider applications of research

Making recommendations for potential future areas for research

One reason we conduct secondary research is to find out what can be done to improve things, for example, we want to know about the Zika virus because we want to avoid babies being born with microcephaly. When you approach your own research, always keep the purpose in mind. What are you looking for and why?

Research is an on-going process. One study may throw up unanswered questions or highlight gaps in knowledge, just as the study we looked at noted that further investigation is needed to find out if alcohol reduces the risk of some types of cancer.

Implications of research for health and social care practice are that guidelines will change as we understand more about risk factors and the causes of disease. Treatments may change too, for example, we used to keep people in bed post-operatively to rest, but research showed this caused blood clots, so now we get people up as soon as possible. Practitioners must keep up-to-date if they are to give the latest advice to service users and maintain public confidence in healthcare.

Implications of research for health and social care service provision will involve planning what services will be needed in future. In the example we discussed, we already know from research that alcohol consumption leads to an increase in certain types of cancer, so planners can ensure sufficient specialists are trained to treat them, and sufficient nurses available to care for them. More importantly, health promotion can focus a campaign aimed at those at risk so the individual can reduce their own alcohol intake and reduce their risk. According to a report by the Nuffield Trust, in England alone, estimates suggest that over 15,000 people die from alcohol-related illnesses each year (Home Office, 2013 quoted in Alcohol-specific activity in hospitals in England – Nuffield Trust report). Preventing or reducing such alcohol related illnesses will benefit society as a whole by reducing the cost of health care and improving the health of the population.

Activity

Search online for either one of the following then answer the questions listed below:

Gringras P., Middleton B., Skene D.J. and Revell V.L. (2015) Bigger, Brighter, Bluer–Better? Current light-emitting devices – adverse sleep properties and preventative strategies. Front. Public Health 3:233. doi: 10.3389/fpubh.2015.00233

Taylor J., Cameron A., Jones C., Franklin A., Stalker K., Fry D. (2015) Deaf and disabled children talking about child protection, NSPCC and University of Edinburgh

1 What was the purpose of the research?
2 Is it qualitative or quantitative research?
3 What methods were used in the research?
4 What were the findings?
5 What are the implications of the findings for individuals?
6 What are the implications for society?

Activity

Define each of the following items:

- Primary research
- Secondary research
- Qualitative research
- Quantitative research
- Ethical issues
- Research methods
- Validity
- Reliability

Check your understanding

1 Name two sources you might use to find out about health or social care research.
2 Why would you use professional sources for research articles?
3 How might statistics be misrepresented on a graph?
4 Which part of a research paper should you read first – the abstract or the methodology? Why?
5 What do we mean by 'valid' research?
6 What do we mean by 'reliable' research?
7 Give one example of how recommendations from research may alter practice.
8 Give one example of how recommendations from research may alter provision.

Case scenario

In April 2003 after years of research by thousands of scientists across the world on the Human Genome Project, scientists managed to work out the sequence of DNA to read the genetic code of a human being. Following on from this work, the UK 100,000 Genomes Project launched in 2012, will sequence 100,000 whole genomes from NHS patients by 2017 from patients with a rare disease (and their families) with cancer.

Rare disease and cancer are both linked to changes in the genome and by comparing DNA from a cancer cell and a normal cell in a person's body, scientists can work out what changes caused the cancer. This gives the possibility that gene therapy can be used to treat rare diseases and cancer much more effectively. You can read more about this project on www.genomicsengland.co.uk

Think about it

Research is expensive and funds are limited. The NHS National Institute for Health Research (NIHR) identified two priorities for research, firstly, preventing the development and spread of antimicrobial resistance as more and more germs become resistant to antibiotics and secondly researching into the prevention, treatment and care of people with dementia.

What are the benefits of targeting funds on these two issues?

What are the disadvantages of targeting funds on these two issues?

Exam practice

First, carry out the following:

1   Read and analyse the article:

    www.nhs.uk/news/2016/04April/Pages/UK-dementia-rates-have-fallen-sharply-in-men.aspx

2   Use at least two secondary sources and research the topic independently.

3   Now write up:

    a) a reference list of your secondary sources

    b) notes, of no more than six pages, on your secondary research.

    (In the real exam you would be allowed up to 18 hours to do this.)

    Now, using just the notes you have made and the original article on the NHS website:

4   Consider this piece of research and the other sources you found on this topic. How was quantitative research used to find out information?

Include in your answer:

a) a detailed discussion of any other research methods used

b) a detailed discussion of the reliability of the research methods used.

5   Why is research that looks at trends in dementia important for individuals? How far does your secondary research support the conclusions drawn in the article?

6   What will you need to consider when planning further research into health services provided for individuals with dementia? Refer to the article and to your own secondary research to support your answer.

7   What are the implications of this research for health service provision for those with dementia? Refer to the article and to your own secondary research to support your answer.

Further reading

Aveyard, H., (2014) *Doing a Literature Review in Health and Social Care: A Practical Guide*, 3rd edition, Open University Press, London

Bell J. and Waters S. (2014*) Doing Your Research Project: A Guide for First-Time Researchers*, 6th edition, Open University Press, London

Boyce T. and Hunter D. (2009) 'Improving partnership working to reduce health inequalities', The King's Fund, London

Gringras P., Middleton B., Skene D.J. and Revell V.L. (2015) 'Bigger, Brighter, Bluer–Better? Current light-emitting devices – adverse sleep properties and preventative strategies', Front. Public Health 3:233. doi: 10.3389/fpubh.2015.00233 available at http://dx.doi.org/10.3389/fpubh.2015.00233

Taylor, J. *et al* (2015) *Deaf and disabled children talking about child protection*. London: NSPCC.

Useful websites

Allen NE, Beral V, Casabonne D, Kan SW, Reeves GK, Brown A, Green J Moderate Alcohol Intake and Cancer Incidence in Women J Natl Cancer Inst 2009; 101 :296-305 doi: 10.1093/jnci/djn514. First published online February 24, 2009. Available at: http://jnci.oxfordjournals.org

Information Commission Office. Data Protection Principles: ico.org.uk

Frontiers in Public Health is a peer-reviewed journal aimed at the scientific community interested in the broad area of public health: http://journal.frontiersin.org

McGuinness B, Craig D, Bullock R, Passmore P. Statins for the prevention of dementia. Cochrane Database of Systematic Reviews 2016, Issue 1. Art. No.: CD003160. DOI: 10.1002/14651858.CD003160.pub3. Available at: www.onlinelibrary.wiley.com

Office for National Statistics: www.ons.gov.uk

France clinical trial: 90 given drug, one man brain-dead. 15 Jan 2016: www.bbc.co.uk/news

Breakthroughs galore: A transformative year in medicine, James Gallagher 28 Dec 2015: www.bbc.co.uk/news

Declaring competing interests: see British Medical Journal, www.bmj.com

The Campbell Collaboration – social care research reviews: www.campbellcollaboration.org

Nearly all men survive testicular cancer (press release, 29 July 2013). Available at: www.cancerresearchuk.org

The Cochrane Review –health care research reviews: www.cochrane.org

CINAHL academic search engine: www.ebscohost.com/academic/cinahl-plus-with-full-text

Equality Human Rights Commission: www.equalityhumanrights.com

Government publications, including Alcohol and Cancer statement, and The health and care system explained: www.gov.uk

Healthwatch, the national consumer champion in health and care: www.healthwatch.co.uk

→

NHS Health Research Authority/National Social Care Research Ethics Committee: www.hra.nhs.uk

Fuller E.(ed), Smoking, drinking and drug use among young people in England in 2014. Available from The Health and Social Care Information Centre (HSCIC): www.hscic.gov.uk

Public Perceptions of the NHS and Social Care 2012, Publication 1469. Available at: www.ipsos-mori.com

What's going on in A&E? The key questions answered – a report into factors influencing waiting times in A & E. Time to think differently – Healthy behaviours: how health and well-being varies with socio economic status. Both available from the King's Fund: www.kingsfund.org.uk

The National Institute for Health Research School for Social Care Research: www.lse.ac.uk/LSEHealthAndSocialCare

Ethnic differences in breast cancer incidence in the UK are explained by differences in known risk factors (Gathani et al 2014). Measuring the impact of overweight and obesity on hospital admissions in women in England (Reeves et al 2014). Both available at: www.millionwomenstudy.org

Change 4 Life, the NHS health promotion site: www.nhs.uk/change4life

The National Institute for Health Research: www.nihr.ac.uk

Gillick principle/Gillick competency Fraser guidelines: www.nspcc.org.uk

Alcohol-specific activity in hospitals in England – Nuffield Trust report: www.nuffieldtrust.org.uk

Lee, P. (2006) 'Understanding and critiquing quantitative research papers', Nursing Times; 102: 28, 28–30: www.nursingtimes.net

RCUK Policy and Guidelines on Governance of Good Research/Conduct, February 2013 (updated July 2015)/'Guidance on best practice in the management of research data'. Available at: www.rcuk.ac.uk

The UK Clinical Trials Gateway: www.ukctg.nihr.ac.uk

World Medical Association (WMA): www.wma.net

5 Meeting individual care and support needs

About this unit

In this unit you will look at the values and skills that guide health and care professionals such as social workers and nurses when they plan how they can meet the needs of individuals. You will learn about different ethical approaches involved in providing care, the laws and guidance around these and some of the ethical dilemmas health workers face. This unit recognises the problems and challenges people face when they need services, and what is being done to make it easier for them to get the help they need. It explores how services are commissioned, and resources balanced, and how risks are reduced to ensure services are available. Personalisation and improved communication operate at the level of the individual service user. You will learn how professionals work together to make sure an individual's needs are fully met and how they share relevant information while maintaining confidentiality and safely managing information.

Learning aims

The aims of this unit are to:

A Examine principles, values and skills which underpin meeting the care and support needs of individuals.

B Examine the ethical issues involved when providing care and support to meet individual needs.

C Investigate the principles behind enabling individuals with care and support needs to overcome challenges.

D Investigate the roles of professionals and how they work together to provide the care and support necessary to meet individual needs.

How will I be assessed?

For learning aims A, B, and C, it is recommended by the awarding body that learners write a report in response to case studies of individuals of different ages that considers the principles, values and skills needed to provide care and support for others while maintaining an ethical approach and enabling individuals to overcome challenges.

For learning aim D, it is recommended by the awarding body that learners write a report based on case studies on how working practices are used to successfully meet individual needs.

How will I be graded?

Pass	Merit	Distinction
Learning aim A: Examine principles, values and skills which underpin meeting the care and support needs of individuals.		
A P1 Explain the importance of promoting equality and diversity for individuals with different needs. **A P2** Explain the skills and personal attributes necessary for professionals who care for individuals with different needs.	**A M1** Analyse the impact of preventing discrimination for individuals with different needs. **A M2** Assess different methods professionals might use when building relationships and establishing trust with individuals with needs.	**A D1** Evaluate the success of promoting anti-discriminatory practice for specific individuals with different needs.

How will I be graded?

Pass	Merit	Distinction
Learning aim B: Examine the ethical issues involved when providing care and support to meet individual needs.		**B C D2** Justify the strategies and techniques used to overcome ethical issues and challenges experienced by individuals with different needs when planning and providing care.
B P3 Explain how to incorporate ethical principles into the provision of support for individuals with different needs.	**B M3** Analyse how an ethical approach to providing support would benefit specific individuals with different needs.	
Learning aim C: Investigate the principles behind enabling individuals with care and support needs to overcome challenges.		
C P4 Explain the strategies and communication techniques used with individuals with different needs to overcome different challenges. **C P5** Explain the benefits of promoting personalisation when overcoming challenges faced by individuals with different needs.	**C M4** Assess the strategies and communication techniques used to overcome different challenges faced by individuals with different care and support needs.	
Learning aim D: Investigate the roles of professionals and how they work together to provide the care and support necessary to meet individual needs.		
D P6 Explain why meeting the needs of the individuals requires the involvement of different agencies. **D P7** Explain the roles and responsibilities of different members of the multidisciplinary team in meeting the needs of specific individuals. **D P8** Explain the arrangements for managing information between professionals.	**D M5** Assess the benefits of multi-disciplinary and multi-agency working for specific individuals with care and support needs. **D M6** Analyse the impact of legislation and codes of practice relating to information management on multi-disciplinary working.	**D D3** Justify how organisations and professionals work together to meet individual needs while managing information and maintaining confidentiality. **D D4** Evaluate how multiagency and multidisciplinary working can meet the care and support needs of specific individuals.

A Examine principles, values and skills which underpin meeting the care and support needs of individuals P1, P2, M1, M2, D1

Working in health and social care is interesting because there is so much variety. Some things however are so fundamental to the work that they underpin the way everything is done. These are the principles, values and skills used in care work.

Promoting equality, diversity and preventing discrimination

A clear definition of equality, diversity and discrimination starts with the Equality and Human Rights Commission, set up by the government to create a fairer society in Britain.

Definitions

So let's look at their definitions.

Equality

Equality is about ensuring that every individual has an equal opportunity to make the most of their lives and talents, and believing that no one should have poorer life chances because of where, what or whom they were born, or because of other characteristics. Equality recognises that historically, certain groups of people with particular characteristics, such as, those of certain races, disabled people, women and gays and lesbians, have experienced discrimination.

Source: www.equalityhumanrights.com

Diversity

Diversity is about difference. It means 'widely varied'. In a diverse population, people are from a range of backgrounds, ethnicities and cultures.

Importance of preventing discrimination

Discrimination can be direct or indirect. According to the Commission, direct discrimination

'refers to less favourable treatment against an individual because of that person's protected characteristic', while indirect discrimination is when 'a provision, criterion or practice is applied in a way that creates disproportionate disadvantage for a person with a protected characteristic as compared to those who do not share that characteristic, and this is not a proportionate means of achieving a legitimate aim.'

Equality and Human Rights Commission

'Protected characteristics are the grounds upon which discrimination is unlawful. The characteristics are: age, disability, gender reassignment, marriage and civil partnership, pregnancy and maternity, race, religion or belief, sex and sexual orientation. In schools, discrimination on grounds of age and marriage and civil partnership do not apply to pupils, although they do apply to employees, for example, teachers. Age applies to students in sixth form colleges and further education institutions.'

Source: www.equalityhumanrights.com

Direct discrimination

Direct discrimination may occur when someone treats you worse because of a specific characteristic, for example, women allowed free entry into a club when men have to pay. Men are being directly discriminated against.

Indirect discrimination is less obvious. A school bans 'cornrow' hairstyles. These hairstyles are more likely to be adopted by specific racial groups so the ban affects one racial group in particular. This is likely to be indirect discrimination.

Initiatives aimed at preventing discrimination in care, for example, the use of advocacy services

Why is it important to prevent discrimination? Does it matter that women get paid less than men? Or does it matter that a poor white boys have the worst start in life? People who work in health and social care think it matters and they

Figure 5.1 The UK has a diverse population

care about trying to make the world a fairer place especially when it comes to health and social care. People who work in care are against discrimination. They are anti-discriminatory and believe everyone should have an equal opportunity to make the most of their lives.

One way we prevent discrimination in care, is by the use of advocacy services. Advocacy means support to have your views heard. The mental health charity MIND provides **advocacy** for people with mental health problems who otherwise might not be listened to.

Activity A P1   A M1

Benjy has learning difficulties. At the clinic another patient who was in a hurry asked the nurse if he could take Benjy's turn because Benjy wouldn't know he had been kept waiting longer than he should. The nurse refused.

1 Explain why it is important to promote equality and diversity for individuals with different needs.
2 Analyse the impact of preventing discrimination for individuals with different needs.

Skills and personal attributes required for developing relationships with individuals

People who work in health and social care need special skills and certain qualities or attributes. These are often called the 6 Cs: care, compassion, competence, communication, courage and commitment. Being able to develop friendly working relationships with people is vital for work in care. People are individuals. They are unpredictable, especially when stressed. They are not machines, doing the same thing every time. A person may be calm one day, angry another day. To work successfully in this sector you have to care about others, to understand them, not judge them, and you have to become skilled in what you do. If you have a quarrel with a partner or friend at home, you have to leave that upset at home, not take it out on others at work. You have to be a skilled communicator, able to hear what others are perhaps unable to put into words, and able to help them understand what they need to know.

At times care work can be scary. If you are a nurse in casualty on Saturday night, drunken people can be violent. A social worker trying to help a drug addict may be attacked. You need courage to work in care. Above all you need commitment. The drunken lout smashing up casualty is someone's son and could be back next day with his elderly parent who has had a heart attack. The drug addict who set the dog on the social worker may eventually go through rehabilitation and become a voluntary worker themselves. It takes commitment to carry on working when people who use the services do not seem to value what you do for them, but sometimes you do see the results of your work. The man who everyone thought would die, recovers. The child knocked over by a speeding car learns to walk again. The drug addict recovers and becomes a loving mother.

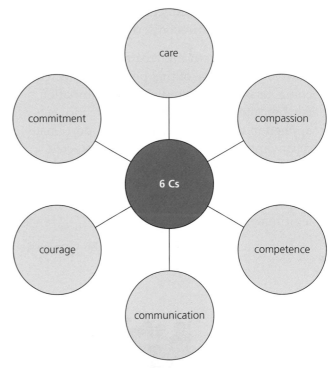

Figure. 5.2 Six Cs of caring

To work in care, you need people skills, communication skills, observation skills and the ability to deal with difficult situations. Empathy, the ability to put yourself in someone else's place and see the world through their eyes, is one of the most important people skills. Empathy helps you to have patience, be flexible and honest in negotiating and solving problems and it encourages people to trust you. A sense of humour in the right situation can help you cope with stress too.

Communication skills – communicating with service users, colleagues and other professionals – includes active listening and responding, using appropriate tone of voice and language, clarifying, questioning, and responding to difficult situations.

Observation skills save lives. A paramedic arrives at the scene of a car crash and observes that the driver has a rapid pulse, is pale and sweaty. The driver might have internal injuries. A midwife delivers a baby and observes that he is blue and not breathing. Both of these are emergencies where observation saves lives. A social worker monitors a family with a young child and observes the child has bruises on his face and legs. The child seems wary. She reports her concerns and the child is taken into care. Later the mother admits that her boyfriend loses his temper with the child and hits him. The social worker's observational skill may have saved the child's life. Observation skills are needed in less critical situations too, for example, when checking children's development. A health visitor notices that a three-year-old is not speaking and does not respond when his name is called. He responds only when he sees her wave at him. She checks his hearing and finds he is deaf. The little boy gets a hearing aid and then learns to speak.

Dealing with difficult situations is part of how we meet individual needs and this is where relationships really matter. There are a lot of difficult situations in care work and how they are handled makes a big difference to how the individual copes. A social worker may have to tell a child that he is to be taken into care. A nurse may have to tell someone that a loved one has died. A care manager may have to tell an elderly resident that their needs can no longer be met in the care home where they lived for the last ten years. Care, compassion, competence, communication, courage and commitment are needed in such situations. A professional who has empathy will support the individual during these difficult times, and will help them come through.

Activity A P2   A M2

An older lady went to have her usual eye test. The optician was new and did not realise the lady had a hearing problem and did not hear the instructions she gave. The optician grew impatient and shouted at the lady.

1   Explain what skills and personal attributes are necessary for professionals who care for individuals with different needs.
2   Assess what different methods the optician might have used to build a relationship and establish trust with this individual.

Empathy and establishing trust with individuals

In order to be able to help people, they must trust you. Many people have had poor experiences of health and care services so it is important to spend time establishing trust. Individuals will know they can trust you if you always do what you say, so if you arrange an appointment at 2.00 p.m. you must be there on time. Health and care professionals have to be honest. If they cannot offer a particular service, they must say so and the individual will then be clear about the limits of the service. At times individuals find it difficult to trust others, especially if they have been let down in the past and not been able to bounce back.

Attachment and emotional resilience theory

John Bowlby and Mary Ainsworth suggested that attachment bonds are formed in the first two years of life and that this bonding could influence later ability to form relationships. Ainsworth observed infants in an experiment called the Strange Situation where a parent briefly leaves the infant playing in a room while a stranger is present. A securely bonded infant will look for the absent parent and may become distressed. On the parent's return, the infant greets them and may seek reassurance in the form of a cuddle. Ainsworth called these 'secure Type B'.

Infants with insecure bonds may react in different ways. Some insecure infants may not get distressed when the parent leaves, and may ignore the returning parent. Ainsworth called these 'insecure-avoidant Type A'. Other infants with insecure bonding may get distressed when a parent leaves, but then behave ambivalently towards the returning parent, getting angry and pushing them away. Ainsworth called these 'insecure-resistant or ambivalent Type C'. Later research identified a further group of infants, 'Type D' who show contradictory behaviours, approaching parents yet seeming apprehensive. Some of these infants may have been maltreated by their parents.

Bowlby and Ainsworth suggested that children form **internal working models** of self, others and the relationship between themselves and others. A child of 'Type A' might expect an inappropriate response from the parent, a difficult relationship with them, and may feel unworthy of love. A child of 'Type B' is secure, confident that parents will return, and they see themselves as worthy of love. Such a child expects warmth and comfort from relationships and is not wary of strangers. A child with a 'Type C' attachment may be upset when the parent leaves, which shows they are attached but they may doubt that the parent will come back, so they are insecure. They may feel that the parent or the stranger in the experiment cannot provide comfort or they may feel they are not worthy of love. Such a child may expect little emotional comfort from relationships.

Children with 'Type D' behaviours may be uncertain how to react when distressed and unsure what to expect from others, seeking instead to comfort themselves.

According to this theory, a child's internal working model of how relationships work influences their approach to new relationships in later life. Securely attached children become adults who are confident that others will respond positively to them. Insecurely attached children grow into adults who find relationships difficult. An insecure-ambivalent attachment may make a person wary of relationships. Those with insecure avoidant attachments may not want relationships. Children with disorganised attachment-related behaviours may become adults who start relationships but fail to sustain them because of their unpredictable behaviour.

Emotional resilience

Emotional resilience is the ability to bounce back after difficulties. Part of this resilience comes from a secure base that includes networks of support such as friends and family, part of it comes from a person's own self-esteem and part comes from a sense of mastery and control knowing one's abilities and strengths. Barnardo's the children's charity, work with children and young people to help them cope with changes.

The triangle of care

The triangle of care involves individuals, their carers and professionals working together to provide the best quality of care for the individual. Previously professionals would talk to the individual who might be able to pass on information to carers, but often might not. Carers were excluded and had very little involvement in planning care, but were left to cope as best they could. With a triangle of care, the individual, their carer and the professionals share information and give a better quality of life for the individual.

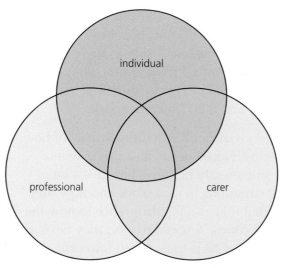

Figure 5.3 The triangle of care: what happens in the overlapping areas?

Empathy

Empathy is the ability to put oneself in the place of others and understand things from their point of view, understand how they feel and why they act as they do. There are several theories that attempt to explain empathy. Robert Vischer used the term 'empathy' in 1873, and it was later used by Johannes Volkelt and Theodor Lipps in the 1890s to mean feeling as others feel. Max Scheler in 1926 drew a distinction between sympathy and empathy, where it might be possible to understand what others are feeling and share their distress (empathy), whereas sympathy is having care or concern for someone without necessarily feeling what they are feeling. It is possible to feel sympathy for a beetle you accidentally step on, but you may not feel what they are feeling.

More recently Martin Hoffman (2002) suggested empathy is the foundation for moral development and there are four stages of empathy: global empathy for example when a baby hears another cry, they cry too; egocentric empathy, from about two years old a child will offer help to someone in a way they would like themselves, so they might offer a teddy to comfort a crying child; empathy for another's feelings emerges around three years old when children role play and begin to realise that other people's feelings may differ from their own. They then respond more appropriately to the needs of others. The fourth stage, empathy for another's life condition, emerges in adolescence, when they begin to empathise with the poor, the sick, or refugees.

Activity A M2

How could empathy help a professional to establish a trusting relationship with a person who needs care and support? Assess how this method helps professionals to build relationships and establish trust with individuals with needs.

Distinction activity A D1

People with learning disabilities and people with mental health issues are sometimes unable to ensure they are treated equally. For this reason it is especially important that health and care professionals are aware of the principles, values and skills which underpin meeting the care and support needs of individuals.

Read 'Learning disabled people will get named social workers to challenge NHS decisions':

www.communitycare.co.uk/2015/11/10/learning-disabled-people-will-get-named-social-workers-challenge-nhs-decisions/

Check your understanding

1 Explain these terms: equality, diversity, discrimination
2 What are protected characteristics?
3 What are the 6 Cs?
4 Outline attachment theory
5 What is emotional resilience?
6 Who is involved in the triangle of care?
7 Explain empathy.

B Examine the ethical issues involved when providing care and support to meet individual needs P3, M3, D2

Ethical issues and approaches

Ethics is concerned with issues of right and wrong. There are several approaches to the study of ethics in care.

Ethical theories

Consequentialism
Consequentialism or results-based ethics says no type of act is inherently wrong – it depends on the result of the act.

The Suicide Act England and Wales says it is wrong to assist anyone to commit suicide. Sometimes people with incurable and painful illnesses want to die. They cannot choose to end their life in a clinic in the UK because that service

Research

What issues surrounding equality and diversity, and preventing discrimination were raised in this article?

How might the application of empathy theories, together with personal skills and attributes successfully promote anti-discriminatory practice?

What are the advantages and disadvantages of empathy theories in this context? Use research to support your argument and come to reasoned and valid conclusions and recommendations.

is not offered but it is offered by Dignitas, a clinic in Switzerland. Any relative who accompanies them is technically guilty of breaking the law.

According to results-based ethics, the relative might feel that their decision to accompany their relative to Dignitas is justified. Their relative will have their wish for a pain free death, surrounded by loved ones and will not face years of suffering.

Deontology

Deontology takes the opposite view to consequentialism. Deontology (duty-based) ethics are concerned with what people do, not with the results, so killing is always wrong, telling lies is always wrong even if it saves someone's life.

Principlism

Principlism combines virtues and practical wisdom with four ethical principles.

1 Autonomy – a person's right to choose how to live their life.

2 Beneficence – when a person is unable to make choices for themselves, health professionals have a duty to act in the best interests of that person, not just in medical terms but also in wider cultural and spiritual terms.

3 Non-maleficence means not causing harm

4 Justice is the moral obligation to act fairly, for example, when resources are scarce, fairly distributing them; respecting people's rights; and respecting laws.

Virtue ethics

Virtue ethics focuses on the virtues or moral character of the health professional rather than the individual so they might ask 'What would a good doctor or nurse do in these circumstances?'

Managing conflict with service users, carers, families or colleagues

Conflict occurs when people are stressed and it can range from obstructive silence through verbal aggression to outbursts of violence. Service users may refuse to say whether they have followed a recommended treatment. Carers and families may feel resentful of professionals 'interfering' or they may expect more than the service can offer. Colleagues may feel there is an unfair workload. Empathy and communication are useful in such situations and can help to diffuse conflict.

Managing a conflict of interests

A conflict of interest may arise when a patient needs an expensive drug and a doctor has been told that the local NHS Trust cannot afford the drug. The first duty of the doctor is to the patient but if all the budget was spent on one patient there would be no money left to treat other people. The strain on resources poses a major ethical dilemma for many health professionals and there are no easy answers. Should a clinical commissioning group fund a place in rehabilitation for a drug addict or should they use that money to provide medication for someone with dementia?

Balancing services and resources

Balancing services and resources is one of the greatest challenges today. Demand for health and social care is increasing, but resources are not. There is a shortage of money and a shortage of staff in health and social care. At the moment, most health care is free at the point of delivery, but social care is not. Those with assets are expected to pay for support and those without who are reliant on welfare benefits find these too are being reduced.

In Unit 2 we looked at how an Occupational Therapist might assess someone's ability to cope before they are discharged from hospital. Minimising risk while promoting individual choice and independence is a routine aspect of everyday care whether in hospital or in the community. We also looked at sharing information and managing confidentiality in Unit 2.

Activity B P3

1 Find out about the cases of Debbie Purdy and Tony Nicklinson.

2 What would a consequentialism or results-based ethics view be on each case?

3 What would a deontological view be?

4 What ethical principles are involved?

5 Explain how a carer could incorporate ethical principles into the provision for individuals with different needs such as these two people.

Legislation and guidance on conflicts of interest, balancing resources and minimising risk

Organisations, legislation and guidance that influence or advise on ethical issues

Organisations

- **The Department of Health** (DH) leads, shapes and funds health and care in England. In Northern Ireland this role is held by the Department for Health, Social Services and Public Safety, Northern Ireland. The Welsh Government sets policy for health and well-being in Wales.

- **National Health Service** (NHS), NHS Wales and Health and Social Care in Northern Ireland are integrated.

- **National Institute for Health and Care Excellence** (NICE) provides national guidance and advice to improve health and social care primarily in England but also advises for Wales and Northern Ireland. It is sponsored by the Department of Health to equalise the availability of treatment and care across England.

- **The Health and Safety Executive** (HSE) encourages, regulates and enforces workplace health, safety and welfare, and researches into occupational risks in England and Wales and Scotland. Responsibility in Northern Ireland lies with the Health and Safety Executive for Northern Ireland.

Legislation

Human Rights Act 1998

This Act sets out the fundamental rights and freedoms that individuals in the UK have access to. These are the rights:

1 Right to life
2 Freedom from torture and inhuman or degrading treatment
3 Right to liberty and security
4 Freedom from slavery and forced labour
5 Right to a fair trial
6 No punishment without law
7 Respect for your private and family life, home and correspondence
8 Freedom of thought, belief and religion
9 Freedom of expression
10 Freedom of assembly and association
11 Right to marry and start a family
12 Protection from discrimination in respect of these rights and freedoms
13 Right to peaceful enjoyment of your property
14 Right to education
15 Right to participate in free elections

Mental Capacity Act 2005

This protects and empowers individuals who lack the mental capacity to make their own decisions about their care and treatment. It applies to individuals aged 16 and over. People working with or caring for adults who lack capacity to make decisions for themselves have a legal duty to consider the associated Mental Capacity Act Code of Practice.

National Health Service Act 2006

This specifies the duty of clinical commissioning groups (CCGs) under Section 140 Mental Health Act 1983 to notify local social services authorities of the availability of suitable hospital places for emergency admissions and for under-18s (section 45 of the Health and Social Care Act 2012).

Mental Health Act 2007

This Act updates the 1983 Act and says what legal powers doctors and Approved Mental Health Professionals (AMHPs) have to detain people in hospital against their will. It introduces Independent Mental Health Advocacy and Deprivation of Liberty Safeguards (DoLS) as well as community treatment orders.

Equality Act 2010

This Act protects the rights of individuals, protects individuals from unfair treatment and promotes a fair and more equal society.

Care Act 2014

This says that local authorities must provide or arrange services that help prevent people developing needs for care and support or delay people deteriorating. They must provide services aimed at reducing needs and helping people regain skills. The Care Act specifies who is entitled to public care and support, who can have their needs assessed, what support there is for planning and how services will be charged for. Personal budgets and the personalisation of services are included in this Act.

Guidance

The DH Decision Support Tool is used following a multidisciplinary assessment to decide if an individual is eligible for NHS continuing healthcare where it can be said that they have a 'primary health need'. This focus is at the individual level.

The Five Step Framework – NICE guidance 'The five steps of health needs assessment' focuses at a wider level on a population.

Step 1 Getting started – What population? What are you trying to achieve? Who needs to be involved? What resources are required? What are the risks?

Step 2 Identifying health priorities - Population profiling; Gathering data; Perceptions of needs; Identifying and assessing health conditions and determinant factors.

Step 3 Assessing a health priority for action such as 'Reduce health inequalities by 10 per cent by 2010 as measured by infant mortality and life expectancy at birth'. Choosing health conditions and determinant factors with the most significant size and severity impact; Determining effective and acceptable interventions and actions.

Step 4 Planning for change - Clarifying aims of intervention; Action planning; Monitoring and evaluation strategy; Risk-management strategy.

Step 5 Moving on/review - Learning from the project; Measuring impact; Choosing the next priority.

NICE and NHS guidance on Care Pathways and Care Plans

Care pathways clearly set out the path of care that an individual might follow. Knowing the outcome can sometimes aid recovery for an individual. Where care pathways are used, recovery is quicker.

An integrated care pathway (ICP) is a multidisciplinary outline of anticipated care, placed in an appropriate timeframe, to help a patient with a specific condition or set of symptoms move progressively through a clinical experience to positive outcomes.

Source: www.medicine.ox.ac.uk

Research following hip and knee replacements, with proactive treatment with specific daily goals for the patient and treating team, and a written protocol listing milestones to be achieved, tests ordered, and daily tasks for patient and team members, meant patients walked sooner and were discharged sooner.

Source: www.medicine.ox.ac.uk/bandolier/Extraforban-do/Forum2.pdf

Managing Conflicts of Interest: Guidance for Clinical Commissioning Groups (2013, NHS)

This guidance is aimed at helping clinicians and members of the CCG to act fairly, legally and ethically when making decisions. They must balance the need for economy with the requirement to provide health care for all in their area.

HSE guidance on risk assessments

The Health and Safety executive provide guidance on assessing and managing risks for organisations. It advises a five step process:

1 identifying what can harm people in your workplace

2 identifying who might be harmed and how

3 evaluating the risks and deciding on the appropriate controls, taking into account the controls you already have in place

4 recording your risk assessment

5 reviewing and updating your assessment.

This guidance is detailed but may be counterbalanced by other factors. An individual may choose not to have an assessment using the Decision Support Tool. They may choose to pay for care even though they might be eligible for free care. Organisations may use the five step process to identify health needs of a population but government policies may change and other priorities be identified, for example a healthy eating campaign may be put on hold while resources are directed at banning smoking in public places. A care pathway may be disrupted by an individual who refuses a blood transfusion for religious reasons.

Clinical Commissioning Groups have to purchase services for a community with a limited budget.

Under Section 140 Mental Health Act 1983 CCGs 'must notify local social services authorities of the availability of suitable hospital places for emergency admissions and for under-18s', so if someone under 18 had a mental health crisis and required emergency admission CCGs must provide a place of safety. Often there is no suitable place and the young person is either accommodated in a police cell, on a ward with adults with mental health issues or in accommodation many miles away.

1   What reasons might a CCG put forward for not providing suitable accommodation?

2   Analyse how an ethical approach to providing support might benefit specific individuals with different needs.

You are a member of a Clinical Commissioning group working on providing safe accommodation for under-18s with a mental health issues.

Justify the strategies and techniques used to overcome ethical issues and challenges experienced by individuals with different needs when planning and providing care.

1   Explain the difference between consequentialism and deontology in ethics.

2   What four principles underpin most ethical theories?

3   Briefly outline three pieces of legislation that influence or advise ethical issues.

4   Briefly explain these: DH Decision Support Tool, NICE guidance 'The five steps of health needs assessment', Care Pathways.

C Investigate the principles behind enabling individuals with care and support needs to overcome challenges C P4, C P5, C M4, B C D2

Enabling individuals to overcome challenges

People have to overcome many problems to live their lives well and to get the services they need.

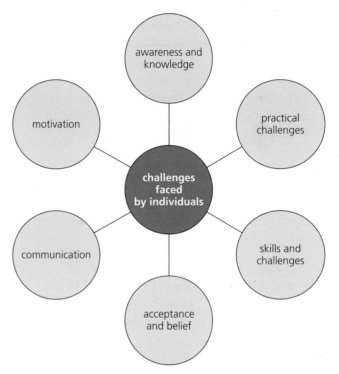

Figure 5.4 Challenges faced by individuals with care and support needs

Care professionals identify the challenges they face through

- observation
- taking part in focus groups (of patients and service users, and of professionals)
- talking to individuals informally
- analysing the results of questionnaires.

Strategies to overcome challenges include:

- educational information materials such as leaflets to increase awareness and knowledge and to aid communication

- training courses for carers and professionals such as, dementia awareness training
- opinion leaders, famous people who can influence public opinion such as a famous chef campaigning against sugary drinks for children
- clinical audits that check organisations are acting fairly without discrimination, and so increase acceptance of the individual
- computer-aided advice systems, such as, online advice that overcome practical challenges of access and make information available in the person's own home
- Patient-mediated strategies such as media campaigns to educate patients and staff. Patients who know about the latest evidence-based practice can influence decisions during consultations about their care. Patients are also more accepting of any changes to their care if they know the evidence behind it.

Role of policy frameworks in minimising challenges

Policy frameworks are plans that help identify good practice.

NHS patient experience framework

This framework describes key elements of the patients' experience of NHS Services. People can measure whether their own experience matches up to this ideal.

1 Respect for patient-centred values, preferences, and expressed needs, including: cultural issues; the dignity, privacy and independence of patients and service users; an awareness of quality-of-life issues; and shared decision making

2 Co-ordination and integration of care across the health and social care system.

3 Information, communication, and education on clinical status, progress, prognosis, and processes of care in order to facilitate autonomy, self-care and health promotion.

4 Physical comfort including pain management, help with activities of daily living, and clean and comfortable surroundings.

5 Emotional support and alleviation of fear and anxiety about issues such as clinical status, prognosis, and the impact of illness on patients, their families and their finances.

6 Welcoming the involvement of family and friends, on whom patients and service users rely, in decision-making and demonstrating awareness and accommodation of their needs as care-givers.

7 Transition and continuity as regards information that will help patients care for themselves away from a clinical setting, and coordination, planning, and support to ease transitions.

8 Access to care with attention for example, to time spent waiting for admission or time between admission and placement in a room in an in-patient setting, and waiting time for an appointment or visit in the out-patient, primary care or social care setting.

Source: www.gov.uk

Health action plans

Health action plans can be used to minimise challenges for people with learning disabilities.

A health action plan is a personal plan about what a person with learning disabilities can do to be healthy. It lists any help people might need and helps to make sure people get the services and support they need to be healthy. It may be shared with professionals and carers if the individual agrees.

Adult Social Care Outcomes Framework (ASCOF)

ASCOF measures the performance of care and support services. The Framework helps councils to improve the quality of care and support services they provide, gives an overview of adult social care outcomes in the previous year and considers future developments.

Common Assessment Framework (CAF)

CAF is a standardised method of assessing a child's additional needs and deciding how those needs should be met. Practitioners across children's services can use it and share information.

Impact of not enabling individuals to overcome challenges

If we do not help people to overcome the challenges and difficulties they face, they will not have the services they need and their health may suffer.

Activity

Look back at the challenges faced by individuals when they require services. Choose one of the strategies listed above and say how the strategy might help a person overcome three of the challenges.

Now choose one policy and say which challenges it might help overcome.

Promoting personalisation

Personalisation, ensuring that every person receiving care and support is able to set their personal goals and has choice and control over the shape of their care and support, was introduced in the Care Act 2014. Local authorities have a duty to assess an individual's needs, and plan with the individual how best to meet the identified needs. Outcomes are measured. Care is paid for from the personal budget allocated to each eligible individual. Sometimes they may be given the budget as a direct payment to use for their care and can employ a personal assistant to help them.

Methods of recognising preferences

Care plans, learning plans, and behavioural plans must relate to the individual as a unique person, noting their individual preferences, for example, the person may be vegetarian or may wish to attend a place of worship. Plans must take account of individual preferences. Specialist support from health and social care professionals must also recognise preferences, for example, a person who is diabetic may require a diet where carbohydrates are controlled. The dietician should find out the individual's preferences before planning a diet. The individual may eat rice or chapatis so may not want a diet where potatoes and bread are the controlled carbohydrates.

The importance of promoting choice and control and the financial impact of this on care provision

Giving people choices of care and giving them control of their own personal budgets is intended to make sure they get the services they need and to reduce the waste resulting from inappropriately provided services. However with rights come responsibilities. The budget holder must keep records of how money has been spent and periodic reviews assess whether the chosen support is effective.

Personal budgets are intended to combine the following funding streams:

- local authority adult social care
- integrated community equipment services
- disabled facilities grants
- Supporting people for housing-related support
- 'Access to Work'
- 'Independent Living Fund'.

Activity

Find out what is happening in your local area. Are individuals given a choice of having a personal budget? What information is available on your local authority website for people wishing to know about personal budgets?

Communication techniques

Promoting effective communication is one of the underlying core principles in care work; however, **there are different approaches for effective communication**. These include:

- **Humanistic** – based on humanist theories such as Maslow's hierarchy of needs. This assumes everyone has basic needs for safety and security. Once these are fulfilled they then seek to feel a sense of belonging and achievement. Effective communication would respond to the level of need in the individual.
- **Behavioural** approaches based on reinforcement and conditioning, as described by Pavlov and Skinner, would focus on giving praise for effort and achievement.

- **Cognitive** approaches such as those described by Piaget would focus on the level of the individual's understanding using symbols, pictures and objects for people with less developed cognition, and using more complex communication for those with a more developed understanding.

- **Psychoanalytical** approaches based on the work of analysts such as Freud and Jung, may use communication focused on early experiences. This approach might be used with people with dementia, as early memories are retained longer.

- **Social** approaches based on Bandura's social learning theory suggest we learn from those around us, so communication using social approaches might focus on modelling appropriate ways of communicating. This might be used with people at the high end of the autistic spectrum who may have difficulty forming social relationships and might require support to learn how to communicate in a social situation.

Verbal communication techniques

Verbal, face-to-face communication has the benefit of being able to see the other person's body language. Professor Albert Mehrabian researched communication in the 1960s and found that in situations where emotions are involved, when words and facial expressions contradict each other, people believe the facial expression rather than what is said. Here is an example, based on a true situation.

A nurse checked a female patient who was due to go to theatre for a termination of pregnancy. As the nurse completed the checklist and confirmed the patient had signed the consent form, she saw the woman was crying and asked her if she was all right. The woman said 'yes', she was fine, then broke down sobbing. The nurse believed the body language not the words and waited rather than taking the patient down to theatre. When the woman stopped sobbing, she asked if it was too late to change her mind – she wanted to keep the baby. The nurse rang the doctor and the operation was cancelled.

In health and social care there are many situations where emotions are involved. In face-to-face situations professionals should read the body language as well as listen to the words and check if the messages contradict each other.

Verbal communication on the telephone works best when factual information is required such as how many children a person has, but this method would not be suitable if a mental health worker wanted to find out how a mother with post-natal depression felt about being a mother.

Even when factual information is required, telephone communication can break down if the care worker uses an inappropriate tone of voice or uses jargon or does not speak the same language.

Mrs Khan rang the doctor's surgery to find out the result of her latest blood test. She was put through to the practice nurse who was very busy. When Mrs Khan struggled to find the words in English the practice nurse grew impatient and her tone of voice became sharp. She asked Mrs Khan whether she wanted the result of the low-density lipoprotein (LDL), high-density lipoprotein (HDL) and triglycerides. Mrs Khan did not understand what the practice nurse meant because she did not understand the jargon and could not understand the nurse's regional dialect.

Body language

Body language, as we saw earlier, can tell us a lot about a person's feelings. How they stand (posture), their facial expression, whether they make eye contact, the gestures they use tell us how they feel.

Figure 5.5 Body language tells us a lot about how people are feeling

Angry people having an argument may stand facing each other 'squaring up', frowning, 'eyeballing' each other and jabbing pointing fingers at each other.

A sad person may slump in a chair or stand apart from others, eyes downcast, avoiding eye contact, perhaps hugging themselves.

A happy confident person holds their head high, makes eye contact in a friendly way and is ready to smile and hold out their hand in friendship.

Body language tells us a lot. If you are not convinced, next time you watch television, turn the sound down and observe what messages body language says.

Written communication using clear language that can be understood by the service user

Written communication lacks the visual context that face-to-face communication gives. Recipients cannot check out what the person means and messages may be misinterpreted.

Written communication should be carefully phrased. Letters are used less often nowadays but when they are, the tone is usually formal. Grammar and spelling should be correct.

Texts may be less formal but if sent from professionals, for example, to remind someone about a hospital appointment, they should be clear, correctly spelled and have the facts. 'Eye clinic tomorrow at 10am' means more than 'hospital appointment tomorrow'.

An e-mail dashed off quickly might be misinterpreted. One typed in CAPITAL LETTERS MEANS YOU ARE SHOUTING. Emails are permanent and may be seen by others, so it is important to be tactful.

Electronic communication techniques

In 2012, Dr Frank Casey of the Royal Belfast hospital for sick children wrote about how they use video conferencing to save children with heart problems having to travel long distances to outpatient appointments in Belfast. Using a laptop with a video conferencing facility, parents can discuss care with the doctor, contact the cardiology department if worried, and test results can be shared on screen. Video conferencing is also used to support the care of new-born babies with heart problems at remote hospitals.

Alternative communication techniques and new technologies

Communication systems such as Makaton, Braille, and British Sign Language, communication boards and symbol systems have been used for many years.

Makaton uses signs, symbols and speech to help people who have no speech or whose speech is unclear to communicate. Signs are used in spoken word order to support speech. Symbols can help people who have limited speech and cannot, or prefer not to sign. Some people use signs and symbols until they find alternatives. Others continue to use them.

Emoticons used in e-mails and texts perform a similar purpose. The Makaton symbol for sleep is similar to the emoticon used in texts and emails.

Figure 5.6 The Makaton symbol for 'sleep'

Braille, a system of raised dots on paper, was invented by Louis Braille in the nineteenth century. It has since been adapted to many languages. The Royal National Institute for the Blind (RNIB) has a library of Braille books. Electronic Braille is available for use with a screen reader, and increasingly technology is helping those with sight loss maintain independence. Screen magnifiers, screen readers and voice activated programmes make computers and the Internet accessible for those with vision impairment. The RNIB has a short video about using screen readers and screen magnifiers.

British Sign Language uses visual communication, including gestures, facial expression, and body language. It is used by those who are Deaf or have hearing impairments and has its own grammar and syntax. Sign language varies according to the language, so someone who knows BSL may not be able to communicate with someone who has learned a different sign language.

Sign Supported English (SSE) uses the same signs as BSL but in the same order as spoken English. SSE supports spoken English, and is used by those who mix with hearing people and in schools where children with hearing impairments learn English grammar while signing.

Communication boards may have words, photos, or pictures commonly used by the person. The pictures may be grouped according to topic, for example, pictures of favourite foods, or activities. Communication boards may be useful for people with autism depending on their individual requirements.

Technology is helping those with communication challenges. Voice Output Communication Aids (VOCAs) or Speech Generating Devices (SGDs) are available. The user may use a pre-recorded message or generate their own messages. Professor Stephen Hawking, the famous physicist, who has motor neurone disease, uses a speech synthesiser to produce his lectures, operates his computer by moving his cheek and surfs the internet, uses email and Skype to communicate with friends.

Theories of communication

Argyle's stages of the communication cycle

In 1972, Michael Argyle, professor of social psychology at Oxford University, described the cycle of communication as an ongoing process (Figure 5.7).

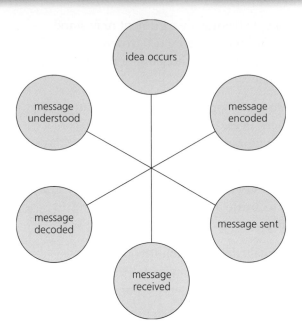

Figure 5.7 Argyle's theory

This is how it works:

1 idea occurs – I haven't seen my friend for ages – could meet them at lunchtime
2 message encoded – compose a text
3 message sent – send text
4 message received – text arrives
5 message decoded – decipher/read text
6 message understood – friend wants to meet at lunchtime.

If the cycle works, you could then think of your reply, encode it, send it and so on, round the cycle. Of course many things can go wrong – you may not think about your friend, or you may think about them but be too busy to send a text. You might have left your phone at home or have no credit, or the battery may be flat. You might send a text to the wrong person, or you send it to the right person but their phone is switched off. Your message might get to the right person but the joke you thought funny is not appreciated by them. Many things can go wrong with communication.

Tuckman's stages of group interaction

Tuckman studied how groups and teams work together and realised that many groups go through the same stages. These are:

- **Forming** – coming together and getting to know each other
- **Storming** – clarifying who does what and what needs to be done. This may involve disagreements.
- **Norming** – agreeing how to proceed. What are the rules or guidelines?
- **Performing** – doing the activity and completing the task

Tuckman added a final stage when the group disbands. He called this adjourning or **mourning**.

Berne's theory of transactional analysis

Eric Berne, a psychotherapist, developed the theory of transactional analysis. A transaction occurs when people meet and communicate. He studied such meetings in detail, analysing what happened. Berne described three states that people operate in

1. Parent – things we are taught by parents or carers when we were small, such as sharing, saying 'please' and 'thank you'
2. Child – emotions we feel such as fear, confidence
3. Adult – things we learn, such as 'there are no monsters hiding under the bed' or 'Dad was right; driving isn't too difficult'

Berne suggested we function in different modes depending on the situation. The whole person is made up of Parent, Adult, and Child.

In simple transactions, for example Adult to Adult, there might be a simple question such as 'Have you seen my keys?' and the response might be 'No, sorry.' It is a factual interchange.

P   P

A ⟷ A

C   C

Or a person in Child mode might ask their spouse 'Can I have a cup of tea?' and the response from their partner in Adult mode might be 'Yes, here you are.'

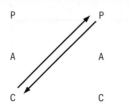

These are complementary transactions, each person staying in the mode. These are healthy transactions.

Sometimes however, transactions do not work well. There might be a person who always makes you feel childish, or irritates you. This is a crossed transaction.

Here is what it might sound like:

'What time will you be in tonight?' (Adult mode asking question, expecting Adult response)

'You are always picking on me' (Child mode responding to perceived Parent figure)

Here is what it might look like using PAC:

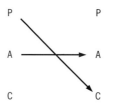

This is a crossed transaction, where the person asking the question might be left wondering what they had said to make the other person respond like that.

This raises the point that it is not just WHAT is said, but HOW it is said, and the importance of non-verbal communication. You can almost imagine the body language of someone storming out saying 'You are always picking on me!'

Activity C P4 A D1

You are preparing for work experience in a residential care home. One of the things you will be expected to do is to talk to the residents. Mr M used to be an accountant and worked in Germany for several years.

1. Explain the strategies and techniques you might use when communicating with him. How could these help you to meet his needs and overcome challenges?
2. Remind yourself of the command word 'evaluate'. Evaluate how successful anti-discriminatory practice might be in meeting his needs.

Activity C P5   C M4

Mrs P is 80 years old and lives alone and has no relatives. She is a little deaf. She is worried because she is about to go into hospital for a hip replacement but does not know much about the operation. Her house does not have a downstairs toilet.

1 What policy frameworks are designed to help her have a better experience?

2 Explain what the benefits of promoting personalisation may be when overcoming challenges faced by this individual. How might the personalisation of care help her recovery?

3 Assess the strategies and communication techniques you would use to overcome different challenges faced by this individual and her care and support needs.

D Investigate the roles of professionals and how they work together to provide the care and support necessary to meet individual needs D P6 , D P7 , D P8 , D M5 , D M6 , D D3 , D D4

How agencies work together to meet individual care and support needs

One of the issues for health and social care is that people, especially politicians, try to improve services by changing the way things are done. This means that there is a lot of change. At the time of writing there are organisations responsible for commissioning or ordering services and others responsible for delivering the services. In England and Wales, health care and social care are commissioned separately. In Northern Ireland health and social care are together.

Organisations responsible for commissioning healthcare services

Clinical Commissioning Groups in England
These are described in Unit 2 'Working in health and social care' on page 35.

Local Health Boards in Wales: In 2009 the 22 Local Health Boards (LHBs) and 7 NHS Trusts

in Wales were replaced by 7 new Health Boards which are much more focused on meeting the needs of patients. Health Boards are responsible within their area for planning, funding and delivering Primary care services such as GPs, pharmacies, dentists and optometrists; Hospital services for inpatients and outpatients; Community services, including those provided through community health centres and mental health services and Health Boards provide information to the public about the services they offer. Health boards also look at complaints against GPs, dentists, pharmacists or optometrists.

Health and Social Care Board in Northern Ireland
The Health and Social Care Board (HSCB) formed on 1st April 2009 by the Health and Social Care (Reform) Act (Northern Ireland) 2009, works with the five local commissioning groups (LCGs) to commission a range of health and social services for the people who live in Northern Ireland. It works with the health and social care trusts that directly provide services to people to ensure that these meet their needs and it manages its annual funding from the Northern Ireland Executive.

Organisations responsible for commissioning social care services, in England and Wales
These are local authorities. Historically social services have been organised on a local scale, whereas health care is organised nationally. Local authorities commission social services according to the needs of their population, so will spend more on services for older people if they have older people in their local community.

Bodies responsible for integrating health and social care
Bodies responsible for integrating health and social care, such as Health and Well-being Boards, are described in detail in Unit 2 'Working in health and social care'.

Assessment and eligibility frameworks
These include:

- The Common Assessment Framework (CAF) described earlier in this unit.

- The National Eligibility Criteria (Care Act 2014) or the Care and Support (Eligibility Criteria) Regulations 2014 which set out national eligibility criteria for access to adult care and support, and for access to carer support.

- The Department of Health sets national policy, creates legislation and allocates funding for health care.

- The National Framework for NHS Continuing Healthcare is published by the Department of health and sets out the principles and processes for NHS continuing healthcare and NHS funded nursing care.

- The Education, Health and Care plan (EHC).

- An education, health and care (EHC) plan is for children and young people aged up to 25 who need more support than is available through special educational needs support. EHC plans identify educational, health and social needs and set out the additional support to meet those needs.

Roles and responsibilities of key professionals on multi-disciplinary teams

Multi-disciplinary teams are described in Unit 2 'Working in health and social care'.

Members of a multi-disciplinary team may work together on a specific case or may work together on a regular basis.

Specific roles and responsibilities are outlined in Unit 2 'Working in health and social care'.

Healthcare professionals work together regularly. Harry, a six-year-old with Attention Deficit Hyperactivity Disorder (ADHD) may see his GP, then be referred to hospital where he sees a nurse, a paediatrician, and clinical psychologist.

Social care professionals work together regularly. Mary, an 80-year-old in hospital for a knee replacement, may see a social worker and an occupational therapist.

Education professionals work together regularly. At school, Harry's progress may be monitored by a special educational needs co-ordinator (SENCO), who discusses Harry's progress with an educational psychologist.

Allied health professionals, such as a speech and language therapist might be involved with supporting a child with a stammer, or might be involved with helping an older person recover speech following a stroke.

Voluntary sector workers, such as Macmillan nurses or Marie Curie nurses may be employed by a charity to provide individualised care for people who are seriously ill; family support workers may be employed by children's charities or by local authority social services.

How multi-agency and multi-disciplinary teams work together to provide co-ordinated support

Figure 5.8 Multidisciplinary care

Choose one of these and decide what input they may need from the NHS, Social services and voluntary services.

Jake a fifteen-year-old who has run away from home and been sleeping rough.

Mia, a mother of two young children who has walked out with the children after years of domestic abuse.

Zia, a 60-year-old diabetic who lives alone and neglects his diet.

Explain why meeting the needs of individuals requires the involvement of different agencies.

Explain the roles and responsibilities of different members of the multidisciplinary team in meeting the needs of your chosen individual.

Assess the benefits of multi-disciplinary and multi-agency working for these individuals with care and support needs. Explain the arrangements for managing information between professionals.

Maintaining confidentiality

Confidentiality has been mentioned in Unit 2 'Working in health and social care' on page 30.

Confidentiality is the right of an individual to have personal, identifiable medical information kept private. Information may only be shared when disclosure is required by law; when patients consent implicitly for purposes of directly providing and supporting their own care and expressly (or explicitly) for other (secondary) purposes; and when the benefits to an individual or society outweigh **both** the public and the patient's interest in keeping the information confidential, according to the General Medical Council (the body which regulates doctors).

Working practices to maintain confidentiality

This includes keeping yourself informed of the relevant laws; keeping information locked away or password protected; sharing information only with people who are entitled to have access to the information, for example, other people in the multi-disciplinary team, service users and their carers or families (depending on the situation). Working practices include being professional about how information is shared.

Codes of practice for care workers

Codes of practice for care workers establish the importance of confidentiality and are described in Unit 2 'Working in health and social care'.

Relevant aspects of legislation

The Health and Social Care Act 2012 created the Health and Social Care Information Centre (HSCIC) as the national provider of information, data and IT systems for health and social care. This Act set out how information must be managed by the Health and Social Care Information Centre (HSCIC).

Activity

Mr K is terminally ill. At his local surgery, a receptionist left the computer screen open on his page. A member of the public who knew Mr K was at the desk and was able to read his medical history. The first thing Mr K knew about this was when his friend expressed his sadness and asked if he could do anything to help.

What effect might this breach of confidence have on Mr K's relationship with his surgery staff?

Managing information

Working practices for managing information

Personal information must be handled sensitively and managed to ensure confidentiality. Information which is anonymised data may require less strict procedures for maintaining confidentiality.

Key points

Managing information

- Why is the information needed?
- What information is needed?
- Where and how can you find the information?
- Information must be used legally and ethically.

The importance of sharing information with colleagues, other professionals, the individual with care needs and their family

If health and care professionals are to offer care that meets individual needs they must share information.

Case scenario

Harry

Harry, the six-year-old with Attention Deficit Hyperactivity Disorder (ADHD) sees his GP who shares Harry's medical information with the hospital staff. The paediatrician will write his findings in Harry's notes and the clinical psychologist will be able to see this information so Harry's mum does not have to repeat it. The clinical psychologist may then refer Harry to an educational psychologist and share information about what investigations and treatment Harry has had. The SENCO at Harry's school can tell the educational psychologist how Harry is responding to treatment. If no one shared information, Harry would have tests repeated, may be given the wrong treatment and his parents would have to repeat everything they'd already said at each visit. Harry's progress would be delayed.

The impact of new technologies mean that we manage information electronically, but that too can lead to breaches of confidentiality, if passwords are not changed and hackers get into the system.

Bodies that control the management of information

- The National Adult Social Care Intelligence Service (NASCIS) provides a single national resource of information for social care services across England. It provides data such as information on the number of adults contacting social services, going through the community care assessment process, and the services they receive.

- The Information Commissioner's Office (ICO) also regulates information and investigates breaches of confidentiality.

- Legislation and codes of practice that relate to the storage and sharing of information in health and social care are discussed in Unit 2 where the Data Protection Act 1998 is explained in detail.

- The Freedom of Information Act 2000 provides public access to information held by public authorities. Public authorities must publish certain information about their activities and members of the public have the right to request information from public authorities. The Act covers any recorded information held by a public authority in England, Wales and Northern Ireland.

- The Mental Health Act 2007 revised the 1983 Act but did not replace it. The 2007 Act brought in a single definition of mental disorder: ' "mental disorder" means any disorder or disability of the mind'. The 2007 Act introduced Independent Mental Health Advocates (IMHAs) who could speak on behalf of those who were too ill to speak for themselves. It also introduced compulsory community treatment orders. An approved mental health professional (AMHP) is responsible for organising and co-ordinating assessments under the Mental Health Act and can recommend that you are detained in hospital under the Mental Health Act (sectioned) or that you receive a community treatment order (CTO).

The Mental Capacity Act 2005

Under this Act people are assumed to have the capacity to make decisions for themselves, unless there is an assessment by a two stage test showing otherwise. All decisions are made in the person's best interests. Any deprivation of liberty should be the least restrictive way of keeping the person safe. Individuals can plan ahead, for example if they have dementia they may wish to appoint an attorney to make financial or personal decisions for them for a time when they have lost capacity. Individuals can make a legally binding advance decision covering refusal of treatment and could also make an advance statement covering wider issues. Advance statements are not legally binding but help people know the person's wishes when they can no longer express them.

The Care Quality Commission (CQC) has a code of practice which gives it a legal duty under the Mental Health Act to visit and interview detained patients, and to see records relating to their detention and treatment, to make sure people are not detained illegally.

The Health and Care Professions Council (HCPC) publish standards of conduct, performance and ethics which members must follow. These include guidelines on fitness to practise. Standard two says 'You must respect the confidentiality of service users.'

Distinction activity D M6 D D3 D D4

Remind yourself of the definitions of the command words 'analyse', 'justify' and 'evaluate'.

Megan is 16-years-old and is anorexic. Which health and care professionals might be involved in her care? How might they work together to help her regain control of her life? What control does she have of who sees her medical information? Which laws might be involved in protecting her right to confidentiality?

Thinking about Megan's case, analyse the impact of legislation and codes of practice relating to information management on multi-disciplinary working.

Justify how organisations and professionals work together to meet individual needs while managing information and maintaining confidentiality.

Evaluate how far multiagency and multidisciplinary working can meet the care and support needs of specific individuals such as Megan.

Check your understanding

1 Explain what is meant by commissioning for health care.
2 Give an example of how professionals work together in health and social care.
3 Why is it important to maintain confidentiality?
4 Give three tips for safely managing computer held information.

Case scenario

Benjy

Benjy is 20-years-old, has learning difficulties and lives in sheltered accommodation. He has an Education, Health and Care plan. How can his support worker Carl ensure Benjy is not discriminated against? Outline the skills and attributes Carl needs to develop a professional relationship with Benjy and then explain the role of empathy in this case.

Benjy's father has strong views about what Benjy should do and thinks Benjy should live at home where he can be taken care of and also keep his elderly parents company. Describe the ethical issues arising from this. How might the triangle of care be applied here?

Activity

Describe some of the challenges Benjy faces in trying to live an independent life and how he can be supported to overcome them. How might personalisation of care services affect Benjy?

What communication techniques might Carl use to ensure Benjy has full information with which to make a decision?

Finally, which other health and care professionals might be involved in supporting Benjy? He has heart problems and requires regular check-ups.

Think about it

This unit is concerned with meeting individual care and support needs. How far do you think that health and care systems currently meet individual needs? Support your answer with examples.

Further reading

Glover J. (2009) *Bouncing back: How can resilience be promoted in vulnerable children and young people?* Barnardo's, Ilford

Grotberg, E. (1997) *A guide to promoting resilience in children: strengthening the human spirit*, Bernard van Leer Foundation, The Hague

Hoffman M. (2002) *Empathy and Moral Development – Implications for Caring and Justice,* Cambridge University Press

Rutter, M. (1985) 'Resilience in the face of adversity: protective factors and resistance to psychiatric disorders', British Journal of Psychiatry, 147: 589-611

Schaffer, H. R. (1996) *Social development*, Blackwell Publishers, Oxford

Seligman, M. (1998) *Learned Optimism*, Pocket Books, New York

Useful websites

The Triangle Of Care – Carers Included: A Guide To Best Practice In Acute Mental Health Care: www.static. carers.org/files/caretriangle-web-5250.pdf

Ethics in nursing: www.advancedpractice.scot.nhs.uk

Information about advocacy: www.advocacymatters.co.uk

Ethics: the four common bioethical principles. Available at: www.alzheimer-europe.org

Bouncing Back – resilience: www.barnardos.org.uk

Information about ethical theories: www.bbc.co.uk/ethics

The Equality and Human Rights Commission. Glossary definitions of key terms: www.equalityhumanrights.com

Health and Social Care Board Northern Ireland: www.hscboard.hscni.net

Integrated care pathways – results from research: www.medicine.ox.ac.uk/bandolier

MIND – The Mental Health Charity: www.mind.org.uk

Information about local services in Wales and changes to local health boards: www.nhsdirect.wales.nhs.uk

Formation of Health and Social Care Board, see: www.niassembly.gov.uk

How to change practice, barriers to change, see NICE: www.nice.org.uk

Attachment In The Early Years – a free Open Learn Course: www.open.edu/openlearn

Guide 47 Personalisation: a rough guide. Care and Support (Eligibility Criteria) Regulations 2014. Both available at: www.scie.org.uk

UK Clinical Ethics Network: www.ukcen.net

6 Work experience in health and social care

About this unit

Work experience in health and social care is extremely important. It can help you decide whether this really is an area you would like to work in and, in doing so, it will aid your own learning and development. Some people do not realise how physically and emotionally demanding working with people can be. For some, it is a challenge they enjoy; for others, the work demands are too much. It is better to find out before you commit to a career in the area whether you enjoy the work. A plan for your work experience will help you get the most from it. Setting clear objectives will ensure you always have something to work towards and do not stand around feeling useless. Finally, reviewing your performance and setting yourself new targets to develop as a result of work experience will introduce you to reflective practice, a skill that every professional is expected to develop.

Learning aims

The aims of this unit are to:

A Examine the benefits of work experience in health and social care for own learning and development.

B Develop a work experience plan to support own learning and development.

C Carry out work experience tasks to meet set objectives.

D Reflect on how work experience influences own personal and professional development.

How will I be assessed?

For learning aims A, B and C, it is recommended by the awarding body that learners write a report evaluating the benefits of work experience and the importance of preparing for placement. The report must include a plan to meet personal and professional goals.

For learning aims C and D, it is recommended by the awarding body that learners are observed on work placement carrying out tasks and activities and interacting with service users and staff, evidenced by an observation report signed by the assessor. The learner should produce a reflective log evaluating their own development on work placement.

How will I be graded?

Pass	Merit	Distinction
Learning aim A: Examine the benefits of work experience in health and social care for own learning and development.		**A B D1** Justify the benefits of preparation in supporting own understanding of the expectations of work experience.
A P1 Explain how work experience can support the development of own professional skills and personal attributes for work in the health and social care sector.	**A M1** Analyse how work experience can provide support in gaining a realistic understanding of the health and social care sector.	
A P2 Discuss ways in which work experience can inform own career choices and help prepare for employment in the health and social care sector.		

→

How will I be graded?

Pass	Merit	Distinction
Learning aim B: Develop a work experience plan to support own learning and development.		
B P3 Explain own responsibilities and limitations on work experience placement. **B P4** Explain how to meet own specific personal and professional development goals while on work placement.	**B M2** Assess the importance of own work experience plan to support own learning and development.	
Learning aim C: Carry out work experience tasks to meet set objectives.		
C P5 Demonstrate work-related skills to meet set objectives for work experience tasks. **C P6** Discuss ways in which work shadowing and observation can support development of own skills while on work placement.	**C M3** Demonstrate work-related skills with confidence and proficiency to meet objectives in different situations.	**C D2** Demonstrate work-related skills proficiently, taking the initiative to carry out activities according to own responsibilities and setting's procedures and selecting appropriate skills and techniques for different situations.
Learning aim D: Reflect on how work experience influences own personal and professional development.		
D P7 Review own strengths and areas for development in response to feedback on work experience placement. **D P8** Produce a personal and professional development plan which identifies improvements to own skills for future development.	**D M4** Assess how self-reflection can contribute to personal and professional development in work experience placement.	**D D3** Justify how planning for and reflecting on skills developed during own work experience placement have informed own future plans for personal and professional development.

A Examine the benefits of work experience in health and social care for own learning and development **A P1** , **A P2** , **A M1** , **A D1**

Work experience of any sort is beneficial. It helps you decide what type of career would suit you.

Developing skills and attributes

Reflecting on own skills and attributes and areas for development

Learning about yourself, your strengths and more importantly your areas for development, is a lifelong activity that brings immense benefits. Your friends and family may be keen to feedback on your strengths, but it is harder to get feedback on areas for improvement. Some people see such feedback as criticism, take it personally and get defensive, but if you can step aside from the personal feelings and learn to work on your areas for development you will develop as a person.

Developing professionalism

Developing professionalism involves aspects of behaviour, communication and appearance, situational awareness and judgement of what is appropriate in different contexts. Having situational awareness and judging what is appropriate is a professional skill. A paramedic called out by a ninety-year-old who lives alone may spend time reassuring them. A paramedic called out by a twenty-year-old who did it for a laugh will not spend time reassuring them.

According to 'Professionalism in Healthcare professions', research published by the Health and Care Professions Council.

'The true skill of professionalism may be not so much in knowing what to do but when to do it.'

Here are some aspects of professionalism that paramedics and other health workers in the study identified.

- Showing clinical judgement and competence.
- Having a clear separation between work and your private life especially where social media is concerned.
- Having a positive attitude and willingness to learn and communicate with people.
- Using appropriate written communication.
- Treating people equally.
- Wearing appropriate clothing such as a uniform.
- Communicating in a way that respects others.
- Having clear rules about accepting gifts.

Communication and interpersonal skills

Communication and interpersonal skills are among the main tools used by health and care professionals. Appropriate verbal and non-verbal communication allows them to find out what problems an individual is experiencing, and allows them to explain the options for care. Interpersonal skills help the care worker tune in to the person's feelings. Empathy, described in Unit 5 'Meeting individual care and support needs', helps the worker understand what the individual may be feeling.

Organisational skills

Organisational skills, the ability to organise oneself by effective time management, and by prioritising tasks, is essential if work is to get done. A social worker who is late for appointments with service users does not inspire confidence. A social worker who tries to meet needs without first assessing

those needs is wasting time and money – both scarce resources.

Technical skills

Technical skills are increasingly required by professionals. Handling data such as being able to calculate a person's income from the information they give, is necessary to find out whether the person is eligible for free social care. A nurse in a critical care unit uses specialist equipment to monitor a person's breathing, heart rate, blood pressure and oxygen levels and then uses that data to decide whether to call the doctor.

Teamwork skills

Teamwork skills are essential in every aspect of health and social care. No one can effectively care for a person all by themselves. Even a full-time carer will have support from a GP and perhaps a care worker. One example of teamwork is in 'Team around the Child', where parents and children together with a lead professional and other professionals work together through a common assessment framework (CAF) to improve outcomes for the child and prevent problems developing. The lead professional, often a social worker, co-ordinates meetings which may involve an educational psychologist, a special educational needs co-ordinator (SENCO) and health professionals such as a GP.

Confidence and personal responsibility

Confidence and personal responsibility are needed by professionals. A confident doctor will inspire confidence in their patients. A doctor lacking confidence will worry patients. A paramedic attending a road traffic accident must inspire confidence in others and does this by being confident themselves. In Unit 2 'Working in health and social care' we saw how important personal responsibility and accountability is to care work.

The ability to link theory with practice

The ability to link theory with practice is shown in Unit 2 'Working in health and social care', where the values and principles of care have to be put into practice, and in Unit 5 'Meeting individual care and support needs' where ethical theories impact on how we provide care.

Activity

Watch an excerpt from a hospital 'soap'. Make a list of the team members. What professional skills do they use? Look out for examples of verbal and non-verbal communication, organisational skills, teamwork, professionalism, confidence and personal responsibility and the ability to link theory with practice.

Clarifying expectations for employment in health and social care

When you are about to undertake work experience in health and social care you will have certain expectations. You will expect to be told where you are going, and who will supervise you. Employers too have expectations of those undertaking work experience and those working in the sector.

Respecting diversity and equality

In Unit 5 'Meeting individual care and support needs', we looked at the importance of promoting equality and diversity and preventing discrimination.

Respecting confidentiality and dignity

In Unit 2 'Working in health and social care', we looked at the importance of respecting the confidentiality and dignity of those using the services.

Confidentiality is important. Members of the public must be able to trust that health and social care professionals will keep their information private, however confidentiality is not absolute. When someone is at risk of harm, information must be shared to safeguard them, following strict procedures. Everyone working in health and social care should know who their safeguarding officer is and the safeguarding procedure in their organisation.

The Caldicott principles, incorporated in the Data Protection Act, govern information sharing in health and social care. The Caldicott principles are:

1 Justify the purpose(s)
2 Don't use personal confidential data unless it is absolutely necessary.
3 Use the minimum personal confidential data necessary for purpose.

4 Access to personal confidential data should be on a strict need-to-know basis.
5 Everyone with access to personal confidential data should be aware of their responsibilities.
6 Comply with the law.

The duty to share information can be as important as the duty to protect patient confidentiality.

The Human Rights Act 1998 – Article 8 of the European Convention on Human Rights says individuals have a right to respect for their private life, but this right can be overridden if necessary to protect health, prevent crime, and protect the rights and freedoms of others.

The Data Protection Act 1998 says that personal information should only be shared if it is:

- necessary for the purpose for which it is being shared
- shared only with those who have a need for it
- accurate and up to date
- shared securely and in a timely fashion
- not kept for longer than necessary for the original purpose.

Under the Data Protection Act 1988, 'vital interest' allows information sharing to prevent serious harm or distress, or in life-threatening situations, however this is not always clear cut. If the only person likely to suffer is the subject of that information, and they have mental capacity to make their own decision about it, then sharing it may not be justified. Mr X decides not to have any more treatment for cancer. He is clear about the decision, knows what is likely to happen and has considered all options. Although he is likely to face distress later, information sharing is not justified in this situation because he is the only person affected and he has mental capacity. If he had made the decision to discontinue treatment for his child who had cancer, then information sharing would be justified in the vital interest of the child.

Section 115 of the Crime and Disorder Act 1998 says that where disclosure is necessary or expedient to reduce and prevent crime and disorder, any person may disclose information to the police, local authorities, health authorities (clinical commissioning groups) and local probation boards.

The Mental Capacity Act 2005 'Code of practice' states that: 'the person who assesses an individual's capacity to make a decision will usually be the person who is directly concerned with the individual at the time the decision needs to be made.' If a person with capacity makes an unwise decision that puts others at risk then it may be justified to share information without their consent.

According to the Care Act 2014, local authorities must set up adult safeguarding boards and share strategic information to improve local safeguarding practice. (They already have children's safeguarding boards and are required to share information between agencies.)

Understanding health, safety and security

Understanding health, safety and security is important for people working in health and social care. They are responsible for the health, safety and security of themselves and of those in their care. Safety and security may be physical and also emotional. Unit 7 'Principles of safe practice in health and social care settings' explains this.

Understanding and applying care values

Understanding and applying care values, discussed in Unit 2 'Working in health and social care', is essential for employment in health and social care. A surgeon may perform an operation but if they are prejudiced, overbearing and do not listen to the patient, they are not doing their job properly because they are not using the care values.

Preparation for employment in the sector

Preparation for employment in the sector requires you to find out about the type of work involved, the people you may be caring for, their expectations of the service and the realities of what services can be offered so you are realistic in the ways you can help.

Activity A P1

Explain how work experience can support the development of the kind of skills and attributes that you will need to work in the health and social care sector.

Exploring career options

In Unit 2 'Working in health and social care' we looked at the roles of people who work in health and social care settings.

Working in different settings

Working in different settings, means that health and care workers must be flexible. A care assistant and a podiatrist may work in a person's own home, and a social worker may conduct an assessment in a person's home. A care assistant may also work in a residential care home and the social worker may also visit to review a service user there. A nurse may work in hospital, but increasingly more nurses are working in the community at clinics. GPs work in clinics and may visit patients at home or in residential care but other doctors may work in hospitals. Care work happens wherever there are people.

Working with different age groups and service users

Health care is free when needed, from antenatal care for the unborn child and the mother, right through life to the end of life. Social care may be free for those without sufficient means to pay. When you work in care you may work with children with special needs, adults with acute physical or mental illness or with older people with dementia.

Sources of information about careers in health and social care

In Unit 2 'Working in health and social care', we looked at different careers in health and social care. Using a website such as the government site National Careers Service https:// nationalcareersservice.direct.gov.uk and the tools available there, you can find out about different careers and what type of career would suit you. The NHS have a website to help you explore different careers and Skills for Care, the employer-led workforce development body for adult social care in England, have a section about careers in care work. The Prospects website offers general careers advice and job and course opportunities to students and graduates.

Using work experience to inform career choices

Using work experience to inform career choices, confirm ideas or consider alternative options is a good use of time. It is much better to discover you do not like an area before embarking on a career in that sector. Alternatively, work experience may confirm your ideas that this might be an area of work you enjoy. During work experience you may meet people in a wider range of professions which may introduce you to new career possibilities.

Activity A P2

Use one of the websites mentioned and find three possible careers you may be interested in.

Discuss how work experience might help prepare you for one of these roles.

Distinction activity A M1

Analyse how work experience can help you to gain a realistic understanding of the health and social care sector. Draw up brief notes and prepare to explain the benefits to a friend who does not see the point of preparation.

B Develop a work experience plan to support own learning and development B P3 , B P4 , B M2 , B D1

Preparation for work experience

Work experience is most beneficial if you prepare for it well.

Expectations for learners on work experience

Employers and service users expect that while you are on work experience you will behave professionally. This means you are dressed in a suitable way for the work to be done. If you are going to be on your feet all day you need comfortable shoes. You may be bending down so clothing should not be revealing. Jewellery can harbour germs and cause cross infection, so must be kept to a minimum and hair should be tied back. Your behaviour should be polite, friendly and professional.

Practical considerations

Practical considerations which should be sorted before work experience is organised include Disclosure and Barring Service (DBS) checks which may take at least four weeks and can take longer. Government guidance 'Post-16 work experience as a part of 16 to 19 study programmes and traineeships (2015)' states that

> 'For young people intending to undertake work experience in the Health Care and Early Years Sector, they will need to have an enhanced DBS check before starting on their placement.'

Other practical considerations might be the needs of the individual on work experience. They may have an education, health and care plan (EHC). If they use a wheelchair it may be necessary to check that the placement has wheelchair access from room to room, not just to the reception area.

Responsibilities and limitations for learners on work experience

Learners should be aware of the care values and their responsibilities to ensure confidentiality of information in the same way that an employed professional would. They should not discuss service users with others and should not discuss work experience on social media sites.

National Minimum Standards

National Minimum Standards issued under the Care Standards Act 2000 require staff providing personal care to be aged at least 18. It is unlikely that someone under 18 on work experience would be requested to give personal care such as changing an incontinence pad or bathing someone. It is important for everyone to have clear boundaries about what they can and cannot do to avoid misunderstandings.

Research your work placement

Researching specific work experience placements such as organisations or job roles is advisable.

Learners could focus on a setting such as a residential care home or a clinic or alternatively focus on a role such as that of a social worker.

The roles of placement supervisors and mentors

These roles are essential for a successful placement. Supervisors and mentors provide ongoing feedback to the student especially in the first few days when a student may be getting to know staff and service users. Supervisors and mentors also are a source of help if a student is uncertain what to do or how to behave in a situation. They can also provide observation feedback as a student learns new skills.

Activity

You are on work placement with a friend. You know she is basically a nice person but on the first day of work experience she arrives late, is wearing torn jeans and is chewing gum. She stands in the corner texting while residents in the care home sit alone with no one to talk to. What impression will the manager have of her? What advice could you give her?

Setting goals and learning objectives

Goals and objectives are like road directions for work experience. They tell you where you want to go and how to get there.

- Reflecting on current knowledge and skills develops self-awareness.
- Identifying one's own strengths and areas for development helps focus on what to work on.

Case scenario

Karim

Karim is going on work experience. He thinks about his current knowledge of care work. His sister is a nurse and his uncle is a doctor. His father is a manager at a care practice, so from talking to them he has some knowledge of health work. He is friendly and finds it easy to talk to people – a useful skill in care work. He is fairly confident, but knows he has little experience of care work so needs to develop in this area. He needs to find out about careers in health care.

Identifying established standards and values required for health and social care professionals

The NHS Constitution sets out rights to which patients, public and staff are entitled. It also sets out responsibilities such as respecting each other, which the public, patients and staff owe to one another in the NHS. Codes of conduct are published by various professional regulators and have been discussed in Unit 2 'Working in health and social care'.

In the 'Guide to the Healthcare System in England Including the Statement of NHS Accountability', the regulators for healthcare professions are listed as follows:

- doctors (the General Medical Council)
- nurses and midwives (Nursing and Midwifery Council)
- dental teams (General Dental Council)
- optical professionals (General Optical Council
- pharmacists (General Pharmaceutical Council)
- chiropractors (General Chiropractic Council)
- osteopaths (General Osteopathic Council)
- health, psychological and social work professionals (Health and Care Professions Council).

Health professionals must be registered with the relevant professional regulator in order to practise and patients may complain to the regulatory body if a registered professional breaches any of the rules of their profession by harming or failing to treat a patient properly.

Identifying SMART targets for own work experience

SMART targets are Specific, Measurable, Achievable, Realistic/Relevant and Timely.

A vague unspecified aim might be to become more confident.

A SMART target might be: To talk to three new people each day while on the work placement.

It is specific – three new people; measurable – three people; this is achievable if you include patients, residents, staff, visitors; realistic because that's what you should be doing on a work placement; and timely – each day you will be attending your work placement. Achieving this SMART target will develop confidence.

Personal development goals

Setting personal development goals, such as improving communication skills and confidence building should be part of your planning for work placement and at this level of study are particularly relevant because these are the basic interpersonal skills used in care work.

Professional development goals

Setting professional development goals such as developing competence, and technical ability should also be part of planning for work placement but learners should be aware of the limitations of what they can actually do on a work placement. It would be inappropriate for a learner to take and record observations such as body temperatures, however, they might be shown how to complete the process while they were on their work placement.

Instead, they may learn how to use and become competent with a specialised communication system such as a communication board used by service users.

All goals should be turned into SMART targets so the degree to which they are achieved can be measured. You might set them out like Table 6.1.

Activity

Set three SMART targets for your period of work experience. Check with a friend whether they are really SMART targets and explain how you will measure whether you have achieved them.

Distinction activity A B D1

Remind yourself of the definition of the command word 'justify'.

Justify the benefits of preparation in supporting your own understanding of the expectations of work experience.

Objective: to gain more confidence					Date achieved and signature of witness
Specific goal	Measurable	Achievable	Realistic	Timely	
Speak to three new people every day while on work placement.	Yes – can count them.	Yes – work placement in clinic means lots of patients and staff.	Yes – you can greet them, help them find their way around, help them find information.	Measured each day of the 5-day placement.	Day 1 Day 2 Day 3 Day 4 Day 5
Talk to two different professionals about their careers in health and social care by the end of the placement.	Yes – either done or not done.	Yes – several different professions represented at clinic e.g. nurses, doctors, health visitors.	Yes – observing them and work shadowing means there is time to ask them.	Measured at the end of the work placement.	

Table 6.1 SMART targets

C Carry out work experience tasks to meet set objectives C P5, C P6, C M3, C D2

Sometimes learners feel they are not allowed to do much while on work experience. This may be true because health and care professionals have a duty of care to patients and service users to keep them safe. They are also accountable for their own practice and for any tasks they delegate. This means if things go wrong, they are responsible. Having said that, there are things that learners can do.

Work experience tasks

Assisting and participating in clinical tasks

Assisting and participating in clinical tasks may be limited. Helping to feed someone may seem an easy task but if they have had a stroke and cannot swallow, they can easily choke. For this reason clinical tasks may not readily be delegated. One of the most important things in care is interacting with service users. Care staff are very busy and do not get much time to sit with, listen and talk to individual service users. Someone on work experience can make a huge difference just by sitting with a service user and getting to know them, perhaps by helping them do a jigsaw or a crossword puzzle. Assisting with meals can involve encouraging people with mobility issues to walk to the dining table, find their seat and get settled.

Assisting and participating in non-clinical tasks

Assisting and participating in non-clinical tasks not directly related to the provision of care for service users, such as tidying the notice board, or putting the shopping away, is useful and shows you can work as part of a team. Attending team meetings helps the learner understand how each role fits with another to offer a seamless service.

Promoting person-centred approaches

Promoting person-centred approaches – as shown earlier, it is important to see the person as an

individual and one of the best ways to do this is to spend time communicating with them.

Case scenario

Sofia

Sofia is on a work placement in a residential care home. She talked to Miss F, a frail eighty-year-old retired teacher who has a poor appetite and is losing weight. Miss F tells Sofia that she really likes a boiled egg and a slice of toast for supper, not all the cooked meals they are offered. Sofia tells her supervisor and the cook at the home adjusts the menu so that is a choice for supper. As a result Miss F gets the care she needs, and begins to eat again and stops losing weight.

Importance of supervision in work experience

If work experience is to be of any use, there must be adequate supervision from staff at the placement and from the learner's place of learning. Learners should of course have a plan of what they need to achieve in placement, and should show this to supervisors who can help them get the range of experience they need to achieve their goals. Learners should also know who to contact at their place of learning if they are concerned about poor practice in the placement. If there is no supervision at the work placement, learners can be left feeling unsure what to do, and what could be a valuable learning experience becomes a wasted opportunity.

Using work experience reflective journals

Reflective journals are useful for all practitioners and form part of a professional practice portfolio that every practitioner is expected to keep. Reflective journals are especially useful on work experience when learners may be meeting new concepts and new ways of working for the first time. Such journals help link theory with practice; for example, having learned about personalisation of care, a learner can apply that to what they see on work experience and decide if personalisation is put into practice in their placement. Reflecting on how a work experience placement influences one's own professional development is a valuable tool for professional development. Learners may see new ways of doing things which they take forward to their own practice, for example, seeing how having an identified lead professional to co-ordinate multiagency team working improves practice.

> **Activity**
>
> What work-related skills do you think you need for your work experience tasks?

Work shadowing and observation

Work shadowing different professionals, over a few days can be used as part of a professional development portfolio (PDP) and to aid career development. It is a useful way to find out if a career would suit you. There are restrictions on work shadowing some roles because of confidentiality and health and safety. Even if there are no issues of confidentiality or health and safety, consent to having the trainee present must always be obtained from the people receiving care services.

Observing specific procedures, as appropriate is again useful in understanding a role. A dental practice may offer a work shadowing opportunity and, provided clients agree, this can be very beneficial for learners. It would not however be appropriate for a learner to work shadow a surgeon in theatre, although they might sit in during an outpatient's clinic with the patient's permission.

Working relationships and agreed ways of working

Working relationships and agreed ways of working in health and social care can be observed at first hand when work shadowing. A shift handover between staff, or the sharing of information between different professionals such as a community nurse and GP, demonstrates agreed ways of working effectively.

Reflecting on work practice and procedures

Reflecting on work practice and procedures used within the setting and writing down what has been learned in the journal is part of developing professionally. A learner who first sees a dressing changed may wonder why the nurse is so particular about hand washing before and after procedures, but as they learn about the potential for cross infection and the decreasing power of antibiotics to control infections, they begin to understand why infection control procedures are carried out. Reflecting helps get the most learning from an experience.

> **Activity** C P6
>
> Discuss the ways in which work shadowing and observation has supported the development of your own skills while on work placement.

> **Distinction activity** C D2
>
> Think again of the work-related skills you need to demonstrate. Make a list of how you might perform them:
>
> - proficiently
> - by taking the initiative. Think about the activities you will perform, the responsibilities you have been given in work-experience and the setting's procedures
> - by selecting appropriate skills and techniques for different situations. Think about the different situations you have been in and what appropriate skills and techniques you needed.

D Reflect on how work experience influences own personal and professional development D P7, D P8, D M4, D D3

If work experience is any good it changes people, influencing them to improve their practice.

Reviewing personal and professional development

Reflective practice is an ongoing activity. No one can ever say they know it all and have nothing more to learn. People change and practice, the way we do things, changes.

Theories and frameworks for reflective practice

Reflective practice is much easier to do if there is a structure to follow. Theories give us structures.

Schön's theory of 'reflection *in* action' and 'reflection *on* action'

In 1984 Donald Schön published *The Reflective Practitioner: How Professionals Think in Action* in which he described 'reflection in action' (thinking during the event) and 'reflection on action' (thinking after the event). Each type of reflection begins with a feeling of surprise or concern, then leads to critical analysis and ends with a new view of the situation, synthesising new ideas. Schön suggested that newly qualified professionals might follow procedures to the letter but as professionals gain experience they learn how to adapt procedures to individual situations.

Case scenario

Reflection on action

Mr A is admitted as an emergency to hospital from the residential care home where he lives. He has a high temperature and is agitated. His tongue is dry and he shows signs of dehydration so the doctor explains to Mr A that he is going to give him intravenous fluid and will put a cannula into Mr A's vein on the back of his hand. Megan, the nurse thinks during this process that Mr A might not understand the terms 'intravenous fluid' and 'cannula' so she gently explains in plain English what the doctor is doing and why he is doing it. Megan is concerned, analyses the situation and adapts her explanation so Mr A can understand. This is reflection in action. Later that evening, the doctor thinks back to the event and decides Megan's communication was much better so decides that next time he is in that situation he will use language the patient can understand. This is reflection on action.

Gibbs' theory of the Reflective Cycle

Gibbs' Reflective Cycle (1988) is another model commonly used in nursing and health related professions. It is a cycle of thinking that continues and is usually represented as a diagram. (See Figure 6.1.)

Gibbs' model is useful for reflection but has the same limitations that Schön's model has. Some argue that reflection should move beyond whether or not their practice is working to critically examining underpinning values, looking at how practice can lead to change, and move towards a commitment to quality and respect for difference.

Kolb's theory of experiential learning

Kolb's theory concerns learning through experience – experiential learning. It is frequently used in education. Kolb describes a four-stage cycle of learning; 'immediate or concrete experiences' provide a basis for 'observations and reflections' which are absorbed as 'abstract concepts' such as equality or confidentiality, which then produce new ways of acting which can be 'actively tested', in turn, creating new experiences.

Kolb linked this process with these learning styles:

- Diverging (CE/RO) people are sensitive, gather information and they see concrete situations from different viewpoints. They are good at brainstorming, working in groups, and listen with an open mind to receive personal feedback.

- Assimilating (AC/RO) people prefer ideas to people and prefer exploring analytical models, and having time to think things through.

- Converging (AC/AE) people are problem solvers. They are more attracted to technical tasks and problems than social or interpersonal issues. They often have specialist abilities.

- Accommodating (CE/AE) people rely on intuition rather than logic and are practical. They rely on others to provide the background information or theory and would rather get on with the job. They prefer to work in teams, set targets and actively try different ways to achieve an objective.

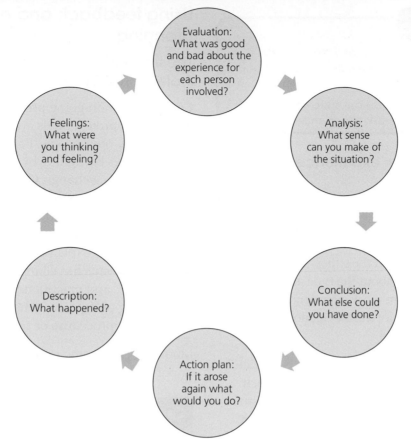

Figure 6.1 Gibbs' reflective cycle

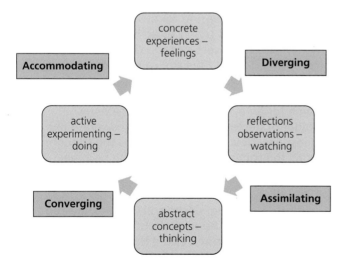

Figure 6.2 Kolb's theory of experiential learning

Kolb's experiential learning cycle has been criticised as having little evidence to support it, nevertheless learning through experience remains as one of several ways of looking at reflection.

The Nursing and Midwifery Council has a format for reflection. Here are the questions nurses must use for reflecting.

1 What was the nature of the CPD activity and/ or practice-related feedback and/or event or experience in your practice?

2 What did you learn from the CPD activity and/ or feedback and/or event or experience in your practice?

3 How did you change or improve your practice as a result?

4 How is this relevant to the Code?

5 Select one or more themes: Prioritise people – Practise effectively – Preserve safety – Promote professionalism and trust.

Source: www.nmc.org.uk

Examples have been given for Schön's model of reflection in action and reflection on action and for Gibbs' reflective cycle.

Assess how self-reflection can help your self-development in work experience.

Reviewing the work experience reflective journal

A review should be done by the learner two or three times a week during placement and again at the end of placement. It is a good idea to review the journal or parts of it, with the supervisor. They may agree with the learner about the type and amount of learning gained from work experience or they may disagree, putting forward evidence the learner may not have considered.

Evaluating one's own performance can be difficult because of bias. You might think your approach was friendly, others might think it was too casual because you used the same informal chatty style with professionals that you use with friends outside work. This is why it is important to gain feedback from others such as the workplace supervisor, or if appropriate from clients and colleagues. If what they say supports what you think, your conclusions are strengthened. If however they disagree, you may have to re-evaluate your views.

Reflecting on one's own personal and professional development is not easy, especially if you think you could have acted in a better way. The important thing is to learn for the future so that you do not make the same mistakes again. Using a reflective model such as those of Schön, Gibbs or Kolb helps to increase the effectiveness of reflective practice.

Following the final review with your workplace supervisor, and the feedback from that, review your own strengths and areas for development.

Produce a personal and professional development plan which identifies improvements to your skills to benefit your future development.

Using feedback and action planning

The importance of Continuing Professional Development (CPD)

Continuous or on-going professional development ensures that professionals are up to date with the services they offer people. Laws change – think of the changes brought in by the Care Act 2014. Ways of working change; GPs no longer work in isolation but are part of a team of health care professionals that includes the CCG, nurses, health care assistants, pharmacists and many more. The way treatment is explained and the various options offered to patients has changed. Consent now must be 'informed' and practitioners must understand the meaning of 'capacity' when obtaining informed consent for a procedure or treatment.

Monitoring, checking one's own practice, is important to make sure standards do not slip.

Case scenario

Neelam

Neelam, an optician, was trained to listen to service users and to treat them with respect. She was very busy, covering for a colleague who was off sick as well as trying to do her own work. At home things were not too good. Her family complained that when she came home she was too tired to give them any attention or cook nice food for them. One day, an older gentleman came for an eye test. He was in the early stages of dementia and slow in answering her questions. Neelam was stressed as she thought of all the things she had to do. She became impatient with the gentleman and told him to hurry up.

Later that evening, as she collapsed exhausted into a chair, she thought about her day and realised she had not treated that service user with respect and had not listened to him. Monitoring her own practice like this led her to evaluate what she had done. She realised that if she had behaved in that way during her training she would never have passed the course and she judged her own behaviour as unacceptable. From then on she decided to learn to manage her stress so that it did not affect the way she treated service users.

Rochelle

Rochelle, a social worker, uses reflective practice to improve her own skills, practice and subject knowledge. Since she qualified, the personalisation agenda has impacted on the way she works. She realised that she needed to improve her skills, practice and knowledge of the personalisation agenda. She went on a training course to update her skills and learn about self-assessment and who to involve when she carries out an assessment of needs with a service user.

Continuous quality improvement (CQI) looks at processes, as a way of improving the quality of a service. It is data driven, for example, if a GPs' surgery receives a large number of complaints from service users who cannot get through on the phone to make an appointment, a CQI approach would be to introduce an extra phone line and a system allowing patients to book appointments by email.

We are all shaped by our beliefs, values, and attitudes. These in turn affect how we approach others and affect our behaviour. How we behave affects how others behave toward us. Rochelle, whose parents came from Jamaica, experienced racial prejudice growing up in England. Rochelle's parents taught her to be strong and that she was equal to others. These beliefs affected her attitude and behaviour. She is confident yet understands how service users may feel when they are discriminated against for whatever reason. Her confidence inspires confidence in others. Service users feel she knows her job and they can rely on her.

Neelam's parents taught her to work hard and she saw her mother always busy looking after the family. Neelam believes she should have a successful career and also be as devoted to the family as her mother was. This puts a strain on her as she strives and fails to meet everyone's expectations including her own. This causes stress which affects her behaviour, making her bad tempered. Her attitude causes colleagues to avoid her and patients leave to go to a different optician.

We have already seen how reflective practice can bring about change in Neelam's behaviour, and in Rochelle's approach to assessment planning. When you are on work experience you can use reflective practice to bring about change. You may lack confidence in talking to new people when you first start but by reflecting on what you do, and planning how to change, you can change your approach and gain confidence. You will find your beliefs change too. At the start of work experience you may believe you are shy, but by the end of it you may realise you are much more confident.

Continuous reflection is used for building on progress and checking that changes in practice are having the desired effect. Your goals which give rise to SMART targets in a work placement have to be checked regularly by you and your supervisor. When you review your SMART target – to speak to three new people each day – you may find that you only spoke to two new people on the first day. Continuous reflection means you can adjust your target, so you may speak to four people the following day to keep on track.

Identifying areas of positive and constructive feedback

Feedback is useful for reinforcing what is done well so a person can build on their strengths.

Highlighting areas for improvement

Highlighting areas for improvement is equally important. Sometimes feedback is given in the form of a praise sandwich: strengths, areas for improvement, strengths.

Creating an action plan

Creating an action plan for personal and professional development is the next stage after receiving feedback. This usually refers to working on areas for improvement. An action plan, much like a plan for a work placement, should be SMART and reviewed regularly.

Identifying career goals

As a result of work experience, learners should have a clearer idea of whether health and social care is an area where they would enjoy working. They may decide to explore other fields for careers or alternatively may find they have a greater understanding of the sector and their future role within it.

Activity

Mary

Mary has finished her work experience at Holly Bank and has a meeting with her workplace supervisor who looks at her reflective journal and the observation report then asks Mary how she thinks it went. Mary says she has enjoyed it and feels more confident about talking to new people after having achieved her SMART target of talking to three new people each day. The supervisor praises Mary's initiative in preventing an accident when Miss F was trying to reach the cup of tea, explaining that Mary's calm approach in talking to Miss F, settling her safely in her chair and picking up the fallen walking stick averted an accident. There are areas for Mary to work on. She made a poster for the noticeboard and there were several spelling mistakes. The supervisor explains that written communication is very important so Mary needs to do something about this issue.

What could Mary do to improve her written communication?

Distinction activity

Remind yourself of the command word 'justify'. Justify and make a list of examples to show how planning for work experience and reflecting on the skills developed during this period have influenced your future plans for personal and professional development. Discuss this with your placement supervisor.

Check your understanding

1 Give three skills and three attributes that might be useful when undertaking work experience.
2 Give five expectations that employers might have when offering work experience to a learner.
3 What are SMART targets?
4 What do we call a record kept by learners to show how they improve in self-management and skill development?
5 Why does a person on work experience need a supervisor?
6 Give three benefits of work shadowing.
7 Why is reflective practice on going?
8 How can feedback help you to develop?

Case scenario

Kamran

Kamran thinks he would like to be a dentist. He is fortunate to have work experience at a dental practice with a good reputation for teaching. At the end of the placement although he gets positive feedback Kamran realises that peering into people's mouths all day is not for him. He would rather know more about the whole body and how it works.

What can he do now?

Think about it

Many health and care professions stress the importance of using reflection to continually improve practice. Every two or three years, nurses and other health and care professionals must provide evidence in a portfolio to show they have developed professionally in order to continue to practise.

What are some of the reasons for requiring health and care professionals to revalidate in this way?

Further reading

Community Care

Nursing Times

Nursing Standard

Useful websites

Professionalism in healthcare professionals: www.hpc-uk.org

The government website for careers advice: https://nationalcareersservice.direct.gov.uk

NHS advice on careers: www.healthcareers.nhs.uk

Care careers advice from the employer organisation for care: www.skillsforcare.org.uk

General careers advice: www.prospects.ac.uk

Guide to the Healthcare System in England Including the Statement of NHS Accountability, available at: www.gov.uk

Department for Work and Pensions employment programmes: Disclosure and Barring Service checks for work placements in adult social care settings registered with the Care Quality Commission- Guidance for providers and registered managers: www.cqc.org.uk

NHS Constitution, see: www.nhs.uk

7 Principles of safe practice in health and social care settings

About this unit

When members of the public need health and social care services they have a right to be kept safe. They expect staff to know their job, and not to put others in danger. Professionals have a duty to make sure they practise safely. Health and care professionals must make sure that anyone who wishes to complain is made aware how to do this. They must be alert for signs of abuse or neglect, understand the factors that may contribute to abuse, and they must know how to respond when abuse or neglect occurs. Practitioners should understand current laws about health and safety, understand their own and other's responsibilities under these laws and know how their practice promotes health and safety.

Learning aims

The aims of this unit are to:

A Examine how a duty of care contributes to safe practice in health and social care settings.

B Understand how to recognise and respond to concerns about abuse and neglect in health and social care settings.

C Investigate the influence of health and safety legislation and policies in health and social care settings.

D Explore procedures and responsibilities to maintain health and safety and respond to accidents and emergencies in health and social care settings.

How will I be assessed?

For learning aims A and B (A.P1, A.P2, B.P3, B.P4, B.P5, A.M1, B.M2, A.D1, B.D2) it is recommended by the awarding body that learners write a report evaluating duty of care and safeguarding procedures in a health and social care setting.

For learning aims C and D (C.P6, D.P7, D.P8, C.M3, D.M4, CD.D3, CD.D4) it is recommended by the awarding body that learners compile a resource file evaluating safe practice principles, procedures and responsibilities in a health and social care setting.

How will I be graded?

Pass	Merit	Distinction
Learning aim A: Examine how a duty of care contributes to safe practice in health and social care settings.		
A P1 Explain the implications of a duty of care in a selected health or social care setting. **A P2** Discuss ways in which complaints and appeals procedures address failure in a duty of care in a selected health or social care setting.	**A M1** Assess the importance of balancing individual rights with a duty of care in a selected health or social care setting.	**A D1** Evaluate the significance of a duty of care and complaints procedures in promoting safe practice in a selected health or social care setting.

How will I be graded?

Pass	Merit	Distinction
Learning aim B: Understand how to recognise and respond to concerns about abuse and neglect in health and social care settings.		
B P3 Describe the types and signs of abuse and neglect that may be experienced by different individuals. **B P4** Explain the factors that may contribute to and reduce the likelihood of abuse and neglect for service users in health and social care. **B P5** Explain how to respond to concerns about abuse and neglect in the selected health or social care setting.	**B M2** Assess the importance of recognising and responding to evidence or concerns about different types of abuse and neglect in health and social care.	**B D2** Justify procedures for responding to concerns about abuse and neglect in the selected health or social care setting.
Learning aim C: Investigate the influence of health and safety legislation and policies in health and social care settings.		**C D D3** Justify the effectiveness of health and safety legislation, policies and procedures in maintaining health and safety in a selected health or social care setting.
C P6 Compare the influence of different health and safety laws or policies on health and social care practice in a selected setting.	**C M3** Analyse how health and safety legislation or policies influence safe practice in a selected health or social care setting.	
Learning aim D: Explore procedures to maintain health and safety and respond to accidents and emergencies in health and social care settings.		**C D D4** Evaluate the importance of safe practice principles in maintaining and promoting the health, safety and welfare of service users in a selected health or social care setting.
D P7 Explain how different procedures maintain health and safety in a selected health or social care setting. **D P8** Explain the health and safety responsibilities of employers, employees and others in a selected health or social care setting.	**D M4** Analyse how individual responsibilities and health, safety and emergency procedures contribute to safe practice in a selected health or social care setting.	

A Examine how a duty of care contributes to safe practice in health and social care settings

A P1 , **A P2** , **A M1** , **A D1**

Doctors, nurses, social workers, occupational therapists, in fact all health and care professionals working in health and social care have a similar duty of care. Employers too have a duty of care to employees, the public and to service users.

Duty of care

Legal obligation to protect well-being and prevent harm

According to the Care Certificate, Standard 3:

> 'A duty of care means that you must aim to provide high quality care to the best of your ability and say if there are any reasons why you may be unable to do so.'

Source: www.skillsforcare.org.uk

According to the 'Unison Duty of Care handbook'

'As a health or social care worker you owe a duty of care to your patients/service users, your colleagues, your employer, yourself and the public interest.'

The NHS constitution explains in detail the legal duties of staff:

- to accept professional accountability and maintain the standards of professional practice as set by the appropriate regulatory body applicable to your profession or role.
- to take reasonable care of health and safety at work for you, your team and others, and to co-operate with employers to ensure compliance with health and safety requirements.
- to act in accordance with the express and implied terms of your contract of employment.
- not to discriminate against patients or staff and to adhere to equal opportunities and equality and human rights legislation.
- to protect the confidentiality of personal information that you hold.
- to be honest and truthful when applying for a job and in carrying out that job.

Source: www.gov.uk NHS Constitution - Staff responsibilities

Upholding the rights and promoting the interests of individuals experiencing abuse or neglect

Upholding the rights of those being cared for is everyone's duty. Nurses, midwives, social workers and other health and care professionals have codes of conduct to guide them in their duty of care. The Code of Professional standards of practice and behaviour for nurses and midwives concentrates on four areas:

1 Prioritise people
2 Practise effectively
3 Preserve safety
4 Promote professionalism and trust

The Nursing and Midwifery Council (NMC) code says nurses and midwives must put the interests of people using or needing nursing or midwifery services first, preserve their dignity, ensure their needs are recognised, assessed and responded to, treat them with respect, uphold their rights and challenge any discriminatory attitudes and behaviours towards them. (NMC Code, March 2015)

Protecting health, safety and well-being

The NMC code says nurses and midwives must work within the limits of their competence, exercising their professional 'duty of candour' and raising concerns immediately whenever they find situations that put patients or public safety at risk. A duty of candour is about openness and honesty with patients when treatment and care do not go according to plan and when there is the potential to cause harm or distress. Nurses and midwives must take necessary action to deal with any concerns where appropriate.

Ensuring safe practice

The NMC code says nurses and midwives must,

'assess need and deliver or advise on treatment, or give help (including preventative or rehabilitative care) without too much delay and to the best of your abilities, on the basis of the best evidence available and best practice. You communicate effectively, keeping clear and accurate records and sharing skills, knowledge and experience where appropriate. You reflect and act on any feedback you receive to improve your practice.'

Balancing individual rights with risks

All health and social care workers must reduce risks but also balance individuals' rights to make their own choices. The Health and Care Professions Council Standards of Conduct, Performance and Ethics which regulate social workers, say that

'A person who is capable of giving their consent has the right to refuse to receive care or services. You must respect this right. You must also make sure that they are fully aware of the risks of refusing care or services, particularly if you think that there is a significant or immediate risk to their life.'

(www.hcpc-uk.org)

Acting in the best interests of people means that they are given full information about the potential consequences of any risks they wish to take. If they have the capacity to make their own decisions, professionals have to respect those decisions even if the professional disagrees. The standards are due for revision in 2016.

Case scenario

Mr X has muscular dystrophy which means he will eventually find it difficult to breath and his final days may be spent on assisted ventilation. He does not want this and makes an advanced directive saying he does not want to be kept alive under such circumstances. His nurse and doctor may disagree but once they have explained the consequences of refusing treatment, they must respect his wishes.

Activity A M1

Look at the revised Health and Care Professions Council Standards from 2016. What do they say about duty of care? Assess the importance of balancing individual rights with a duty of care in a selected health and social care setting. Why would it matter if a doctor forced treatment on an unwilling patient?

Complaints procedures

Complaints policies and procedures

All organisations inspected and regulated by the Care Quality Commission must have a complaints procedure and staff should be familiar with that procedure so they can assist people who wish to make a complaint. The care provider must investigate the complaint thoroughly and take action if problems are identified.

Reasons why complaints may be made, e.g. failure in a duty of care, dissatisfaction with quality of care

Complaints may be made because of something done, an act committed, or they may be because of something that should have been done and was omitted. Some reasons for complaints against both NHS and Social Services may be:

- Attitudes or behaviour of individual care workers, for example, rudeness, abuse or persistent lateness
- Discrimination for example by not providing information in alternative formats for those with visual impairments.
- Poor delivery of services, such as not providing menu choices for vegetarians.

Some complaints may relate to social care, for example:

- the local authority refusing to assess a person's need for adult social care
- unreasonable delays in assessing needs or providing services to meet assessed needs. The Local Government Ombudsman suggested that a reasonable time for an assessment should normally be between four and six weeks from the date of the first request
- how the cost of a service is worked out if an individual has to pay.

Investigating complaints

In the NHS, complaints should first be sent to the service provider. Many issues can be resolved locally and do not become full complaints. If the situation is not resolved then the complaints procedure is as follows:

Stage one
Make a formal complaint to the service provider, for example, a GP, dentist, hospital or pharmacist or to the organisation that commissioned their services, such as the local Clinical Commissioning Group or NHS England which purchases primary care services. CCGs oversee the commissioning of secondary care, such as hospital care and some community services. Healthwatch and PALS are organisations that represent the views of people who use NHS services.

Stage two
If you are not happy with the outcome of the complaint you can refer the matter to the Parliamentary and Health Service Ombudsman, who is independent of the NHS and government.

Complaints relating to social care should be made to the local authority providing the care but if a person privately arranges and pays for their own care, or uses a direct payment from the local authority to pay for care that they themselves arrange, they must complain to the organisation that is providing the care who will have their own complaints procedure. If the problem is not sorted, the Local Government Ombudsman makes final decisions on complaints that have not been resolved by the NHS in England and UK government departments and other UK public organisations.

In Wales, the NHS Wales Putting Things Right complaints process investigates complaints through Health Boards. The Public Services Ombudsman for Wales has a similar role to that of the English Parliamentary and Health Service Ombudsman.

Charities welcome feedback from people who use their services. Mencap have an online forum for service users and their families. The NSPCC website includes their complaints policy and encourages people who use their services and professionals to get in touch. The Prince's Trust has a feedback area on their website and a complaints policy.

The Citizens Advice Bureau sums up different options for complaints procedures

- first speak to the person providing the care, or their manager
- use the local authority complaints procedure or the complaints procedure of the care provider if this isn't the local authority
- report your complaint to the Local Government Ombudsman
- take legal action, for example, for personal injury, negligence, discrimination or for breach of your human rights
- report concerns to a regulatory body
- report concerns to other bodies such as the Care Quality Commission or your local Healthwatch
- talk to your local councillor about your concerns.

Source: www.citizensadvice.org.uk

Complaints against individual practitioners may be made to their regulating body. If they have breached their duty of care or behaved unprofessionally, for example, by having sexual relationships with clients, falsifying records or breaching confidentiality, their regulating body will investigate. If the complaint is proved, the professional body may caution the individual, impose conditions, suspend them or strike them off the professional register altogether so they cannot work in that profession.

In the UK, and covering England, Wales and Northern Ireland, regulatory bodies include

- the Nursing and Midwifery Council (NMC)
- the Health and Care Professions Council (HCPC)
- the General Medical Council (GMC).

In addition to the above, in Wales; the Care Council for Wales (Social Care) and in Northern Ireland; the Northern Ireland Social Care Council (NISCC) regulate social workers.

Health boards investigate complaints against GPs, dentists, pharmacists or optometrists. Healthwatch makes sure that the health and social care system listens to people's views and experiences and acts on them. It works in partnership with the public, health and social care sectors and the voluntary and community sector to improve services. Some NHS providers have a Patient Advice and Liaison Service (PALS) to help patients and carers when making a complaint. Local Authorities also arrange advocacy services to support people who wish to complain about the NHS.

Responding to complaints with respect and treating them seriously

All organisations should treat complaints seriously and with respect. Healthwatch, the consumer champion for health and social care say that people should have the right to have complaints and feedback taken seriously and acted upon when things go wrong.

Using complaints to improve the quality of service provision

Organisations should use complaints to improve services. In 'Complaints Matter' a report published by the Care Quality Commission in 2014, the CQC reported that too often complaints were not handled well in hospitals, mental health services, community health services, GP practices, out-of-hours services and adult social care service.

Some organisations listen to complaints and improve services. According to the NHS Institute for Innovation and Improvement, King's College Hospital NHS Foundation Trust used the 'How are we doing?' feedback programme to find out the views of people using their services. As a result of feedback they changed visiting hours, increased cleaning and set up an adolescent room with entertainment system for teenage cancer patients. (www.institute.nhs.uk)

Legal proceedings and clinical negligence

Taking legal action against the NHS or a member of staff can be expensive and complicated, so it is advisable to take legal advice. The charity Action against Medical Accidents offers specialist advice on legal action, inquests and other procedures when harm may have been caused. The Citizens Advice Bureau also offers advice on how to take legal action.

A judicial review challenges a decision of an NHS body or the secretary of state for health on the basis that it's unlawful. A decision might be unlawful if the decision-maker does not have power to make the decision, or is using their power improperly, if the decision is irrational, or the procedure followed was unfair or if the decision was in breach of the Human Rights Act or breaches European Community (EC) law. In order to make a claim for judicial review, the person must have a direct, personal interest in the action or decision being challenged.

In 2009, Debbie Purdy, who suffered from Multiple Sclerosis, forced a judicial review to clarify the law on assisted suicide. She wanted to know whether her husband would be arrested if he helped her end her life. She died in 2014 but not before the director of Public Prosecutions had clarified how decisions were made. It still remains an offence to encourage or assist a suicide or a suicide attempt in England and Wales.

If someone has been harmed as a result of medical negligence they may take legal action for compensation. A person can also take legal action for compensation if they are the next of kin of someone who has died because of negligent medical treatment or who lack capacity and cannot take legal action themselves. The NHS Litigation Authority (NHS LA) represents the NHS in such claims.

Activity

How could the complaints procedure help promote safe practice in a residential care home? Give examples to support what you say.

Discuss ways in which complaints and appeals procedures address failure in a duty of care in a selected health and social care setting.

Distinction Activity A D1

Remind yourself of what the command word 'evaluate' means.

1 Evaluate the significance of a duty of care in promoting safe practice in a hospital setting. Give examples to support what you say.

2 Evaluate the significance of complaints procedures in promoting safe practice in a hospital setting. Give examples to support what you say.

Check your understanding

1 What is the difference between 'duty of care' and 'duty of candour'?

2 Give three reasons why people might complain about health and care services.

3 A service user has direct payments and arranges their own care. Who should they complain to if the service they receive is poor?

4 An elderly patient in hospital is left unattended and not given food. Who should her daughter complain to?

B Understand how to recognise and respond to concerns about abuse and neglect in health and social care settings B P3 , B P4 , B P5 , B M2 , B D2

Abuse is a misuse of power and control that one person has over another. Abuse is defined by the effect it has on an individual. It does not matter whether or not the person misusing their power intended to abuse the individual. What matters is the effect their actions have.

Neglect results from failure to provide the amount and type of care that a reasonable person would be expected to provide. It may be intentional or unintentional.

Types and signs of abuse and neglect

Guidance published by the Social Care Institute for Excellence, *Protecting adults at risk: Good practice guide*, is an authoritative guide on this topic.

Neglect

Neglect happens when there is a failure to provide care, for example, putting food in front of a person but failing to check whether they can feed themselves. Neglect can be the deliberate withholding of, or failure to provide necessary care and support, for example, ignoring a resident's request to be taken to the toilet resulting in a loss of dignity when they wet themselves, or leaving the door wide open when helping them undress.

An act of omission
An act of omission is when a health or social care professional fails to meet the standards required of them by their professional code of conduct, for example, a nurse failing to give medication to a patient, or a social worker failing to check on a child at risk.

Physical abuse

Physical abuse, the non-accidental infliction of physical force that results in bodily injury, pain or impairment includes hitting, pushing, burning and misuse of medication.

Signs of physical abuse may include the following.

1 Unexplained injuries or whose explanation is inconsistent, multiple injuries healing at different rates indicating they occurred at different times.

2 Bruising, cuts, welts or marks on the body such as slap and finger marks, unexplained loss of clumps of hair.

3 Burns (especially if the person does not smoke).

4 A pattern of injuries or physical symptoms that occur when a particular carer is on duty.

5 Misuse of medication, e.g. administering sleeping tablets to keep the individual drowsy.

6 Subdued behaviour in the presence of a carer.

7 Skin breakdown, ulcers and bed sores from being left in wet clothing or bedding.

8 Malnutrition when the adult at risk is not living alone, unexplained weight loss.

9 Seeking medical treatment too late or not at all.

10 Frequent changes of GP, or a reluctance of carers to assist someone to the GP.

Psychological abuse

Psychological abuse, includes emotional abuse, verbal abuse, humiliation and threats of punishment.

Emotional abuse
Emotional abuse includes actions or behaviour that have a harmful effect on the emotional health and development of an adult at risk.

Signs of emotional or psychological abuse may include the following.

1 An air of silence when the person who caused the harm is present.

2 Changes in the psychological state of the adult at risk e.g. withdrawal, fear, paranoia, confusion, resignation, tearfulness or agitation, uncharacteristically manipulative, uncooperative and aggressive behaviour, low self-esteem.

3 Insomnia.

4 A change of appetite resulting in weight loss or gain.

A carer's behaviour
A carer's behaviour may indicate that psychological abuse is happening. They may prevent an adult at risk from using or gaining access to services, including educational and social opportunities in the wider community. They may deny them access to religious and cultural provision, deny access to friends, not allow them to express their views, and restrict their freedom of movement by locking the person in a room, tying them to a chair or leaving

them for long periods of time on a commode, and they may deny their rights to privacy in relation to care, feelings and other aspects of life.

There may be inappropriate communication methods, patronising or belittling the adult at risk, or failing to respond to calls for assistance with toileting. There may be intimidation and/ or harassment with the use of threats, humiliation, bullying, swearing and other abuse. There may be a general lack of consideration for the needs of the adult at risk, a lack of stimulation and meaningful occupation or activities and a lack of positive reinforcement and no choice about activities of daily living. The adult at risk may not have their individual abilities and skills recognised, and may be prevented from developing independence. They may not be given information about how to raise concerns and those offering help may be denied access to them.

Sexual abuse

Sexual abuse, includes sexual activity where the individual cannot give consent, and includes sexual harassment. It may be abuse which does not involve contact, but is still sexual abuse, for example inappropriate looking, sexual photography, indecent exposure, sexual teasing or innuendo, being forced to watch pornographic films or images, enforced witnessing of sexual acts or sexual media and sexual harassment. Sexual abuse involving contact may include rape or attempted rape, sexual assault, inappropriate touch anywhere, masturbation of either or both persons, penetration or attempted penetration of the vagina, anus or mouth with penis or other objects and sexual activity that the person lacks the capacity to consent to.

Signs of sexual abuse

Signs of sexual abuse may include physical signs such as bruising, bleeding, pain, itching, infections or discharges in the genital area, or sexually transmitted diseases (STDs), unusual difficulty in walking or sitting, foreign bodies in genital or rectal openings, wetting or soiling, torn, stained underclothing and pregnancy in a woman who is at risk or unable to consent to sexual intercourse.

Behaviours may change and the person at risk may start to use explicit sexual language or may begin to self-harm. They may develop overt sexual behaviour and inappropriate attitudes towards others, copying the behaviour that was used towards them by the abuser. They may become withdrawn, have poor concentration and disturbed sleep, develop fear of relationships, and show fear of staff or other carers offering help with dressing, bathing, and become reluctant to be alone with a specific individual.

Financial abuse

Financial abuse includes misuse or theft of money, fraud, and exploitation of property or inheritance. It includes stealing money or possessions directly or by fraud. Loans between the adult at risk and a member of staff, loans made by anyone under duress, threat or undue influence and loans dishonestly extracted are financially abusive.

It is financial abuse when the family of the adult at risk provides a lower standard of care than is needed or wanted, in order to maintain assets to maximise an inheritance or when undue pressure is put on the adult at risk in connection with wills, property, inheritance or financial transactions.

Preventing the adult at risk accessing their money, property or inheritance, not giving them appropriate assistance to manage and monitor their financial affairs and to access benefits – and neglecting to act in the best financial interests of the adult at risk is also financial abuse. People who move into the adult at risk's home and live rent free without any clearly set out financial arrangements may be committing financial abuse. There may be misuse of the personal allowance by the person managing the finances of the adult at risk who is in a care home or service or misuse of a power of attorney, deputy, or other legal authority through an abuse of position e.g. exploitation of a person's money or assets and by false representation, using another person's bank account, cards or documents, or impersonating them.

Signs of financial abuse

Signs of financial abuse may be an unexplained shortage of money, missing personal possessions, and unexplained withdrawal of funds from accounts, by anyone. There may be financial hardship where financial affairs are managed by a court appointed deputy, attorney or LPA and money is withheld and there are no receipts for financial transactions carried out on behalf of the adult at risk. A lack of clear financial accounts held by a care home or service may indicate financial abuse. Financial abuse may be indicated if a power of attorney or lasting power of attorney (LPA) is obtained after the adult at risk has lost mental capacity and the person managing the financial affairs of the adult at risk is being evasive or uncooperative. Failing to register an LPA after the adult at risk has lost mental capacity may indicate financial abuse, if it seems the adult at risk is continuing to manage their own financial affairs, especially if there is a discrepancy between their standard of living and financial resources and the family or others show unusual interest in their assets. Recent changes in deeds or title to property and rent arrears and eviction notices may indicate financial abuse.

Discriminatory abuse

Discriminatory abuse includes abuse based on sex, race, culture, religion, age, ability, sexual orientation, class, culture, language, and race or ethnic origin. It is a misuse of power that denies opportunity to some groups or individuals excluding them from services to which they are entitled. There may be a lack of respect and unequal treatment of the adult at risk based on their protected characteristics, with inappropriate use of language and verbal abuse or offensive remarks about the individual's age, disability, race or sexuality. There may be disregard of the individual's communication needs e.g. not allowing access to an interpreter or signer. Individuals may be harassed or excluded from services. When there is discriminatory abuse, the support offered does not cater for individual needs in terms of race, age, sex, disability, marital status, sexual orientation, religion or belief, gender reassignment or pregnancy/maternity status - the 'protected characteristics' under the Equality Act 2010.

Signs of discriminatory abuse
Signs of discriminatory abuse may include offering an individual a substandard service or repeatedly excluding them from basic rights such as health, education, employment, criminal justice and civic status. The individual may therefore become anxious, withdrawn and isolated or may lash out in anger, frustration and fear.

Institutional abuse

Institutional abuse is seen when the needs of the institution are more important than the needs of the service users, when there is poor management and poor leadership. Individuals are isolated, visitors discouraged and complaints are ignored. There may be a failure to investigate and act on reports of abuse and verbal and physical abuse becomes the norm. Procedures and routines serve the needs of the organisation, not the individual, for example, individuals in residential care may not be given a choice of bed time – everyone is put to bed at the same time before night staff come on duty.

Signs of institutional abuse
Signs of institutional abuse may include a high staff turnover, inadequate staffing levels, poor staff morale and poor standards of care with little respect for the dignity, privacy and confidentiality of individuals. Physical and psychological abuse may be present. Residents may be hungry or dehydrated, lack personal clothing and possessions and have little to do. Residents may be abusive to staff and other residents or withdrawn and isolated within the environment. There are few visitors. Management is poor – with inadequate financial management, poor record keeping, inadequate procedures for managing medication and an absence of individual care plans and inadequate or incorrect care given. Staff have little or no training.

Domestic abuse

Domestic abuse is defined by the government as

'any incident or pattern of incidents of controlling, coercive, threatening behaviour, violence or abuse between those aged 16 or over who are or have been intimate partners or family members regardless of gender or sexuality. This can encompass but is not limited to psychological, physical, sexual, financial and emotional abuse.'

Source: Home Office press release - New definition of domestic violence and abuse to include 16 and 17 year olds, 5 November 2012

- Controlling behaviour is defined as: a range of acts designed to make a person subordinate and/ or dependent by isolating them from sources of support, exploiting their resources and capacities for personal gain, depriving them of the means needed for independence, resistance and escape and regulating their everyday behaviour.

- Coercive behaviour is defined as: an act or a pattern of acts of assault, threats, humiliation and intimidation or other abuse that is used to harm, punish, or frighten their victim.

Domestic abuse includes so called 'honour' based violence, female genital mutilation (FGM) and forced marriage, and protects victims of different genders and ethnic groups.

From 31 October 2015, as part of the Serious Crime Act 2015, there is a mandatory duty requiring regulated health and social care professionals and teachers in England and Wales to report to the police known cases of Female Genital Mutilation (FGM) in under 18-year-olds.

Activity B P3

Winterbourne View Care Home ('Winterbourne') provided specialist residential care for up to 24 service users aged 18 and over with learning difficulties and autism. In 2011 an undercover reporter filmed the care at Winterbourne. This was later shown on television. Staff were later convicted and sentenced for the abuse that happened. According to the film footage, service user A, a young woman with significant physical problems and profound learning difficulties, was put fully clothed under a running shower. She was screaming and saying no. It also shows water was thrown over her by a support worker. On the same day she had water thrown over her outside and was taunted by members of staff. She was then brought inside soaking wet and shaking. The nurse manager in charge saw this and did nothing.

Source: adapted from Conduct and Competence Committee Substantive Hearing 16 August 2013 www.nmc.org.uk

Which types of abuse can you identify in this incident?

You can check your answers by reading the decision of the Conduct and Competence Committee Substantive Hearing 16 August 2013 Nursing and Midwifery Council.

Describe the types and signs of abuse and neglect that may be experiences by different individuals.

Factors that could contribute to an individual being vulnerable to abuse and neglect

Unfortunately abuse continues to happen. Anyone can become a victim of abuse and anyone can be an abuser. In this section we look at the factors that contribute to an individual becoming vulnerable to both abuse and to neglect.

Vulnerable groups

People may see themselves as isolated and alone but they often belong to certain groups which are vulnerable. Babies, children, and some older people are seen as more likely to be abused because they are seen as powerless because of their age and ability and because they have no one to defend their best interests. Children with increased vulnerability include those under one year, those with disabilities, looked-after children, and those who witness domestic violence. Adults in need of care and support are vulnerable, especially those who lack mental capacity, have communication difficulties, or are socially isolated. Children and adults who are vulnerable may suffer neglect or abuse if their care giver abuses substances.

Physical vulnerability
Physical vulnerability may come from having physical disabilities. A wheelchair user who cannot get away from taunting bullies is vulnerable. A child with a chronic medical condition such as asthma may not be able to get away from the school bully who steals their lunch. A deaf eighty-year-old resident may not hear the cruel comments carers make when she rings the bell yet again for the toilet.

Cognitive impairment
Cognitive impairment can make people vulnerable. An older person with a type of dementia such as Alzheimer's disease may be out on their own and get confused by their surroundings then ask a stranger to take them home. A young person with special educational needs may not understand when a carer behaves inappropriately. A child with a speech impairment may have difficulty expressing themselves and their views might be neglected by social workers keen to place them with a foster family.

Emotional vulnerability

Emotional vulnerability, includes depression, anxiety, and phobias. Relationships that involve influence or power have the potential for abuse. Someone who is depressed and has low self-esteem may easily be intimidated by a stronger partner in a relationship, or by a forceful carer who makes their decisions for them. People with anxiety and phobias are especially vulnerable, if someone deliberately tries to coerce them into making decisions in their favour. One elderly lady who lived alone received a telephone call supposedly from her bank, saying her account had been hacked. In order to prove they were genuine and not a scam, the fraudsters asked her to ring the bank back using the phone number printed on the back of her bank card. However, the fraudster kept the telephone line open so even though the person called the bank, the call did not go through. Instead she is unknowingly connected straight back to the fraudster. The fraudster then pretends to be from the bank and asks the lady to provide her full bank card details and key in her PIN so that their existing card can be 'cancelled' and the new one 'activated' or 'authorised.' They explained that she would have to return her bank cards at once and they would send a courier to collect them. She gives her cards to the courier. The next day she finds her bank account has been emptied. Her anxiety made her emotionally vulnerable to financial abuse.

Social vulnerability

Social vulnerability is an increasing problem in our ageing society, where older people live in social isolation and are lonely. One elderly lady answered the door to find two strangers who said they had just moved in next door and had brought her some cakes. She invited them in, made a cup of tea and was chatting to them when one asked to go to the toilet. He was some time. When he came back downstairs the couple left. A few minutes later the elderly lady found her handbag had been emptied of the hundred pounds she had withdrawn earlier that afternoon from the bank.

Socially vulnerable people are susceptible to controlling and institutionalised behaviour. Service user A in the Winterbourne case in the previous Activity was subject to institutionalised

behaviour – forcibly showered and soaked in water to make her stop spitting at carers.

Staffing issues

Staffing issues that may lead to institutional abuse and neglect include a lack of staff training, lack of leadership, and low staff levels. In the Winterbourne case, outlined in the previous Activity, staff had little training in managing challenging behaviour and there was no leadership or support from management to show how to manage A's spitting behaviour. In the example of the failure of care in Mid-Staffordshire NHS Foundation Trust at the end of this unit, low staffing levels meant patients were neglected and poor quality care became the norm. The culture of the organisation, lack of staff training and lack of monitoring of practice contributed to institutional abuse.

Activity B P4

1   Explain the factors that may contribute to the likelihood of abuse and neglect for service users in health and social care.

2   Find out what happened in the Winterbourne case and in the case of Mid Staffordshire NHS Foundation Trust. What can we learn from these cases? Explain the factors that can reduce the likelihood of abuse and neglect for service users in health and social care.

Responding to suspected abuse and neglect

Following safeguarding policies and procedures

> 'Safeguarding means protecting an adult's right to live in safety, free from abuse and neglect.'
>
> Source: p 230, para 14.7 Care and Support Statutory Guidance for the Care Act 2014

Safeguarding regulations also form part 5 of the Protection of Freedoms Act 2012. Sections 42–46 of the Care Act 2014 set out the new legal framework for Safeguarding including how local authorities and other parts of the system should protect adults at risk of abuse or neglect. It replaced 'No secrets', the previous safeguarding guidance.

According to the Care Act 2014, the aims of adult safeguarding are to:

- stop abuse or neglect wherever possible
- prevent harm and reduce the risk of abuse or neglect to adults with care and support needs
- safeguard adults in a way that supports them in making choices and having control about how they want to live
- promote an approach that concentrates on improving life for the adults concerned
- raise public awareness so that communities as a whole, alongside professionals, play their part in preventing, identifying and responding to abuse and neglect
- provide information and support in accessible ways to help people understand the different types of abuse, how to stay safe and what to do to raise a concern about the safety or well-being of an adult and
- address what has caused the abuse or neglect.

Source: p 231, para 14.11 Care and Support Statutory Guidance

Safeguarding adults is part of the duty of care of every professional in health and care. Every organisation should have adult safeguarding policies and procedures.

Procedures may include

1 a statement of purpose relating to promoting well-being, preventing harm and responding effectively if concerns are raised

2 a statement of specific roles and responsibility, authority and accountability so that all staff and volunteers understand their role and limitations

3 a statement of the procedures for dealing with allegations of abuse, including those for dealing with emergencies by ensuring immediate safety, the processes for initially assessing abuse and neglect and deciding when intervention is appropriate, and the arrangements for reporting to the police, urgently when necessary

4 a full list of points of referral indicating how to access support and advice at all times, in normal working hours and outside them, with a comprehensive list of contact addresses and telephone numbers, including relevant national and local voluntary bodies

5 an indication of how to record allegations of abuse and neglect, any enquiry and all subsequent action

6 a list of sources of expert advice

7 a full description of channels of inter-agency communication and procedures for information sharing and for decision making

8 a list of all services which might offer access to support or redress

9 an explanation of how professional disagreements are resolved especially with regard to whether decisions should be made, enquiries undertaken for example.

Adapted from p 241, para 14.41 Care and Support Statutory Guidance

Different agencies will be involved at different levels. Locally, social services, health services, police, education and voluntary organisations may be represented on Safeguarding Boards. The local authority, NHS and police, must work together to develop, share and implement a joint safeguarding strategy.

The Care Quality Commission as regulator oversees and monitors quality. Following the introduction of the Care Act 2014 and the Francis Report on the care at Mid Staffordshire Hospital, the CQC reviewed its statement of fundamental standards which they expect to see when inspecting care providers.

This is the CQC statement for Safeguarding:

You must not suffer any form of abuse or improper treatment while receiving care.

This includes:

Neglect

Degrading treatment

Unnecessary or disproportionate restraint

Inappropriate limits on your freedom.

Source: www.cqc.org.uk

Professional roles and legal responsibilities

Six key principles underpin all adult safeguarding work whether in the NHS, the police, education or social services. They are

- Empowerment – people supported to make their own decisions and informed consent.
- Prevention – it is better to take action before harm occurs.
- Proportionality – the least intrusive response appropriate to the risk presented.
- Protection – support and representation for those in greatest need.
- Partnership – local solutions through services working with their communities to prevent, detect and report neglect and abuse.
- Accountability – accountability and transparency in delivering safeguarding.

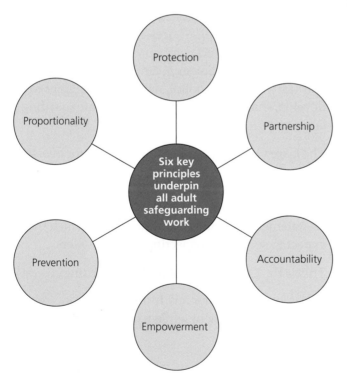

Figure 7.1 Six key principles that underpin safeguarding

All regulated health and care professionals such as nurses, social workers and doctors, have a duty to safeguard individuals in their care. This is set out in their professional code. The Code for nurses and midwives says:

17 Raise concerns immediately if you believe a person is vulnerable or at risk and needs extra support and protection

17.1 take all reasonable steps to protect people who are vulnerable or at risk from harm, neglect or abuse

17.2 share information if you believe someone may be at risk of harm, in line with the laws relating to the disclosure of information, and

17.3 have knowledge of and keep to the relevant laws and policies about protecting and caring for vulnerable people

Source: www.nmc.org.uk

The Health and Care Professionals Council (HCPC) code is under revision at the time of writing and will be published for 2016 but meanwhile the standards guide social workers and other practitioners registered with the HCPC in raising concerns.

Standard 1 requires you to act in the best interests of your service users. You must act immediately if you become aware of a situation where a service user may be put in danger, and take appropriate action to protect the rights of children and vulnerable adults who are at risk. You must place the safety of service users before any personal or professional loyalties at all times.

Standard 4 requires you to tell us (or any other relevant regulators) any important information about your own, or other registrants' or health and care professionals' conduct or competence.

Local authorities are required by the Care Act to use a person-centred approach to working with risk, making information accessible to involve more people in safeguarding support, and using advocacy to support service users. Professionals should work with the adult to establish what being safe means to them and how that can be best achieved. There is a greater emphasis on the experiences of service users with a focus on qualitative reporting on outcomes as well as quantitative measures, so service users are asked how well services meet their needs, not just how many services meet their needs. Making safeguarding personal means it should be person-led and outcome-focused.

Local authorities must set up *Safeguarding Adults Boards*, which include the local authority, NHS and police, to develop, share and implement a joint safeguarding strategy.

According to the Care Act 2014, local authorities must:

Lead a multi-agency local adult safeguarding system that seeks to prevent abuse and neglect and stop it quickly when it happens

Make enquiries, or request others to make them, when they think an adult with care and support needs may be at risk of abuse or neglect and they need to find out what action may be needed

Establish Safeguarding Adults Boards, including the local authority, NHS and police, which will develop, share and implement a joint safeguarding strategy

Carry out Safeguarding Adults Reviews when someone with care and support needs dies as a result of neglect or abuse and there is a concern that the local authority or its partners could have done more to protect them

Arrange for an independent advocate to represent and support a person who is the subject of a safeguarding enquiry or review, if required.

Any relevant person or organisation must provide information to Safeguarding Adults Boards as requested.

Source: www.scie.org.uk

Adult safeguarding partnerships must ensure that everyone is clear about their roles and responsibilities. They must create strong multi-agency partnerships that aim to prevent abuse and that respond quickly to abuse or neglect. They must change the culture to become a positive learning environment and break down current 'blame' cultures. Local authorities and their partners must provide access to community resources such as leisure facilities, safe town centres and community groups to reduce the social and physical isolation which increases vulnerability; and they must clarify how to respond to safeguarding concerns arising from poor quality service provision.

Role and duties of Safeguarding Adults Boards (SABs). SABs have three core duties. They must:

- develop and publish a strategic plan setting out how they will meet their objectives and how their member and partner agencies will contribute
- publish an annual report detailing how effective their work has been
- commission safeguarding adults reviews (SARs) for any cases which meet the criteria for review.

The terms 'adult protection coordinator' or 'adult safeguarding co-ordinator/lead' describe an individual who has safeguarding lead responsibilities across an authority. They support the work of the Safeguarding Adults Board (SAB) and advise the local authority on adult safeguarding cases. The role varies from council to council, and carries different titles.

Each Local Safeguarding Children Board (LSCB) has a statutory duty to co-ordinate how agencies work together to safeguard and promote the well-being of children and young people under the age of 18 years old in their local area. The LSCB must ensure the effectiveness of the safeguarding arrangements in their area. As part of this LSCBs must undertake serious case reviews (SCRs) for every case where abuse or neglect is known or suspected and either: a child dies, or is seriously harmed and there are concerns about how organisations or professionals worked together to protect the child.

Responding to disclosure

When safeguarding children, Sections 11 and 12 of the Children Act 2004 place a statutory duty on agencies to co-operate to safeguard and promote the welfare of children. The statutory guidance 'Working together to safeguard children - A guide to inter-agency working to safeguard and promote the welfare of children' (2015) focuses on a child-centred and coordinated approach to safeguarding. It says that everyone has a responsibility to keep children safe.

Concerns about children should never be ignored. If you think a child is in immediate danger phone the police on 999 or the NSPCC on 0808 800 5000. If the child is not in immediate danger but there is a concern, contact your local authority children's services child protection team, or your own organisation's designated child protection officer as listed in your organisation's child protection procedure. If your organisation is not keeping children safe you can contact the NSPCC directly.

Paragraph 32 of the 2015 government guidance 'What to do if you're worried a child is being abused – Advice for practitioners' says, 'If you have concerns about the safety or welfare of a child and feel they are not being acted upon by your manager or named/designated safeguarding lead, it is your responsibility to take action.

Once a referral has been made, a social worker should respond within one working day telling you what further action they have decided to take. Practitioners may be called to a further assessment of the child, through an early help assessment, through a child in need assessment (section 17 of the Children Act 1989) or a child protection enquiry (section 47 of the Children Act 1989), which will be led by a social worker. If a social worker suspects that a child is suffering, or is likely to suffer, significant harm the local authority holds a strategy discussion to determine the child's welfare. If the child is judged to be at continuing risk of significant harm an initial child protection conference is convened to make decisions about the child's future safety, health and development. Professionals involved in the child's care such as teachers or nursery nurses may be called to contribute to this conference. A core group meets within ten days to develop and implement the child protection plan. Information sharing is mandatory to protect the child. Confidentiality may be broken in such circumstances as sharing information with other involved professionals is necessary to protect the child's vital interests under the government guidance to the Data Protection Act.

Clause 45 of the Care Act 2014 focuses on 'supply of information'. This relates to the responsibilities of others to comply with requests for information from the safeguarding adults board. Anyone can become aware of abuse or neglect of an adult with care and support needs. In cases of adult abuse, if an abusive act is witnessed, or there is disclosure from a third party or the adult themselves, or suspicion

or concern that something is not right or there is evidence of possible abuse or neglect, if safe to do so, speak to the adult concerned, get their views and what they would like to see happen next. If the person is in immediate danger take immediate actions to safeguard anyone at immediate risk, e.g. call emergency services or medical assistance.

If there is no immediate danger – ask, has a criminal offence occurred, or likely to occur? If so, call the police.

Reporting and recording procedures

After immediately responding to disclosure of abuse, the incident must be reported within the same day. If a criminal offence has or is likely to occur, the police must be notified at once and then the incident reported to the local lead agency. If no criminal offence is involved, the incident must be reported immediately to the local lead agency, which is likely to be local social services.

Whistle-blowing

Whistle-blowing is disclosure by an individual to the public, or those in authority, of mismanagement, corruption, illegality, or some other form of wrong-doing in the workplace.

The law protecting whistle blowers is the Public Interest Disclosure Act 1998 (PIDA).

The usual steps are first, check your employer's whistle-blowing policy and follow the steps set out in it. The policy should give details of the contact person for raising concerns within your organisation. Raise concerns internally with the line manager so issues can be addressed at a local level. You should be kept informed about the action taken to deal with it.

If nothing happens escalate your concerns internally with higher management.

If nothing happens after raising concerns with higher management, escalate your concerns externally with a prescribed regulator.

If there is a concern about the health, behaviour, or practice of another professional, raise your concerns internally and also notify the appropriate regulator for their profession. The Professional Standards

Authority is responsible for overseeing the UK's nine health and care professional regulatory bodies which are:

1 General Chiropractic Council (GCC) regulating the chiropractic profession.

2 General Dental Council (GDC) protects patients and regulates dental teams.

3 General Medical Council (GMC) regulates doctors.

4 General Optical Council (GOC) regulates the optical professions in the UK.

5 General Osteopathic Council (GOsC) regulates the practice of osteopathy in the UK.

6 General Pharmaceutical Council (GPhC) regulates pharmacists, pharmacy technicians and pharmacy premises in Great Britain.

7 Health and Care Professions Council (HCPC) regulates health, psychological and social work.

8 Nursing and Midwifery Council (NMC) regulates nurses and midwives in England, Wales, Scotland, Northern Ireland and the Islands.

9 Pharmaceutical Society of Northern Ireland (PSNI) is the Northern Ireland regulatory and professional body for pharmacists.

The government publication 'Blowing the Whistle to a Prescribed Person – List of prescribed persons and bodies' (2015) lists the following as prescribed persons and bodies for healthcare concerns:

- Care Quality Commission for matters relating to the provision of health and social care.

- Monitor for the regulation and performance of NHS foundation trusts.

- NHS Trust Development Authority about the performance of English NHS trusts, including clinical quality, governance and management of risk.

- Healthcare Inspectorate Wales and Welsh Ministers about the review of, and investigation into the provision of health care by and for Welsh NHS bodies.

If the regulator fails to act, as happened in the Mid-Staffordshire hospital case, it is wise to take legal advice. Raising your concern publicly is a serious step.

Activity

Sara started working at Beeches care home but is worried about the way some staff shout at residents. The staff also refuse to take them to the toilet, then leave the residents in wet and smelly clothes when they wet themselves.

1 What should Sara do?

2 What should the manager do?

3 Explain how to respond to concerns about abuse and neglect in a health or social care setting.

Reducing the likelihood of abuse and neglect

People who abuse others look for those who are vulnerable. Those who work in health and social care can reduce the likelihood of abuse by supporting vulnerable individuals.

Identifying people at risk of abuse and neglect and the importance of observation

Health and care workers play an important role in identifying those at risk of abuse or neglect because as part of their work they observe people. In the case of Baby Peter, a GP and a social worker both identified Peter as at risk of abuse and neglect. His mother was arrested each time. Perhaps if others around had been more observant, he might not have died.

Case scenario

Peter Connolly, Baby P

1 March 2006 Baby P, Peter Connolly was born.

December 2006: his mother was arrested after bruises were spotted on the boy's face and chest by a GP.

April 2007: Baby Peter was admitted to North Middlesex hospital with bruises, two black eyes and swelling on the left side of his head.

May 2007: After seeing marks on the boy's face, a social worker sent Baby Peter to the North Middlesex where 12 areas of bruises and scratches were found. His mother Tracey Connolly was re-arrested.

30 July 2007: Injuries to Baby Peter's face and hands were missed by a social worker after the boy was deliberately smeared with chocolate to hide them.

3 August 2007: Baby Peter was found dead in his cot.

4 Tell someone (your employer, supervisor, or health and safety representative) if you think the work or inadequate precautions are putting anyone's health and safety at serious risk.

Source: Health and Safety Law: What you need to know, www.hse.gov.uk

The Manual Handling Operations and Regulations (2002)

The Manual Handling Operations and Regulations (2002) originally published in 1992 apply to many different manual handling activities such as lifting, lowering, pushing, pulling or carrying animate loads which may move unpredictably, such as a person, or inanimate ones, such as a box or a trolley. Incorrect manual handling can cause injury. Employers must consider the risks to employees, consult and involve employees in reducing risks.

The Regulations require employers to:

- avoid the need for hazardous manual handling, so far as is reasonably practicable

- assess the risk of injury from any hazardous manual handling that can't be avoided and

- reduce the risk of injury from hazardous manual handling, so far as is reasonably practicable.

Employees must:

- follow systems of work in place for their safety

- use equipment provided for their safety properly

- co-operate with their employer on health and safety matters

- inform their employer if they identify hazardous handling activities

- take care to make sure their activities do not put others at risk.

The Food Hygiene Regulations (2006)

The Food Hygiene Regulations (2006) apply throughout the UK and consolidated and simplified previous EU food hygiene legislation. They control throughout the food chain, from primary production to sale or supply to the final consumer (from 'farm to fork'), focus on public health protection and clarify that it is the primary responsibility of food business operators to produce food safely.

Food businesses must be registered and inspected. They must have a Hazard Analysis and Critical Control Point (HACCP) plan to keep food safe from biological, chemical and physical safety hazards. Staff must receive hygiene training. Inspections are without notice and inspectors may issue a Hygiene Improvement Notice or Hygiene Emergency Prohibition Notices – banning the use of certain equipment or certain processes.

The 4 Cs of food hygiene
Prevent cross-contamination:

- Clean and disinfect work surfaces, boards and equipment thoroughly before and after preparing food.

- Use different equipment (including chopping boards and knives) for raw meat/poultry and ready-to-eat food.

- Wash hands before preparing food and after touching raw food.

- Keep raw and ready-to-eat food apart at all times. Store raw food below ready-to-eat food in the fridge.

- Separate cloths, sponges and mops, should be used in areas where ready-to-eat foods are stored, handled and prepared.

Cleaning:

- Wash and dry hands thoroughly before handling food.

- Clean and disinfect food areas and equipment between different tasks, especially after handling raw food.

- Clear and clean as you go.

- Disinfection products should meet British and European Standards.

- Do not let food waste build up.

Chilling:

- Put food that needs to be kept chilled in the fridge straight away.

- Cool cooked food as quickly as possible and then put it in the fridge.

- Keep chilled food out of the fridge for the shortest time possible during preparation.
- Check regularly that your fridge and display units are cold enough.

Cooking: thoroughly cook poultry, pork, rolled joints and products made from minced meat, such as burgers and sausages.

In addition to the 4 Cs, food handlers must be fit to work. Staff handling food or working in a food handling area must report symptoms of diarrhoea and/or vomiting to management immediately. Managers must exclude staff with these symptoms from working with or around open food, normally for 48 hours from when symptoms stop naturally.

Control of Substances Hazardous to Health (COSHH) 2002

Employers must control substances that are hazardous to health. They can prevent or reduce workers' exposure to hazardous substances by:

- finding out what the health hazards are, for example, risk of harm from cleaning chemicals or from body fluids for care workers
- deciding how to prevent harm to health (risk assessment)
- providing control measures to reduce harm to health such as locking away chemicals, ensuring medicines are kept in a locked cupboard, providing gloves, aprons and other protective equipment
- making sure they are used
- keeping all control measures in good working order
- providing information, instruction and training for employees and others
- providing monitoring and health surveillance in appropriate cases
- planning for emergencies.

Reporting of Injuries, Diseases and Dangerous Occurrences Regulations (RIDDOR) 2013

RIDDOR requires employers and others to report deaths, certain types of injury, some occupational diseases and dangerous occurrences linked to work and incidents where the work activities, equipment or environment contributed to the accident.

These must be reported, if they arise 'out of or in connection with work':

- the death of any person, whether or not they are at work
- accidents which result in an employee or a self-employed person dying, suffering a specified injury, being absent from work or unable to do their normal duties for more than seven days for example, a care worker injuring themselves while trying to lift a heavy patient
- accidents which result in a person not at work (e.g. a patient, service user, visitor) suffering an injury and being taken directly to a hospital for treatment, or if the accident happens at a hospital, if they suffer a specified injury, for example, an elderly person falling out of a hospital bed and fracturing their leg would be reported
- an employee or self-employed person has one of the specified occupational diseases or is exposed to carcinogens, mutagens and biological agents
- specified dangerous occurrences, which may not result in a reportable injury, but have the potential to do significant harm.

The report should be made online no longer than ten days after the incident, by the employer of an injured person, a self-employed person or someone in control of premises where work is carried out. Records must be kept for three years and should include:

- the date and method of reporting
- the date, time and place of the event
- personal details of those involved
- the injury
- a brief description of the nature of the event or disease.

Data Protection Act (1989)

Data Protection Act (1989) is described in detail in Unit 2.

Information sharing has proved a barrier to effective joint working but is permitted where it is of *vital interest* – a term used in the Data Protection

Act (DPA) 1998 to permit sharing of information where it is critical to prevent serious harm or distress, or in life-threatening situations.

Care Standards Act (2000)

This set national minimum standards for care. It established the predecessor of the CQC.

The Equality Act (2010)

This Act brought together previous laws into one discrimination law which protects individuals from unfair treatment and promotes a fair and more equal society. The protected characteristics were listed earlier in this unit. Under this Act you are protected from discrimination in the workplace, when using public services like health care or education, when using businesses and other organisations that provide services and goods, when using transport, joining a club or association (e.g. your local tennis club); and when you have contact with public bodies such as the local council or government departments. The Act protects against direct and indirect discrimination, harassment and victimisation. The Act requires public bodies such as local councils, hospitals, and publicly-funded service providers to show how they have considered whether their decisions and policies affect people with different protected characteristics.

The Care Act (2014)

This Act brought in some of the biggest changes for 60 years to the way care is delivered.

It placed a duty on local authorities to promote well-being, to focus on preventing, reducing or delaying needs, to provide information and advice to service users and change from a service led system to a person-centred one that focuses on outcomes for service users. Local authorities have a legal duty to assess needs and eligibility and provide independent advocacy. The system of charging and financial assessment was changed to allow people to have deferred payment agreements so their home did not have to be sold to pay for care until after their death. Person-centred care and support planning, personal budgets, direct payments and a review of care and support plans were brought in along with new provisions for adult safeguarding. Integration and partnership working became mandatory helping

those in transition between children's services and adult care, or between prisons, approved premises and bail accommodation.

Care Quality Commission Standards

These are the fundamental standards below which care must never fall. They concern:

- person-centred care
- dignity and respect
- consent
- safety
- safeguarding from abuse
- food and drink to keep you in good health while you receive care and treatment
- premises and equipment
- complaints
- good governance
- staffing
- fit and proper staff with checks on applicants' criminal records and work history
- duty of candour
- display of ratings.

Disclosure and Barring Service (DBS) checks

The Disclosure and Barring Service (DBS) prevents unsuitable people from working with vulnerable groups, including children. It replaces the Criminal Records Bureau (CRB) and Independent Safeguarding Authority (ISA). Safeguarding regulations include information about the Disclosure and Barring Service and are Part 5 of the Protection of Freedoms Act 2012.

Activity C P6

Compare the influence of different health and safety laws or policies on health and social care practice in a selected setting.

You may want to look at:

- Health and Safety at Work Act (1974)
- The Manual Handling Operations and Regulations (2002)
- Control of Substances Hazardous to Health (COSHH) 2002

What are the similarities in their influence?

Influence of legislation and policies on health and social care practice

Legislation and policies improve services. Monitor, the sector regulator for health services in England, and the NHS Trust Development Authority publish quarterly reports on NHS performance. The National Audit Office is studying progress with personalised commissioning in adult social care. The report is due to be published in 2016.

Safeguarding vulnerable adults, children and young people

Safeguarding policies and legislation influence practice by clarifying what to do, who should be involved in safeguarding, and have emphasised training for staff around their responsibilities in this area.

Protection from accidents, injuries and illness, including infection control, food preparation, hazardous substances

National minimum standards have clear guidelines for employers and employees meaning more people are aware of what good care is and what it is not. Staff and service users are protected by this legislation.

Managing risk assessments and maintaining a safe working environment, including safe moving and handling

Managing risk assessments and maintaining a safe working environment, including safe moving and handling has become everyone's business. Staff are trained to risk assess situations and have safe practice, including the storage and handling of medication.

Promoting health and well-being

Promoting health and well-being is emphasised and the shift from cure to prevention has influenced practice as more funding is directed into maintaining health. Better care, a joint initiative between local authorities and CCGs aims to reduce the number of hospital admissions.

Legislation

Legislation provides confidence and reassurance for families and other carers. The Care Act 2014 brought together different laws and put the patient at the heart of care, focusing on outcomes for them as a measure of the service.

Meet legal and regulatory requirements, including record keeping. Legislation and policy clarify requirements for record keeping according to the Data Protection Act and the Care Act. Self-assessment involves the person at the heart of their care. Personal budgets and direct payments involve record keeping on the part of the budget holder and give a tighter control on finances.

Recruitment of staff in health and social care

Recruitment of staff in health and social care remains an issue. Agency staff maintain many services where there are insufficient permanent staff. Disclosure and Barring Service checks help to ensure that the many thousands of staff employed in health and care have clear criminal records.

Activity C M3

Analyse how health and safety legislation or policies influence safe practice in a selected health or social care setting.

Choose from these:

- Care Standards Act (2000)
- Control of Substances Hazardous to Health (COSHH) 2002
- Data Protection Act (1988)
- Health and Safety at Work Act (1974)
- Reporting of Injuries, Diseases and Dangerous Occurrences Regulations (RIDDOR) 2013
- The Care Act (2014)
- The Equality Act (2010)
- The Manual Handling Operations and Regulations (2002)

Distinction activity C D3

Remind yourself of what the command word 'justify' means.

Justify the effectiveness of health and safety legislation, policies and procedures in maintaining health and safety.

Use the full range of legislation and policies listed in the previous section and give examples from a range of these. Use examples from a range of settings to illustrate your answer.

Check your understanding

1 Who is responsible for health and safety?
2 What do the Manual Handling Operations and Regulations advise you should do before starting to lift or move an object?
3 What type of plan must food businesses have under the Food Hygiene Regulations 2006?
4 Give three examples of substances hazardous to health.
5 According to the Data Protection Act 1988 when is it permissible to share information?
6 What did the Care Standards Act introduce?
7 Give three key points of the following: The Equality Act 2010, The Care Act 2014

D Explore procedures and responsibilities to maintain health and safety and respond to accidents and emergencies in health and social care settings

D P7 , D P8 , D M4 , C D D3 , C D D4

Procedures to maintain health and safety

Procedures are ways of doing something, so procedures to maintain health and safety are ways of ensuring a healthy and safe environment.

Infection control and prevention

Infections such as Clostridium difficile spread rapidly when hygiene is poor. Infections are less of a threat to healthy people but in hospitals and care homes where people may have less resistance to organisms, infections can be deadly. According to the National Institute for Health and Care Excellence (NICE), people should receive healthcare from healthcare workers who decontaminate their hands immediately by using hand rub or soap and water before and after every episode of direct contact or care even when they wear gloves. An alcohol-based hand rub should be used for hand decontamination before and after direct contact or care, except when hands are visibly soiled or potentially contaminated with body fluids or when caring for patients

with vomiting or diarrhoeal illness, regardless of whether or not gloves have been worn. In these last examples, soap and water must be used.

Safe moving and handling of equipment and individuals

If done badly, moving and handling can cause injury, accidents to care workers and service users and may result in lack of dignity for patients. All tasks should be risk assessed, unnecessary risks avoided and where moving and handling cannot be avoided, employers should put measures in place to reduce the risk, where reasonably practicable.

Food preparation and storage procedures

This should include the advice outlined earlier in this Unit.

Storage and administration of medication

According to NICE, care home providers and other health and care organisations where medication is used, should have an up-to-date medicines policy, which includes written processes for:

● sharing information about a resident's medicines, including when they transfer between care settings
● ensuring that records are accurate and up to date
● identifying, reporting and reviewing medicines-related problems
● keeping residents safe (safeguarding)
● accurately listing a resident's medicines (medicines reconciliation)
● reviewing medicines (medication review)
● ordering medicines
● receiving, storing and disposing of medicines
● helping residents to look after and take their medicines themselves (self-administration)
● care home staff administering medicines to residents, including staff training and competence requirements
● care home staff giving medicines to residents without their knowledge (covert administration)

Figure 7.2 Helping a care home resident to manage their medication

- care home staff giving non-prescription and over-the-counter products to residents (homely remedies), if appropriate.

Care home staff (registered nurses and social care practitioners working in care homes) should record the reasons why a resident refuses a medicine in the resident's care record and medicines administration record.

Storage and disposal of hazardous substances

Hazardous chemicals used in cleaning, such as bleach must be kept in a locked cupboard when not in use. According to the Royal College of Nursing guidance, hazardous waste includes items, or parts of them, that can harm the environment or human health. Used dressings, waste chemotherapy drugs, needles, and soiled incontinence pads are typical of hazardous clinical waste in health care. Offensive waste may include material contaminated with body fluids, and may have an odour. Material should be separated and placed in the relevant receptacle.

Colour-coded segregation ensures the correct disposal method for each item. The Department of Health published 'Environment and Sustainability Health Technical Memorandum

07-01: Safe management of healthcare waste with guidance on the colour coding and disposal of waste', which states:

- Infectious Clinical Waste goes into a yellow clinical waste bag or rigid yellow hard burn bins.
- Infectious Clinical Waste from known or suspected infectious sources contaminated with cytotoxic/cytostatic products is put into purple clinical waste bags.
- Infectious Clinical Waste from known or suspected infectious sources suitable for alternative treatment technologies is put into orange clinical waste bags.
- Offensive Waste that does not meet the definition of infectious waste but may cause offence due to material contaminated with body fluids is put into a yellow and black striped bag (Tiger Bag).
- Sharps not contaminated with medicinal products are put into an orange-lidded sharps bin.
- Sharps contaminated with medicines but not cytotoxic or cytostatic are put in yellow-lidded sharps bins.
- Non-hazardous pharmaceutical products such as waste medicines are put in blue-lidded rigid hard burn bins.

procedures for responding to accidents and sudden illness, understand medication and healthcare tasks, handle hazardous substances, promote fire safety, work securely, and manage stress. The Care Certificate Standard 14 explains care worker duties for handling information.

Responsibilities of others in the setting, such as visitors, includes following health and safety guidance and emergency procedures if required, and abiding by relevant regulations, policies and procedures such as signing in and out if required.

Activity D P8 D M4

In your work placement, interview a member of staff about their responsibilities then interview a care home manager about their responsibilities for health, safety and welfare. How do their responsibilities differ?

Explain the health and safety responsibilities of employers, employees and others in a health or social care setting.

Analyse how individual responsibilities and health, safety and emergency procedures contribute to safe practice in a health or social care setting.

Distinction activity C D D4

Remind yourself of what the command word 'evaluate' means.

Evaluate the importance of safe practice principles in maintaining and promoting the health, safety and welfare of service users in a residential care home.

Give examples to support what you say.

Check your understanding

1. What is the purpose of a procedure?
2. Who is responsible for health and safety?
3. Give three examples of procedures to maintain health and safety. Which of these have you seen put into practice in your work placement?
4. Give three examples of procedures for responding to accidents and emergencies. Which of these have you seen put into practice in your work placement?
5. Were there any ways these procedures could be improved?

Case scenario

Mid Staffordshire NHS Foundation Trust

Extracts from Executive summary, Report of the Mid Staffordshire NHS Foundation Trust Public Inquiry February 2013, Chaired by Robert Francis QC.

Between 2005 and 2008 conditions of appalling care were able to flourish in the main hospital serving the people of Stafford and its surrounding area. (p.7)

The first inquiry in 2010 found that:

Patients were left in excrement in soiled bed clothes for lengthy periods;

Assistance was not provided with feeding for patients who could not eat without help;

Water was left out of reach;

In spite of persistent requests for help, patients were not assisted in their toileting;

Wards and toilet facilities were left in a filthy condition;

Privacy and dignity, even in death, were denied;

Triage in A&E was undertaken by untrained staff;

Staff treated patients and those close to them with what appeared to be callous indifference

(p. 13 of the Report)

1. In what way was the duty of care ignored by staff in this hospital?
2. What was the process for complaining?
3. Find out how complaints were dealt with in this hospital.
4. What examples of abuse and neglect are listed in the above excerpt?
5. What failures in health and safety are apparent in this list of findings?

Think about it

Learning organisations improve their services by listening to feedback from those who use their services. In 'Complaints Matter' a report by the Care Quality Commission in 2014, it was found that too often complaints were not handled well in hospitals, mental health services, community health services, GP practices, out-of-hours services and adult social care service.

What are the implications for organisations of not handling complaints well?

Further reading

Community Care

Nursing Times

Useful websites

Report of the Mid Staffordshire NHS Foundation Trust Public Inquiry Chaired by Robert Francis QC, February 2013, search: http://webarchive.nationalarchives.gov.uk/

NHS and social care complaints – Citizens Advice: www.citizensadvice.org.uk

Fundamental standards; complaints procedure; Report – Complaints Matter 2014. All available at: www.cqc.org.uk

NHS Constitution for England; Care and Support Statutory Guidance – Care Act 2014; Quarterly report on the performance of the NHS foundation trusts and NHS trusts, 6 months ended 30 September 2015 (published by Monitor). All available via: www.gov.uk

The Health and Care Professions Council – Standards of conduct, performance and ethics: www.hcpc-uk.co.uk

Healthwatch provides support for complaining about health and social care services: www.healthwatch.co.uk

Health and Safety at Work: Reporting injuries, diseases and dangerous occurrences in health and social care. Guidance for employers: www.hse.gov.uk

Patient experience case studies: www.institute.nhs.uk

Out of Sight Campaign – raising awareness for people with learning disabilities: www.mencap.org.uk/outofsight

Patient Advice and Liaison Service (PALS): www.nhs.uk

National Institute for Health and Care Excellence. Quality Standard 61. Medicines policy: www.nice.org.uk

Nursing and Midwifery Council; revised Nursing and Midwifery Council code 2015; Conduct and Competence Committee; Substantive Hearing 16 August 2013: www.nmc.org.uk

Safe care – evidence and evaluation report, available at: www.nspcc.org.uk

Parliamentary and Health Service Ombudsman: www.ombudsman.org.uk/complain-for-change/home

Public Law Project (PLP), a national legal charity which aims to improve access to public law remedies for those whose access to justice is restricted by poverty or some other form of disadvantage: www.publiclawproject.org.uk

Adult safeguarding resource –e learning; Identifying the signs of abuse; Social Care Institute for Excellence (2011) 'Protecting adults at risk: London multi-agency policy and procedures to safeguard adults from abuse', Adults' Services Report 39; Care Act 2014 - Safeguarding Adults. All available at: www.scie.org.uk

UNISON duty of care handbook for members working in health and social care, see: www.unison.org.uk

A Examine strategies for developing public health policy to improve the health of individuals and the population

A P1, **A P2**, **A M1**, **A B D1**

The origins and aims of public health policy

In Victorian times, outbreaks of cholera, typhoid and influenza killed thousands and the Great Stink of London, when raw sewage filled the Thames, forced politicians to move Parliament. Edwin Chadwick demonstrated the link between poor living conditions and disease and reduced life expectancy. The government realised that they would have to organise a public approach to health and from these beginnings, public health was born.

Contributors to public health systems from 1942

In 1942, the Beveridge Report identified five 'Giant Evils' in society: squalor (dirtiness), ignorance, want (poverty), idleness and disease. These affected poor people most. The report was published during the Second World War, but in 1945 when the war ended, the government decided to act on Beveridge's suggestions.

To overcome squalor they built council houses with bathrooms and flushing toilets. To overcome ignorance they introduced free education up to the age of 15. To overcome poverty, the government introduced a system of benefits. People in work had to contribute, as did employers, but in exchange people got sick pay when they were too ill to work. To overcome idleness the government introduced Labour Exchanges, now called Job Centres. To overcome disease they set up the National Health Service. These reforms made up the Welfare State and provided care for people from 'cradle to grave.'

The NHS Act 1946, which came into force in 1948, was welcomed by the public who were worried about the risk of epidemics spreading from other parts of the world. Measles, a highly contagious virus, for which there was no vaccine as yet, was particularly feared because in some people it resulted in blindness and brain damage.

Aims of public health policy

Public health policies or plans include the following.

- Planning national provision of healthcare and to promote the health of the population.

Figure 8.1 A cartoon of the time by George Whitelaw, published in the *Daily Herald*, showing Beveridge fighting the five 'Giant Evils'

- Identifying and monitoring the needs of the population.
- Identifying and reducing inequalities between groups and communities in society.
- Protecting individuals, groups and communities in society from threats to health and well-being that arise from environmental hazards and communicable diseases.
- Addressing specific national health problems over a period of time.
- Developing programmes to screen for early diagnosis of disease.
- Since 2013, public health has been devolved to local authorities who under guidance from Public Health England (or Wales or Northern Ireland) support them in their core duties.

There are five core mandatory public health functions which are as follows.

1 Appropriate access to sexual health services.
2 Ensuring there are plans in place to protect the health of the population, including immunisation and screening plans.
3 Ensuring NHS commissioners (Clinical Commissioning Groups or CCGs) receive the public health advice they need.
4 The National Childhood Measurement Programme (NCMP).
5 NHS Health Check assessments.

Activity

Public Health England, Public Health Wales and the Public Health Agency in Northern Ireland are responsible for supporting local authorities in public health in their areas. Check out the public health website for where you live.

Strategies for developing public health policy

Identifying health needs

Identifying health needs and promoting the health of the population. Public Health England (PHE) identified the need for people to reduce their alcohol consumption following 'Booze's Black Friday 2015' when alcohol consumption was expected to be at record levels for the festive period. Public Health England and their counterparts in the rest of Britain develop programmes to reduce risk such as a vaccination programme to protect against meningitis. They also screen for disease, warning of high numbers of infections of scarlet fever in 2015 to 2016 and organising screening programmes for bowel and cervical cancer.

Planning and evaluating

Planning and evaluating the national provision of health and social care target setting to include local and national provision.

PHE published their priorities based on evidence. In 'From evidence into action: opportunities to protect and improve the nation's health' and the NHS Five Year Forward View, it sets out the following areas as targets:

- obesity
- smoking
- alcohol
- ensuring a better start in life,
- reducing dementia risk
- tackling tuberculosis
- tackling antimicrobial resistance.

Minimising harm of environmental factors to include recycling, waste management, pollution reduction, ensuring food safety

In 'Recycling and Public Health 2009' a study produced for the Network of Public Health Observatories, recycling and waste management were found to produce minimal risks to health. The Health Protection Agency, the predecessor of PHE, reviewed research to examine links between emissions from municipal waste incinerators and effects on health and found risks were minimal. PHE publish reports on air pollution. They found that 'more than five percent of 'deaths' in England are attributable to long-term exposure to particulate air pollution' and 'This estimate makes air pollution the largest environmental risk linked to deaths every year'.

Source: https://publichealthmatters.blog.gov.uk/2015/11/03/understanding-the-impact-of-particulate-air-pollution/

Groups that influence public health policy

Key groups in setting and influencing public health policy development

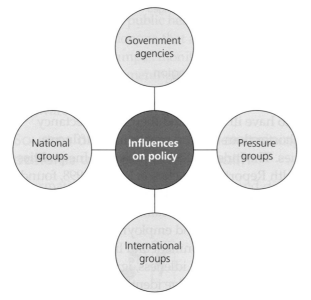

Figure 8.4 Influences on policy

Government and government agencies, such as the Department of Health and Public Health have a direct influence on public health policy. The government decides the level of taxes on alcohol and cigarettes, making them more or less affordable. The Department of Health influences where funds are allocated, for example, to big hospitals rather than to mental health services. Public Health, part of the Department of Health provides information to help local authorities prioritise services.

Pressure groups, such as Age UK and British Heart Foundation keep the needs of those they represent in the headlines, so people are more aware of what they do and how they can help.

Action on Smoking and Health (ASH) campaigned successfully to get smoking banned in public places.

International groups, such as the World Health Organization (WHO) and the United Nations raise awareness of global health issues. Avian flu spread across continents but because of the international awareness raised, countries were able to cope. WHO published a fact sheet about Antibiotic resistance in October 2015, highlighting the overuse of antibiotics and the emergence of drug resistant organisms against which we have no defence.

National groups, such as the government body the National Institute for Health and Care Excellence (NICE) advise doctors and the public about the most economical drugs to use. Cancer Research UK, a charity, funds research into potential cures.

Check your understanding

1 What did the 1942 Beveridge report identify as the 'giant evils' in society?
2 How did the government try to overcome these evils?
3 What is another word for 'strategy'?
4 What is the role of Public Health England (or Wales or Northern Ireland)?
5 According to the Acheson report and the Black report, why do some people have poorer life chances and poorer health?
6 Why do we need international data on health?

B Examine the factors affecting health and the impact of addressing these factors to improve public health B P3 , B P4 , B M2 , A B D1

Both the Acheson report in 1998 and the earlier Black report in 1980 drew attention to the factors that affect health.

Factors affecting health

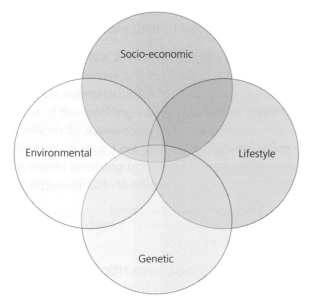

Figure 8.5 Factors affecting health

Socio-economic

Social class is based on social status which is linked to income and education. Generally speaking, the higher the social class, the more money someone has, so a doctor who is in a higher social class earns more than a nurse. This in turn allows the doctor to send their children to better schools. They have access to a better education and more chance of going on to a professional occupation.

Environmental

Those who live in good housing, where there is enough space to relax, perhaps with a garden where children can play, are more likely to have better health than those who live in damp, overcrowded accommodation with no space to exercise. Good housing is related to income too, so factors overlap as in the diagram.

Genetic

Genetic factors affect everyone whether they are rich or poor. Sickle cell anaemia is an inherited blood disorder where the red blood cells, which carry oxygen around the body, develop abnormally. People with sickle cell anaemia may have joint pain or back pain and tire easily. Other genetic disorders are cystic fibrosis and muscular dystrophies. Although genetic disorders are not caused by socio-economic or environmental factors, those children born with genetic disorders are likely to have a better quality of life if they are raised in a healthier environment.

Lifestyle

Lifestyle factors are usually acquired. Children learn from those around them, so if mum rewards her children with sweets, they are likely to grow up with a preference for sweets and see food as a reward, which lays the foundation for obesity. If parents usually eat healthy foods such as salads and sit with children at meal times, children learn those habits too and are more likely to be a healthy weight.

Children learn substance misuse from others. If mum or dad regularly take drugs or get drunk, small children will think that is normal and may learn to do the same. When they are teenagers and learning what it means to be adult and have fun, they may then see drugs and alcohol as a source of fun. Later, when they have alcohol poisoning or liver failure, they will suffer the effects of their lifestyle choices.

The current system

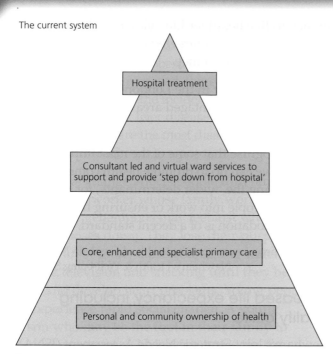

The system we want to see

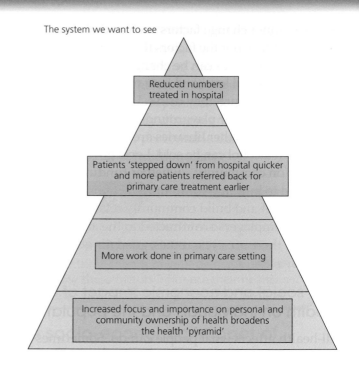

Figure 8.7 The current system and the system we want

- social and community networks including community development programmes such as Well London and Activate London, and use of volunteers and peer support alongside 'social prescriptions' of exercise or better diet.

According to the strategy

'The wider determinants of health are important – social inequalities in unemployment, crime, housing etc. are the biggest causes of health problems in Newham. You are more likely to smoke, misuse drugs or alcohol, live in overcrowded housing, be out of work if you are from a poor area – all of these factors will damage your health. Tackling these root causes will be the best long term way of tackling health inequalities.'

Reduced demand for or pressure on health and social care services

Newham's Health and Well-being Strategy aims to reduce pressure on hospital services as they explain in their strategy:

'As we develop integrated care pathways we need to make sure that these step people down from costly and intensive interventions like

hospitalisation into more community-based care that will be better for them, and more cost effective.'

Activity B M2 B M3

1 Assess the extent to which factors affect current patterns of health and ill-health in older people.

2 Assess how minimising the factors affecting health contribute to improving the health of the population in a specific area.

Distinction activity A B D1

How far can strategies and monitoring help public health policy to meet its aims in reducing the factors that negatively influence public health? Base your answer on a specific demographic area.

Remind yourself of what the command word 'evaluate' means.

Evaluate how far the use of strategies and monitoring the health status of the population helps public health policy to meet its aims in reducing the negative factors that influence public health.

Check your understanding

1 What are socio-economic factors?
2 How can they impact on health?
3 How can the environment affect health?
4 Give three examples of genetic factors affecting health.
5 How can lifestyle factors impact on health? Give three examples.
6 How can local government influence health and reduce inequality?

C Investigate how health is promoted to improve the health of the population C P5 , C P6 , C M4 , C D2

The role of health promoters

Aims

Health promoters aim to improve the health of individuals and the population and reduce health inequalities globally, nationally and locally.

Global health promotion

The World Health Organization, within the United Nations promotes and protects good health worldwide, by providing information about disease outbreaks, co-ordinating crisis intervention and the response to humanitarian emergencies; establishing International Health Regulations and an international system of classifying diseases.

National, regional and local health structures in England, Wales and Northern Ireland, include the

- Department of Health
- Public Health Agency
- clinical commissioning groups (CCGs) as described in Units 2 and 3
- health professionals.

England

In England, the Department of Health (DH) leads, shapes and funds health and care while Public Health England protects and improves the nation's health and well-being, and reduces health inequalities. As described in Unit 2 'Working

in health and social care', local authorities (or councils) are responsible for public health and do this through health and well-being boards which include representatives of all CCGs in the health and well-being board's area, among others. Health and well-being boards assess the needs of their local community through Joint Strategic Needs Assessments (JSNAs) then agree priorities in Joint Health and Well-being Strategies (JHWSs). Together, JSNAs and JHWSs form the basis of commissioning plans for public health for CCGs. (See Figure 8.8.)

Wales

In Wales, NHS Wales is the publically funded National Health Service of Wales and Public Health Wales has responsibility for health protection, for collecting information on ill-health and for screening health conditions. Seven Local Health Boards (LHBs) in Wales now plan, secure and deliver healthcare services in their areas fulfilling the role that CCGs do in England. (See Figure 8.9.)

Northern Ireland

In Northern Ireland, the Department of Health, Social Services and Public Safety (DHSSPS), the Health and Social Care Board (HSCB) and the Public Health Agency (PHA) work in partnership with the Health and Social Care Trusts.

Activity

Find out how health promotion is organised where you live nationally and then look at the local organisation of health promotion.

Approaches to promoting public health and well-being

Promoting public health and well-being includes:

- monitoring the health status of the community and identifying those most at risk, e.g. children, unemployed, older people, minority ethnic groups
- health surveillance programmes
- targeted education and health awareness and health promotion programmes
- socio-economic support to reduce health inequality between individuals and communities, e.g. winter fuel payments, free school meals, housing support

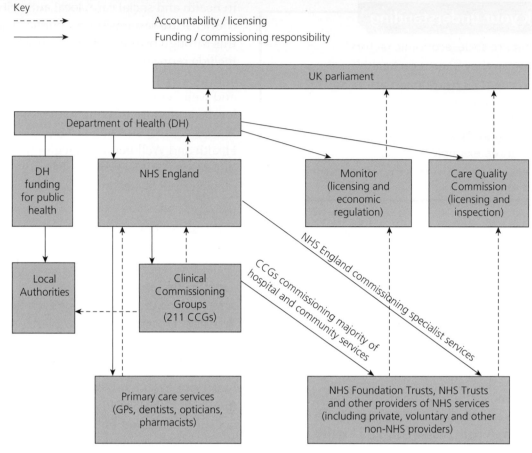

Source: House of Commons Library

Figure 8.8 Structure of the NHS in England (post April 2013)

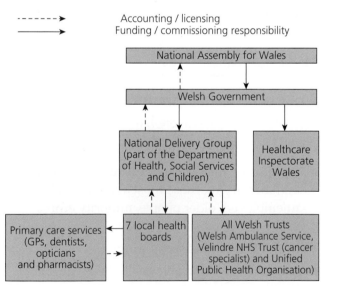

Source: Wales Audit Office, www.publications. parliament.uk/pa/cm201415/cmselect/ cmwelaf/404/40406.htm

Figure 8.9 Structure of the NHS in Wales

- improving access to health and care services
- co-ordinating national and local services
- disease registration to inform of health trends and for strategic health planning
- statutory duty to notify certain communicable diseases, e.g. measles, tuberculosis.

In Newham, monitoring the health status of the local community showed that the biggest causes of death are circulatory diseases, cancer and respiratory diseases. In 2010 it was the second most deprived local authority area in the country. By 2015 it was the eighth most deprived in the country.

The Health Profile of Newham provided in 2015 by Public Health England shows:

Deprivation is higher than average and about 27.2 per cent (19,700) children live in poverty. Life expectancy for both men and women is lower than the England average. In Year 6, 25.1 per cent (949) of children are classified as obese, worse than the average for England. In 2012, 20.0 per cent of adults were classified as obese. Estimated levels of adult physical activity are worse than the England average. Rates of sexually transmitted infections and TB are also worse than average.

Targeted education and health awareness and health promotion programmes are focused towards improving healthy life expectancy, increasing levels of physical activity and reducing smoking.

Newham Clinical Commissioning Group developed Social prescriptions such as the 'Newham Community Prescriptions' approach, encouraging healthy lifestyles and social inclusion. There are a wide range of physical activity options, developed through partnerships with local organisations and activities to support healthy eating.

Socio-economic approaches in Newham include tackling mental health barriers to employment. Putting employment at the centre of addressing health problems is Newham's employment service Workplace which partners with local businesses to help local people find work. Nationally, the winter fuel allowance for pensioners and free school meals for children from poorer families, combined with housing support has helped to improve the quality of life for children, families and older people.

Improving access to health and care services is essential for early diagnosis and treatment. Newham has the highest cardiovascular disease (CVD) mortality rate in the Capital. Using an Integrated Care Strategy, collaborating with nearby areas, supports people to have more appropriate care in the community.

Co-ordinating national and local services through partnerships with schools and children's centres, Newham local authority focus on interventions and preventative work such as additional speech and language therapy, family therapy, nutrition and active lifestyles advice to older age ranges. The local authority public health department also organise and pay for height and weight checks for primary school children.

Disease registration

Registered Medical Practitioners in England and Wales have a statutory duty to notify a Proper Officer of the local authority, often the CCDC (Consultant in Communicable Disease Control), of suspected cases of certain infectious diseases such as mumps, food poisoning, malaria, scarlet fever, tuberculosis and many more notifiable diseases.

The notifiable diseases specified by Public Health England are:

- Acute encephalitis
- Acute infectious hepatitis
- Acute meningitis
- Acute poliomyelitis
- Anthrax
- Botulism
- Brucellosis
- Cholera
- Diphtheria
- Enteric fever (typhoid or paratyphoid)
- Food poisoning
- Haemolytic uraemic syndrome (HUS)
- Infectious bloody diarrhoea
- Invasive group A Streptococcal disease
- Legionnaires' disease
- Leprosy
- Malaria
- Measles
- Meningococcal septicaemia
- Mumps
- Plague
- Rabies
- Rubella

- Scarlet fever
- Severe Acute Respiratory Syndrome (SARS)
- Smallpox
- Tetanus
- Tuberculosis
- Typhus
- Viral haemorrhagic fever (VHF)
- Whooping cough
- Yellow fever.

Notifications prompt local investigation and action to control the diseases. Public Health England collates the weekly returns and publishes analyses of local and national trends.

The system of reporting helps spot patterns and enables action to be taken. In 2013, Newham had the highest rate of TB in London and the UK but because the pattern of disease was identified by the London Health Observatory which is now part of Public Health England, 84 per cent of cases had completed their treatment within a year, while others continued for longer. By 2014 rates in Newham and Brent had decreased by more than 25 per cent compared with 2013.

Activity

Look at your local public health data online and find the Joint Strategic Needs Assessment (JSNA) for your local area. What are the immediate priorities for public health in your area? You may have to look on your local health and well-being board website to find the JSNA.

Approaches to protecting public health and well-being

National and local services work together

Evidence-based responses through environmental surveillance and intelligence gathering can be seen in this example from Public Health England.

PHE figures show that cases of meningococcal disease peak each year during winter: December through to March as appears in the graph in Figure 8.10.

Meningococcal infection spreads through close contact and so PHE encourages students to have the vaccine from their GP before they return to university and halls of residence.

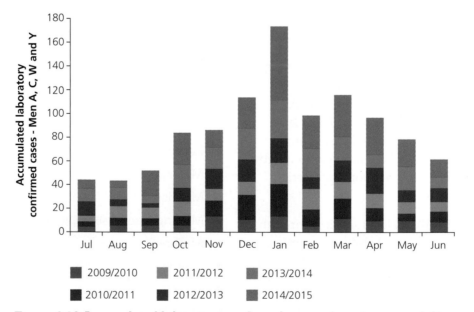

Figure 8.10 Accumulated laboratory confirmed cases of meningococcal diseases

Adapted from www.gov.uk/government/news/meningococcal-disease-cases-peak-in-winter-phe-urges-vaccination

Environmental controls

Environmental controls, such as waste disposal and treatment, water supply, food production, preparation, storage and sales are monitored and managed locally and regionally. Your local council arranges waste disposal and treatment, monitors food production, preparation, storage and sales. The Drinking Water Inspectorate work with Public Health England to monitor and ensure the quality and supply of drinking water. DEFRA, the Department for Environment, Food and Rural Affairs oversee this area nationally.

Regulations, control and monitoring of public areas and work environments

The Health and Safety at Work Act established the Health and Safety Executive to regulate, control and monitor work place health and safety in Great Britain. Public Health England published a review of the impact of physical environments on employee well-being, but the HSE remains the lead body on health and safety in work and public environments.

The role of microbiology services to identify and control outbreaks of food-, water- or airborne disease

Public Health England's food, water and environmental laboratories provide specialist microbiology tests on food, dairy, water and environmental samples, offer advice and training and conduct research and development to respond to emerging dangers from new pathogens. Local health professionals who diagnose notifiable diseases send samples to PHE laboratories to confirm their diagnoses.

The role of field epidemiology in controlling communicable disease

Public Health remains the lead body nationally in controlling communicable disease for example in preparedness and response to pandemic influenza. Public Health issues an annual programme to inform health professionals about the vaccines available, which groups are most vulnerable, and PHE offers training in administering the vaccines. In the winter of 2015, PHE raised awareness of the increased incidence of scarlet fever and the likelihood of an outbreak among children. PHE published information about symptoms, diagnosis, management and epidemiology of scarlet fever (scarletina) and the management of it in schools and nurseries.

Specific programmes for health protection

There is overlap between the Department of Health, Public Health England and NHS England, however, Public Health provides immunisation, health and genetic screening programmes. It offers information for immunisation practitioners and other health professionals about immunisation programmes such as Childhood immunisation schedules for diphtheria, tetanus, pertussis (whooping cough), polio and Haemophilus influenza type b (Hib) Pneumococcal, Meningococcal group B and Rotavirus gastroenteritis.

PHE health screening programmes include the NHS diabetic eye screening (DES) programme, and the NHS breast screening (BSP) programme.

PHE genetic screening programmes include the NHS sickle cell and thalassaemia (SCT) screening programme, the NHS new-born blood spot (NBS) screening programme to identify rare conditions that can lead to serious illness, development problems and even death.

Activity

How have approaches to protecting public health and well-being been applied in reducing the spread of influenza? Look at what is being done nationally and locally.

Disease prevention and control methods

Prevention and control of communicable diseases

Public Health and the local authority website give advice on preventing the spread of communicable diseases which can be passed from one person to another. They give guidance on hygiene, BCG vaccination to protect against tuberculosis, and the use of antibiotics to prevent the spread of bacterial meningitis among other things. They also warn about the indiscriminate use of antibiotics which results in bacteria developing resistance to antibiotics.

	Year 1 target	Year 1 achievement
Reach (% of all mothers of children under 11 who had an opportunity to see the advertising campaign)	99%	99%
Awareness (% of all mothers with children under 11 who recalled seeing the Change4Life advertising)	82%	87%
Logo recognition (5 of all mothers with children under 11 who recognised the Change4Life logo)	44%	88%
Response to 'How are the kids?' (total number of questionnaires returned electronically, by post or from face-to-face marketing	100,000	346,609
Total responses (including website visits, telephone calls, returned questionnaires)	1,500,000	1,992,456
Sign-up (total number of families who joined Change4Life)	200,000	413,466
Sustained interest (total number of families who were proven to still be interacting with Change4Life six months after joining)	33,333	44,833

Source: Change4Life One Year On

Table 8.1 Change for Life: analysis of the data obtained during and after promotion to evaluate outcomes against original objectives

The influence of campaign focus, target audience and ethical considerations on chosen model

The Change4Life campaign aims at behaviour change and uses a stage model and the theory of planned behaviour model, attempting to change beliefs and behaviours.

- Reaching at-risk families.
- Helping families understand health consequences.
- Convincing parents that their children are at risk.
- Teaching behaviours to reduce risk.
- Inspiring people to believe they can do the behaviours.
- Creating desire to change.
- Triggering action.
- Supporting sustained change.

To reach the target audience it used the advertisements and also linked with partners in business and in schools to reinforce the message and to change norms. It used case studies to encourage people to believe that they too could change.

Currently it uses achievable targets such as 'From couch to 5K' to motivate desired behaviours. The chosen model fits well with the target audience, campaign focus and ethical considerations.

Source: www.nhs.uk/change4life

Activity

Choose one current health campaign. How does it

- relate to health policy,
- explain the objectives.
- decide their target audience.
- justify the chosen approach
- consider ethics.

Barriers to participation and challenging indifference

There are several barriers that prevent people participating in health campaigns.

Cost

The cost of transport may put people off attending health services and treatments. If they have to pay three or more pounds to get to the hospital, they may not attend a diabetic clinic or chiropody appointment. The cost of gym membership or swimming sessions might be too much for those with children. People on a limited income may not be able to afford the cost of nutritional food and instead eat cheap food which tends to be high in fats and carbohydrates. A bag of chips may be cheaper than fresh fruit, vegetables and pasta, especially as there are no costs for cooking chips.

Individual resistance

For example, where someone refuses to give up an unhealthy lifestyle because people think that illness will not happen to them. They do not see the need to stop smoking/ get fit/ reduce alcohol intake/ lose weight. Sometimes they are indifferent, not caring what happens to them because they feel they have nothing much to live for.

Accessibility

Resources can be a problem. There may not be a swimming pool or gym near-by, or getting to one may be difficult. They may have mobility issues and find it difficult to access transport.

Lifestyle

Factors such as an unhealthy diet, lack of exercise and smoking may be linked to work patterns. Someone who works long hours at a stressful desk bound job may grab a sandwich while working through their lunch break. Some people smoke to reduce stress. Such lifestyle factors, if continued, lead to cardiovascular problems including heart attack.

The media can focus too much on an issue. Over-exposure can lead to public indifference, for example, warning about drinking and driving every Christmas can be ignored. Inaccurate reporting can discourage participation, for example, changing advice about the safe limit of units of alcohol can make people unsure what advice is correct.

Activity

Choose a current health campaign. What barriers may stop people from participating in the campaign?

Models and theories that justify health behaviour change

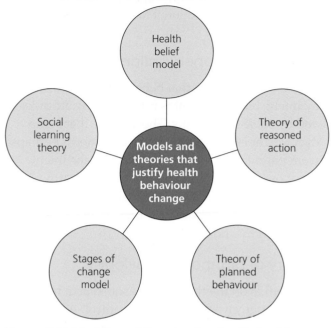

Figure 8.12 Models and theories that justify health behaviour change

Health belief model (HBM)

This model is based on the following.

- Perceived susceptibility: a person's perception that the health problem is personally relevant and a diagnosis of illness is accurate.
- Perceived severity: the individual only acts when they perceive the severity to be high enough to have serious consequences.
- Perceived benefits: the patient's belief that treatment will cure the illness or help to prevent it.
- Perceived costs: if the person thinks action is too complicated, takes too long, or is not accessible they will not comply
- Motivation: the desire to comply with a treatment.

Modifying factors: include personality variables, patient satisfaction, and socio-demographic factors such as cultural values like being fat is healthy.

Weaknesses of the model – it assumes people are rational; it ignores socio-economic factors such as the cost of joining a gym or the cultural acceptability of women being outside the home or women working long hours. It fails to recognise emotional factors such as fear of change.

Theory of reasoned action

This theory suggests that behaviour is preceded by intent, but that intent is influenced by attitudes and by subjective norms. The attitude that being overweight is OK, and the subjective norm perhaps from parental pressure to eat, leads to the intent to eat one more biscuit and the action of eating a packet of them. It follows from this that any action towards healthy eating must first change attitudes and subjective norms.

Theory of planned behaviour

This builds on the theory of reasoned action but includes perceived behavioural control. Attitude plus subjective norm plus behavioural control affect intent which in turn affects behaviour BUT behavioural control intervenes and decides the behaviour.

The attitude that being overweight is ok, and the subjective norm that eating is good, leads to the intent to eat only one more biscuit. This time, behavioural control comes in and helps the individual resist temptation. Behavioural control is linked to the idea of self-efficacy – the confidence in one's ability to do something.

Stages of change model

The stages are:

- Pre-contemplation – before considering change
- Contemplation – considering change
- Preparation – planning and envisioning change
- Action – making the change
- Maintenance
- Relapse
- Pre-contemplation and so on, in a repeating spiral, learning from each attempt.

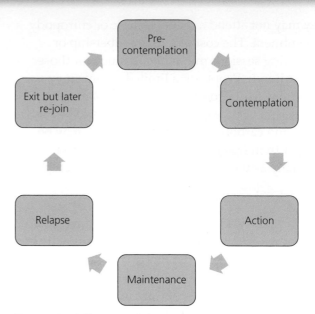

Figure 8.13 Stages of change

Social learning theory

According to Bandura, we learn by observing others. Learning is a cognitive process that takes place in a social context and can occur purely through observation or direct instruction.

Activity D P7

Look at the health campaign you chose earlier.

Explain how models, or theories, that justify behaviour change can be used to overcome barriers in relation to that health promotion campaign.

Approaches to increasing public awareness of health promotion

Increasing public awareness is essential if a health campaign is to be effective. There are various approaches to raise awareness of health promotion.

Health education activities

Health education activities, especially those targeted at young people in school or college can be effective if supported by action. It is no good teaching young people about a healthy diet and then making chips the cheapest option on the menu. Healthy eating campaigns such as the Five a Day rule for fruit and vegetables, and the 2014 government standards for school lunches which limit fried and batter coated food are one way to improve the nutritional standard of young people.

Social marketing approach

A social marketing approach such as the Change4Life programme examined earlier, looks at the marketing mix of a product or service, place, promotion and price. The product was a healthy lifestyle. A key issue was to reach families with young children, promoting it through the media they use, such as television. The price was free in terms of money but demanded some time and commitment. The benefits of social marketing are that it is targeted to a specific group rather than a broad approach, and it uses an approach that many find appealing. Limitations are that it is expensive and requires a lot of organisation to co-ordinate all those who could contribute.

The role of mass media

The role of mass media is seen as increasingly important in health promotion. Television adverts are targeted at specific groups and shown between programmes they watch. Social media such as Facebook and Twitter are used for health promotion campaigns. #StayWellThisWinter campaign is used on Twitter. Brook Manchester, a charity that provides free and confidential sexual health services and advice for young people under 25, worked with Salford University as part of a campaign to reduce Manchester's high youth pregnancy rates. They used a mobile phone app to show young men how to use a condom. They also used a focused mixed media campaign with the Lesbian and Gay Foundation to encourage people to have cervical screening. One advantage of social media is that it is relatively cheap but the disadvantages are that it can be difficult to assess its effectiveness and it may not be equally accessible to all.

Community development approach

A community development approach is holistic, encouraging community participation, and empowerment. Moseley Community Alcohol Partnership was set up by local people in Moseley Birmingham to tackle the problem of street drinking, aggressive begging and anti-social

behaviour. An Injunction Order was obtained under Section 222 of the Local Government Act 1972. Anyone found to be breaching the order was reported and an individual package of support organised for them. This might include counselling, referral to agencies who support those with drug or alcohol misuse, help with benefit advice and even re-housing. The police, fire service, local housing associations, local councillors and specialist charities including the Big Issue supported local residents to make the area safer for all. An alternative giving scheme was set up so that local residents could, instead of giving money to street beggars, donate to the fund and those in need could apply for help to enable them to develop and sustain a settled lifestyle. The benefits of a community approach are that people feel ownership of such projects and the projects can be tailored to meet local needs. Limitations are that many such projects rely on key individuals to sustain the momentum and funding may be restricted to one-off grants.

Two-way communication

This is effective in health promotion in health and social care settings, and one way communication can turn people off. Two way communication is used by peer educators, and peer mentors. Interactive theatre and drama that deals with problems of bullying can be effective. Interactive video and computer packages are effective for learning about sexual health, and they also improve self-efficacy, intention and sexual behaviour, but there is not enough evidence yet to show whether they reduce sexually transmitted infections and pregnancy.

National campaigns

National campaigns can tackle national health issues. Currently heart disease is one of the main causes of death. Risks from heart disease can be reduced by increasing physical activity, having a healthy diet, and not smoking, which is why many health promotion campaigns focus on these areas.

Drink Wise

This campaign encourages safer drinking to reduce accidents and reduce the admission to hospital from alcohol poisoning. The reduction of teenage pregnancies and sexually transmitted diseases is also the focus of health promotion for young people.

Activity

Choose one specific health campaign that encourages behaviour change. How successful has it been?

Distinction activity D P7

Explain factors affecting current patterns of health and ill-health in a specific demographic area.

You may wish to look at a campaign directed at sexual health of young people, or alcohol consumption and young people, or obesity in children.

Check your understanding

1 What are the features of health promotion campaigns?
2 What barriers may prevent people responding to health campaigns?
3 Explain:
   (a) health belief model
   (b) theory of reasoned action
   (c) theory of planned behaviour
   (d) stages of change model
   (e) social learning theory
4 Describe three approaches to increasing public awareness of health promotion.

Case scenario

Katy and her friends are celebrating her eighteenth birthday. Health promotion is the last thing they want to think about. What aspects of health promotion might be relevant to her and her friends and which ways are better suited to getting her age group to celebrate safely?

Think about it

According to the Nuffield Trust report 'Alcohol-specific activity in hospitals in England', from 2008/09 to 2013/14, A&E attendance rates likely to be due to alcohol poisoning doubled, yet one in four hospitals do not have an alcohol service available. Cut backs to local public health budgets in England mean less money is available for health promotion and those at risk of becoming alcoholic may not be referred for treatment. What impact might this have on their life expectancy?

Further reading

Marmot M., (2015) *The Health Gap: The Challenge of an Unequal World*, Bloomsbury Publishing

Marmot M., (2015) *Status Syndrome: How Your Place on the Social Gradient Directly Affects Your Health*, Bloomsbury Publishing

Naidoo J. and Wills J., (2016) *Foundations for Health Promotion, Fourth edition*, Bailliere Tindall

Useful websites

Birmingham Public Health: www.birminghampublichealth.co.uk

'Understanding the impact of particulate air pollution' (3 November 2015): https://publichealthmatters. blog.gov.uk/2015/11/03/understanding-the-impact-of-particulate-air-pollution/

Action on Smoking and Health: www.ash.org.uk

Recycling and Public Health (2009) – an evidence report by M. Lyons, P. Luria and J. Harris, Liverpool John Moores University: www.cph.org.uk/publication/recycling-and-public-health/

Food Standards Agency: www.food.gov.uk

Acheson D, Independent Inquiry into Inequalities in Health Report, London: HMSO, 1998; Black D, Morris J, Smith C, Townsend P. Inequalities in health: report of a Research Working Group. London: Department of Health and Social Security, 1980; Annual review of tuberculosis in London 2014; all available from: www gov.uk

Public Health England website: www.phe.gov.uk

Moseley Community Alcohol Partnership: www.moseleycap.co.uk

Newham Health and Well-being Strategy: www.newham.gov.uk

Health Profile 2015 Newham and updated Newham Key Facts document (October 2015): www.newham.info

Change4Life campaign: www.nhs.uk/change4life

Health inequalities and population health, NICE advice [LGB4] October 2012: www.nice.org.uk

Alcohol-specific activity in hospitals in England, Research report (December 2015): www.nuffieldtrust.org.uk

Office for National Statistics: www.ons.gov.uk

Cochrane Review: Interactive computer-based interventions for sexual health promotion: www.researchgate.net

'Campaigns in rude health thanks to social media', *Research Perspectives* magazine Vol.1 Issue 1: www. salford.ac.uk/research/perspectives-magazine/volume-1/issue-1/campaigns-in-rude-health-thanks-to-social-media

World Health Organisation: www.who.int

9 Infection prevention and control

About this unit

Everyone working in health and social care has a role in minimising the possible transmission of infections. People who use our services are vulnerable and it is important to ensure that their health status is not further affected when using health and social care services. This unit will explore the causes and transmission of infection, how these can be prevented and controlled. It will develop knowledge of policies and procedures, legislations and policies that apply to health and social care settings. The roles and responsibilities of employees and organisations will be examined.

Learning aims

The aims of this unit are to:

A Understand the causes of infections and transmission of infection.

B Explore how to prevent and control the transmission of infection in health and social care settings.

C Investigate roles and responsibilities of health and social care organisations and workers in preventing and controlling infections.

How will I be assessed?

For learning aim A, it is recommended that a report is produced exploring how infections occur and how they are transmitted.

For learning aim B, a practical demonstration of following infection control and decontamination procedures along with a reflective account is advised.

For learning aim C, a report based on a real health and social care setting explaining the procedures in place to minimise infection and the roles and responsibilities of the setting and workers in minimising infection is recommended. This could be a work placement.

How will I be graded?

Pass	Merit	Distinction
Learning aim A: Understand the causes of infections and the transmission of infection.		
A P1 Explain the causes of different infections and the diseases that can result from them. **A P2** Explain how these diseases can be transmitted and contracted.	**A M1** Assess how the transmission and contraction of infectious diseases can be influenced by different factors.	**A D1** Analyse potential ways in which infections are caused, transmitted and disease is contracted.
Learning aim B: Explore how to prevent and control the transmission of infection in health and social care settings.		
B P3 Demonstrate the correct use of standard procedures to prevent infection in a health or social care setting. **B P4** Demonstrate correct decontamination techniques in a health or social care setting. **B P5** Review how successful use of own techniques prevented and controlled infection.	**B M2** Demonstrate the correct use of procedures to prevent and control infection, adapting them for different situations.	**B D2** Justify the procedures and techniques selected and adapted to prevent and control infection with reference to the different situations.

How will I be graded?

Pass	Merit	Distinction
Learning aim C: Investigate the roles and responsibilities of health and social care organisations and workers in preventing and controlling infections.		
C P6 Explain how organisational policies and procedures apply legislation to prevent the transmission of different infections in a named health or social care organisation. **C P7** Discuss the roles and responsibilities of different health and social care workers in preventing and controlling infection in a named health or social care organisation.	**C M3** Analyse how, by implementing and following infection control policies and procedures, the health or social care organisation and workers help to prevent the transmission of infection.	**C D3** Evaluate how procedures and workers' roles and responsibilities in a named health or social care organisation successfully prevent and control the transmission of infection.

A Understand the causes of infections and the transmission of infection **A P1** , **A P2** , **A M1** , **A D1**

There are many different causes of infections and disease that may result. This section will examine causes of some diseases along with ways in which these can be transmitted.

Causes of infection

Agents of infection

An agent of infection is the micro-organism that can cause infection.

Bacteria

Bacteria are commonly found within the body and the environment. If it is a bacterium that causes infection, it is known as 'pathogenic'. Bacteria are one cell and can multiply by dividing themselves. This is known as binary fusion. Bacteria do not have a nucleus like most cells. Some bacteria cells have a flagellum which helps the bacteria move.

Viruses

Viruses are incredibly small and only visible under an electron microscope. They can only replicate within another cell such as a human cell. Once inside the cell (known as a host cell), they damage the cell and make copies of the viruses. Once the host cell is open, the viruses exit the cell and pass around the body. Viruses do not survive for very long outside of the body.

Parasites

Parasites are organisms that live on their hosts and are dependent upon them for food. They are often associated with tropical diseases, but there are examples of parasites outside tropical areas. Pathogens are spread via a host organism or 'vector'. An example is malaria, a parasite that is hosted on mosquitoes. If an infected mosquito bites a person, the parasite is transmitted to them. The mosquito is the **vector** and the malaria is the **parasite**. (In humans, the malaria parasite can cause malaria disease.)

Fungi

Fungi are parasitic on humans. These are opportunistic infectious agents that can grow in dead keratin cells of the skin. Single cell microbes reproduce in a similar way to bacteria called budding.

Protozoa

Protozoa are single cell animals and are a major public health issue in some parts of the world. The life cycle of each protozoon varies, but the majority are parasitic.

Reservoirs of infection

Reservoirs of infection is the source of where micro-organisms can be found. Organisms causing disease may be found in humans, the environment, or spores and cysts. Human contact could include other people that you may come into contact with who had the disease. Human reservoirs may have symptoms of the infection, but can also be asymptomatic (showing no symptoms). Bacteria can remain and be transmitted as spores in situations such as lack of moisture, or heat. The bacterium remains alive, but inert. Cysts are common and often seen as a sac like structure. They can be caused by infection and as a result may appear red, inflamed or have pus coming from them. The environment includes anything the organism may have come into contact with. Door handles, bedding, stethoscopes and clothing such as neckties are examples.

A carrier of infection is a person or organism that is infected with the agent but shows no symptoms. Water-borne diseases are diseases carried in water. They are transmitted when contaminated water is used, for example for drinking or for making ice cubes to chill drinks. Typhoid is an example of a water-borne disease. Disease can be transmitted via a vector such as insects, for example a tick. It may not be obvious that the vector has the disease until transmission. Humans can be carriers of infection and pass the infection onto other people through contact. HIV for example is passed on through different means, most commonly through unprotected sex. Raw or infected food can carry diseases like salmonella or listeria. Through eating these, the infection is passed on.

Symptoms of diseases

Table 9.1 summarises types of, and signs and symptoms of infections.

Activity A P1

Create a fact file to explain the different causes of infections that result in diseases.

Collect information and pictures.

Identify some extra resources that you can use to help write your assignment task.

Types of infection and resulting diseases

Systematic infection and localised infection

When an individual experiences an infection, the body's immune response will be activated. There are two types of infection.

- 'A systemic' infection means one affecting the entire body. Symptoms will often be a temperature and aches. Influenza (flu) is one example.

- 'A localised' infection will affect only one part of the body. They will often be inflammation symptoms such as redness or swelling. An example of this would be an infected wound.

Micro-organism	Disease	Signs and symptoms
Fungi	Athlete's foot **Figure 9.1**	Fungus that usually appears between the toes or on the bottom of the feet. Can also affect toenails. Skin may be dry, red, scaly and flaky or white, soggy and cracked. It will be itchy
	Ringworm **Figure 9.2**	The most common affected areas are the arms and legs. It appears like a ring-like patch of skin that is either red or silvery. It can also be inflamed and itchy. The ring spreads outwards as it progresses. It is nothing to do with worms!

Micro-organism	Disease	Signs and symptoms
Viruses	Influenza (flu)	Pyrexia (high temperature), weakness and exhaustion, chills, aches and pains, cough. Loss of appetite. Symptoms will come on quickly and will include a fever as well as muscles that ache. The person will feel unwell.
	Common cold	Mild infection of nose, throat, upper airway. Individual will have sore throat, blocked or runny nose, sneezes and a cough. Symptoms come on gradually and will not be as severe as influenza.
	Norovirus	Most common stomach bug. Causes watery diarrhoea and a sudden feeling of being sick along with projectile vomiting.
	HIV	A virus that attacks and weakens the immune system. Most people will experience a short illness that occurs two to six weeks after infection. After that, no symptoms may occur for several years.
	Hepatitis B	A virus that affects the liver. Symptoms include nausea and vomiting, diarrhoea, lack of appetite, jaundice (see Figure 9.6) and flu-like symptoms.
	Poliomyelitis	A virus that invades the nervous system, causing total paralysis very quickly. Initial symptoms include fever, headache, vomiting, neck stiffness and pain in the limbs. Most countries are not polio-endemic.
Bacteria	MRSA (Methicillin-resistant *Staphylococcus aureus*) Figure 9.3	A bacteria that is resistant to many antibiotics. A common type of bacteria that is carried on the skin, if it is able to enter the body, it can cause blood poisoning. Symptoms include redness, swelling, pain, and a feeling of being unwell.
	Tetanus	Bacteria enters a wound and affects the nerves. Symptoms include stiffness in jaw muscles (lockjaw – see Figure 9.7), fever, sweating and rapid heartbeat.
	Legionnaires' disease	A lung infection causing flu-like symptoms such as muscle pain, high temperature, chills and confusion. Once in the lungs, it can cause a cough, shortness of breath and chest pains.
	Tuberculosis	A serious condition that affects the lungs. Symptoms include a persistent cough which brings up phlegm, weight loss, night sweats, high temperature, tiredness and fatigue.
	Cholera	A potentially fatal infection caused by consuming contaminated food or water. Symptoms include severe diarrhoea, cramps, nausea and vomiting.
	Salmonellosis	Can cause food poisoning. Symptoms include diarrhoea, stomach cramps, vomiting and fever.

Micro-organism	Disease	Signs and symptoms
Vector-borne	Malaria	A serious disease spread by mosquitoes. Symptoms include high temperature, headaches, vomiting, muscle pains and diarrhoea.
	Lyme disease 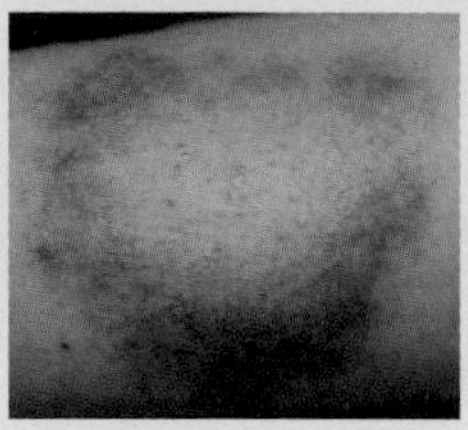  **Figure 9.4**	A bacterial infection spread to humans through ticks. A circular rash shaped like a 'bulls eye' on a dart board appears at the site of the tick bite, the skin will be red. Later symptoms can include pain and swelling in the joints, nervous system problems and heart problems.

Table 9.1 Infections

Figure 9.5 Symptoms of influenza are more severe than those of the common cold

Figure 9.6 Jaundice (a symptom of Hepatitis B)

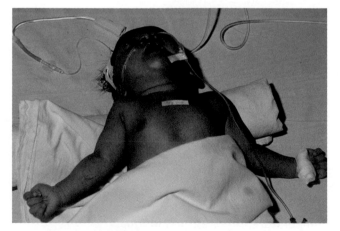

Figure 9.7 Lockjaw (a symptom of tetanus)

Activity A2 P2

Make a poster to explain how the diseases we've discussed can be transmitted and contracted.

Ways infections are transmitted

Conditions needed for growth of micro-organisms

Certain conditions are needed for micro-organisms to grow. Micro-organisms feed on protein and carbohydrates, warmth can depend on the microbe. Some grow at low temperatures and others at high temperatures. Some micro-organisms such as bacteria grow rapidly in warm conditions, between the two extremes of non-activity for a low temperature and death caused by high temperatures. This ideal temperature is known as 'optimum'. Micro-organisms need water for growth. They cannot take in solids and so the nutrients frequently come from water solutions. This provides a source of energy for growth for the micro-organism.

Factors aiding transmission

Certain factors can help the transmission. Some people are more vulnerable or susceptible to particular infection. Ages such as children who are very young and have not built up their immune system or people who are older who may not have as an efficient immune system are more vulnerable. Poor nutrition is one of the most common causes of immunodeficiency and is critical to help the immune response. The immune system can also be affected by lifestyle choices such as stress. These can all assist with transmission of micro-organisms.

Environmental factors that affect the transmission of infections include: climate; the presence of organisms that can carry pathogens from one host to another (a 'vector presence'); sanitation; and pollution. For example, in the UK, ticks act as the vector for Lyme disease. The effect of the climate on infectious diseases is less obvious, but one example is heavy rain: this can cause flooding, leading to sewage overflow, which causes increased disease.

Social factors such as poverty and poor housing can greatly increase the chance of infectious disease spreading. Travel and migration can result in aiding transmission due to placing the individual at greater risk of acquiring infections. Typhoid for example is only present in some parts of the world such as the Indian subcontinent. Nutrition can affect the immune response and therefore make individuals more or less susceptible to infections.

How infective agents can be transmitted	Infectious agency
Food-borne – through poor cooking of food, or storing foods causing cross-contamination.	Salmonellosis (Salmonella) Norovirus
Water-borne – this can be through raw sewage contaminated drinking water.	Poliomyelitis Cholera

How infective agents can be transmitted	Infectious agency
Droplet infection can be transmitted through the air such as coughing; sneezing releases tiny droplets of water which the microns cling to.	Influenza, common cold, tuberculosis, Legionnaires' disease
Body fluids can pass on micro-organisms that can only live inside a body.	HIV Hepatitis B
Vector-borne diseases are organisms that spread disease from one individual to another by an animal or insect or anthropods. Anthropods are small animals that have an external skeleton. The most common anthropods are ticks, mosquitoes and lice.	Malaria Lyme disease

Table 9.2 How infective agents can be transmitted and enter the body

Activity A M1

Assess how different factors affect the transmission and contraction of diseases.

Distinction activity A D1

Remind yourself of what the command word 'analyse' means.

Analyse the ways in which infections are caused and transmitted, and disease contracted.

Check your understanding

1 Identify four causes of infections.
2 Identify four diseases that can result from each cause identified in 1.
3 Explain two ways in which disease can be transmitted and contracted.
4 Identify two factors that can influence the transmission of disease.

B Explore how to prevent and control the transmission of infection in health and social care settings

The prevention and control of transmission of infection is fundamental and can take many different forms.

The use of standard procedures to prevent and control the transmission of infection in health and social care settings

Cleanliness

Hand washing

People's hands are the most common way in which micro-organisms spread and therefore the most important step in preventing the spread of infections. The World Health Organisation has identified five crucially important times for hand hygiene. These are before and after touching a patient, before a clean or aseptic procedure, after body fluid exposure risk and after touching patient surroundings. This aims to ensure that hand hygiene is performed at required moments within the flow of care. An effective hand hygiene technique is essential to ensure that hands are washed correctly, as there are common areas that are missed. The procedure shown in Figure 9.8 illustrates how to carry out this technique. It is commonly displayed in health and social care settings as a reminder to staff. In health and social care settings, staff should always set a good example to those around them, by washing hands effectively and regularly.

Antiseptic hand gels

Hand gels have some advantages as they take less time to use than hand washing, can be more accessible and cause less skin irritation. Hand gels are effective for disinfecting hands, but soap and water should always be used when hands are visibly soiled, if there is an outbreak of norovirus or clostridium difficile spores or if a patient is experiencing vomiting and or diarrhoea as hand gel will not be as effective. Care should always be taken to ensure all areas of the hand are cleaned in the same way as shown in Figure 9.8 and given time to dry naturally.

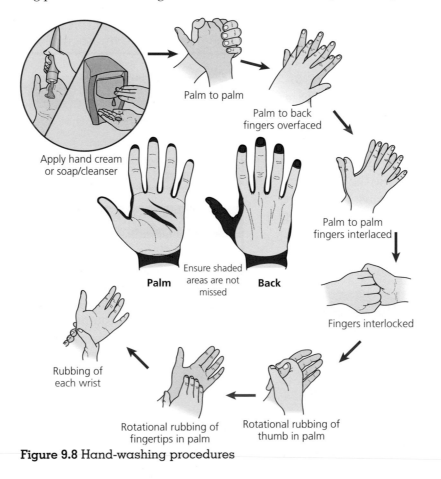

Apply hand cream or soap/cleanser

Palm to palm

Palm to back fingers overfaced

Palm to palm fingers interlaced

Fingers interlocked

Palm Ensure shaded areas are not missed **Back**

Rotational rubbing of thumb in palm

Rotational rubbing of fingertips in palm

Rubbing of each wrist

Figure 9.8 Hand-washing procedures

Washing facilities

Appropriate washing facilities should be available in every setting. This includes somewhere to wash hands, separate facility for clinical related duties and food.

Maintaining a clean environment

A clean and safe environment is essential for infection prevention and control and a key priority for the NHS. Hospitals and other care settings need to ensure they can also demonstrate how they are being kept clean and the standards that they keep. Cleaning services should also be available as and when required.

Maintaining equipment

Health and Social Care Settings such as hospitals have a range of equipment both for clinical and non-clinical purposes. The responsibility for this can vary, but it is important that all items are cleaned on a regular basis and not forgotten about.

Food handling procedures

Food has potential to be a source of infectious disease and therefore care must be taken to ensure safe practices. There is potential for infection during preparation, serving and storage. Before preparing food, hands should always be washed and clean clothes worn. If a worker has been unwell with diarrhoea and vomiting then they must not work with food. Raw food should be kept away from any ready-to-eat foods such as bread or fruit. Different chopping boards should be used to prevent cross-contamination between food products. When cooking foods, the right temperature must be used to ensure that any harmful bacteria are killed. Foods such as poultry, pork and burgers must be cooked thoroughly before eating. When serving foods, hot food should be kept hot and cold food cold. If food is not going to be eaten immediately it should be cooled at room temperature (ideally within 90 minutes) and stored in the fridge (NHS 2014). A 'use by date' indicates that a food goes off quickly and it can be dangerous to eat after this date. A 'best before date' is generally for food that is longer-lasting. It is generally safe to eat after this time, but may not be at its best quality.

When storing foods in a fridge or freezer, a fridge should be below 5°C. Food in a freezer should be kept below −18°C. Raw meat and poultry should be kept in clean, sealed containers so they do not touch or drip onto other food. This is another source of cross-contamination.

Correct handling and disposal of waste

Spillages should always be promptly cleared up, using appropriate equipment following the procedures of the setting. This may include specific coloured mops or cleaning products. Waste should always be disposed following the workplace policy. Waste management is crucial within health and social care settings to ensure infection control is well managed. Care should always be taken to ensure that bags are not overfilled and not more than two thirds full. They should be tied securely.

Waste colour codes

Although this can vary between organisations, a use of a colour coding system enables everyone to be aware of the hazards presented by the waste.

YELLOW: infectious waste which requires disposal by incineration.

ORANGE: Infectious waste which may be treated to make sure it's safe prior to disposal or incineration.

PURPLE: Cytotoxic waste. This must be incinerated in a licensed facility.

YELLOW and BLACK: Offensive hygiene waste and may be landfilled in licensed sites.

BLACK: Domestic waste which does not contain sharps, medicinal waste or infectious materials.

Soiled laundry management

Laundry is a potential hazard as linen can be a source of transfer of micro-organisms. The main hazards are body fluids, needles or scissors or other sharps, infectious micro-organisms and parasite infections. Safe working methods when handling laundry include the use of PPE (see below), linen should never be placed on the floor or shaken into the environment and linen should not be changed at the same time as wound dressing. Soiled laundry should be placed in an appropriate bag (many settings use special bags that can be placed directly

Type of waste	Examples	How to handle	How to dispose
Household waste	Cardboard Broken furniture Confidential waste	Ensure own safety. Take care to not leave accessible to others.	Recycle when appropriate Landfill Shredded
Sharps; needles or scissors	Sharps injury Risk of cross infection	Do not carry sharps across settings. Wear gloves	In sharps bin. This should be near where the sharp is. Many settings have small portable bins that can be brought to the patient or service user's bed side. The sharps bin will be incinerated
Clinical waste	Infectious waste Cytotoxic and cytotoxic waste Medicines other than cytotoxic	Disposable gloves and apron	Orange bag Licensed or permitted treatment facility Incineration Incineration
Biological spillages	Micro-organisms, chemicals	Depends on type. PPE including gloves, aprons and possibly shoe covers and eye wear and mask	Depends on type of spillage Treatment facility or incineration

Table 9.3 Types of waste

into the washing machine, avoiding contact) and removed from the clinical area. The public should not be able to access the laundry storage area and the area should be kept dry.

Use of personal protective equipment (PPE)
Personal protective equipment (PPE) helps protect health and social care workers from infectious agents and can help stop the spread of disease. Gloves (powder free) along with non-latex alternatives, aprons or gowns, eye and mouth protection (such as masks, goggles and face shields) are all examples used within health and social care settings. The level of protection required will depend upon the risk of infection. Gloves should be used when there is the potential for exposure to blood or bodily fluids, or when there is potential for contact with non-intact skin, mucous membranes or invasive procedures. Aprons should be used when it is anticipated that clothing may come into close contact with micro-organisms, or blood and body fluids. Facemasks can prevent airborne respiratory particles entering the body and eyewear can offer some protection against physical splashing of infected substances into the eyes.

All of these examples can protect the skin, mouth and eyes from contamination or spoiling/splashing and therefore exposure to micro-organisms. Efficient and effective hand hygiene is still required, and after use, the PPE must be disposed of safely and properly. PPE should be changed between patients even if two patients have the same infectious condition. The PPE should be removed without touching it with bare hands. The first glove can be pulled off inside out and the second can be removed by slipping the thumb of the ungloved hand inside the wrist of the glove and pulling it off while turning it inside out. Gloves should then be disposed of in the clinical waste bin. Aprons should be removed without touching the middle of the apron.

Decontamination techniques

Following organisational policy on decontamination

Decontamination means removing unwanted substances, which include micro-organisms (as well as dirt or dust). Following organisational policy on decontamination is essential to ensure that health care workers are carrying out decontamination correctly. Failure to do so can increase the risk of hospital-acquired infections, cross-contamination or injury through poor use to staff or patients / service users.

Role of PPE

The use of personal protective equipment is important throughout this process. PPE helps prevent the spread of micro-organisms to, from and between patients or service users, and protects care staff, their clothes or uniforms. The use of PPE such as disposable gloves and disposable aprons creates a barrier to protect skin or clothing from contact. As decontamination uses hazardous substances, PPE can protect the skin from these as well.

The three-step decontamination process and its importance

A clean environment is important in a health care setting. It will assist in preventing dust and dirt build-up which can increase the risk of infection. Decontamination is a combination of processes to remove or destroy organisms to prevent the spread of disease.

There are three steps of decontamination: cleaning, disinfection and sterilisation. The level of risk for an item a patient or service user comes into contact with determines the level of safety procedures required. If an item is likely to have come into contact with blood or bodily fluids, such as surgical equipment, a higher level of cleaning is required as these have a higher risk of infection.

Contamination risks

Contamination risks:

- low risk, e.g. floors, furniture, mobility aids
- medium risk, e.g. bedpans, urinals, commodes
- high risk, e.g. instruments used for invasive techniques.

Activity B P3 B P4

Review the hand washing and decontamination techniques and use of standard procedures to prevent infection. Practise these for different scenarios. With a friend, observe each other's practice and provide some peer feedback.

Step	Function	What items?
Cleaning	Significantly reduces number of micro-organisms and debris where they may live. Necessary before sterilisation or disinfection.	Low-risk items such as floors, furniture. Used on re-useable medical instruments before they are sterilised..
Disinfection	Only carried out after initial clean has taken place. Stronger than cleaning for reducing the number of micro-organisms. May not eradicate some viruses and bacterial spores.	Medium-risk items such as bedpans, commodes, dressing trolleys, sinks.
Sterilisation	Only carried out after initial clean. Renders an object free from micro-organisms including spores and viruses. Items must be not be left exposed as this can causes re-contamination.	High-risk items such as surgical instruments or babies feeding equipment.

Table 9.4 The three steps of decontamination

Check your understanding

1 Demonstrate the hand-washing techniques shown in Figure 9.8. Why is each step required?
2 Identify one way of handling food correctly when preparing, cooking and serving food.
3 Name two items of PPE and describe how they would be used and disposed of safely.
4 What is the difference between cleaning, disinfection and sterilisation?
5 Identify one item of contamination risk in each of these categories: low, medium and high risk.

Activity B M2

Describe the correct use of procedures to prevent and control infection, adapting them for different situations. For assessment you will need to be able to demonstrate this.

In placement identify waste that is generated and how this is disposed of, along with policies and procedures in place. Compare this with a friend who is in a different setting.

How are they similar? How are they different?

Distinction activity

Make a list of all the procedures and techniques used for infection control. Find clinical evidence to explain why these are important and how they help reduce the spread of infection.

C Investigate the roles and responsibilities of health and social care organisations and workers in preventing and controlling infections

Organisational policies and procedures to minimise infections in health and social care settings

Everyone who works in health and social care settings have roles and responsibilities to prevent and control infections. Visitors, patients or service users also have a role to play.

Legislation	How it applies to infection control
Health and Safety at Work Act 1974	Covers a wide range of health and safety issues and gives all employees and employers responsibility for health and safety.
Health and Social Care Act 2008 Updated July 2015	Code of practice on the prevention and control of infections.
The Personal Protective Equipment at Work Regulations 2002	Requires employers and managers to supply their employees with PPE.
Control of Substances Hazardous to Health Regulations (COSHH) 2002	Employers have the responsibility to control exposure to hazardous substances.
Hazardous Waste Regulations 2005	Employers that reduce waste have a duty to ensure that it does not harm the public.
Environmental Protection Regulations 2011	Requires that waste is disposed of correctly.
Reporting of Injuries, Diseases and Dangerous Occurrences Regulations (RIDDOR) 2013	Exposure to infections acquired at work are reportable (disease that can be caught in the community are not reportable). A health care worker that has had a needle stick injury from a patient with hepatitis would be reportable, for example.

Table 9.5 Some infection prevention and control legislation

Impact of relevant legislation on organisational policies and procedures

A number of legislations apply to infection prevention and control, some are summarised in Table 9.5. These are important as they provide rules that organisations must follow. Settings will put policies into place to provide guidance to employees. By having legislation, compliance can be monitored and actions taken against companies that do not abide by the regulations.

Roles of organisations in preventing and controlling infections

All organisations have a role in preventing and controlling infections. Workers should have a thorough induction and training in methods to prevent cross contamination, and then re-training to ensure methods used are still correct. The employers have a duty to provide the correct equipment including personal protective equipment such as aprons, gloves, eye protection or masks. These should fit the worker and training should be

provided on use. All settings should have a policy on decontamination which should be accessible to all staff. It should be reviewed at regular intervals and reflect national guidance, best practice, legislation and regulation.

Ensuring policies and procedures are in place

All organisations should have policies and procedures and Figure 9.9 covers some of the policies and procedures that should be in place in your setting. These provide guidance to staff about how to work in situations. Some reflect legal responsibilities. All will help prevent cross-infection and promote the safety and well-being of all staff and patients and visitors.

Activity

In your work placement, identify all policies and procedures that link to infection control.

Write a summary of each and link this to legislation.

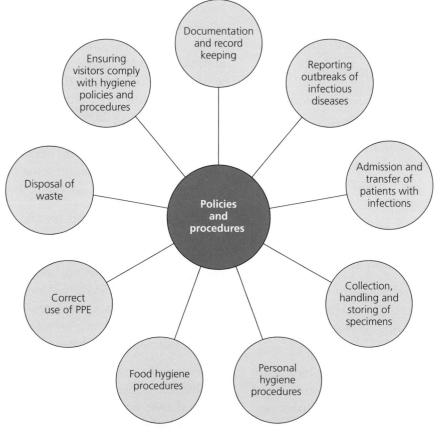

Figure 9.9 Policies and procedures

Roles and responsibilities of health and social care workers

Roles

Everyone who works with people in health and social care are involved in infection control. Formal and informal carers have frequent direct patient contact. They should ensure they maintain a high level of personal hygiene, and wear and use and dispose of PPE correctly. There are some individuals who take a specialised role.

Infection Control Nurses have a specific role in helping prevent infections in hospitals and clinics. They train and support staff on proper infection control procedures, and monitor infections that may have arisen from care. They will create infection control plans and may be involved with reporting disease outbreaks.

Environmental Health Officers are responsible for making sure that living and working surroundings are safe. They will investigate health hazards and take required actions.

Health Protection Services such as Public Health England protects and promotes the health and well-being of the public. They advise the government and NHS and will prepare for public health emergencies.

Following policies and procedures

Health and social care workers have a responsibility to follow all policies and procedures.

Cleaning and clearing service areas according to a schedule. This may include what items and services are to be cleaned, how often, what chemicals and what safety precautions should be taken.

Decontamination ensures that systems are in place for decontamination of equipment before and between each patient to minimise risks.

Record keeping is a legal requirement for health and social care professionals. It will show the measures taken to prevent and reduce infections.

Some diseases are reportable under RIDDOR. Injuries that are caused through a work practice are reportable. A disease, such as a nurse contracting TB after caring for a patient with the condition, is reportable. A near accident which may not have resulted in a reportable injury, but has potential to cause harm, such as a needle stick injury from a contaminated needle is reportable. There is a requirement for notification of infectious disease to be made under the Health Protection (Notification) Regulations 2010. Examples include whooping cough, malaria, measles and rubella.

Food preparation, storing and serving correctly will include ensuring the correct temperature of food items and storage facilities (see page 205). Nutrition is linked to a healthy immune system, so this is also a responsibility of the health and social care worker.

Some nutrients can be lost during the cooking process, especially vitamins and minerals. It is important to eat a range of fruit and vegetables. The eatwell guide highlights the different types of food and proportions. Once the health and social care worker is trained in procedures of food safety such as checking fridge temperatures daily or using specific utensils, these must be followed.

Each organisation will have its own dress code, with some organisations such as hospitals requiring uniforms to be worn. The main concern is infection prevention and control, and to enable effective hand hygiene which is crucial in helping to prevent infections. All clinical areas require staff to be 'bare below the elbow' so long-sleeved clothing such as jumpers or jackets are not allowed. Long nails and jewellery are forbidden as these can harbour bacteria. (A plain wedding band is permissible.) False nails and nail polish should not be worn. Footwear needs to be clean, in good repair and plain so it can be easily cleaned. Open-toed shoes do not protect the foot from injury. Clogs may be worn in some operating theatres, but should not be worn outside of these areas.

At patient admission, transfer and discharge infection control should be considered. If a patient is being admitted with an infection, then a care plan should be in place. On admission staff must take into consideration any infection control risk the patient or service user may present. They should check if the patient has a known infection and if so, refer to isolation procedures for guidance.

Screening often takes place for infections such as MRSA. On transfer either to another ward, or hospital, then again checks should be made as to whether the patient has any known infections. On discharge, staff have a duty to inform any carers of the risks posed if a patient has infections. On either transfer or discharge of a patient with a known infection, a thorough clean known as a 'terminal clean' should take place and the bed curtains changed.

Even after a person has died, there are still infection control issues. Although most micro-organisms are unlikely to infect healthy people, there are other ways of spreading infection such as from needle stick injuries or through abrasions, wounds and sores. Standard precautions such as hand hygiene and PPE should be used. To transfer the deceased person, a body bag may be used depending on the infection to prevent infection risk.

Taking specimens such as blood samples, urine and stool samples or wound swabs poses an increased risk of infection. Before and after taking any specimens, hands should be decontaminated thoroughly. Specimens should only be collected when there are clinical signs and symptoms, or at the request of a consultant, or member of the infection control team. They should only be taken by staff trained in the sample process. PPE should be worn and care taken to ensure that specimen containers are not being overfilled. Different containers will be used for different samples. Specimens should be stored according to the policy of the setting. The sample bottle should be checked to ensure that it is clearly and correctly labelled. Some specimens should be taken directly to the laboratory or collected as close to collection times as possible.

Urine samples can be taken as a MSU or a CSU. A MSU is a Midstream Specimen of Urine. The patient passes a small amount of urine before collecting the specimen. This is to reduce the risk of contamination from any naturally occurring micro-organisms in the urethra. The patient and, if they require assistance, the practitioner should wash their hands to prevent cross-infection. The area at the opening of the urethra should be cleaned. A CSU is a Catheter Specimen of Urine. Hands should be washed and sterile gloves worm to prevent cross-contamination. The port of the catheter should be decontaminated to prevent inaccurate results.

Faeces samples should be taken into a clean bedpan or receiver to prevent cross-infection and contamination. A faeces container has a built-in spoon which should be used to collect the sample. Samples should be sent to the lab as soon as possible, or refrigerated and sent within 12 hours. Samples should be sent immediately if the patient has repeated diarrhoea to determine if it is caused by C. difficile.

Blood samples should be taken after the area has been cleaned and always with a sterile needle. Different colour bottle tops will be used for testing of different samples. Volume of blood taken and the order in which they are collected will depend upon the specimens required. Blood cultures to determine infection are generally taken first to minimise the risk of contamination.

Vomit should be collected in sterile containers. If they cannot be sent to the lab straight away, they should be refrigerated or frozen. It may also be advisable to double bag such specimens.

Sputum samples are helpful to determine respiratory infections. Apron, gloves and eye protection should be worn. A physiotherapist can assist in obtaining the specimen. A clean container with a secure lid should be used to prevent contamination and it should be taken to the lab within 2 hours.

Wound swabs: When collecting a wound swab, an apron and gloves should be worn. A zig-zag motion while rotating the swab will enable sufficient quantity of sample to be taken to enable analysis. The wound swab should not be stored for too long as this can increase the likelihood of contamination. Wound swab containers come with a built in swab.

Visitors entering the care setting should also follow infection control procedures. Staff have a responsibility to encourage this process. This may include washing hands, not sitting on patients' beds and any PPE that may be required for patients in isolation such as masks or aprons.

Protection of service users

As well as preventing cross infection, service users are protected through both primary and secondary methods.

Primary methods include immunisation, prophylactic drugs, national health initiatives. Immunisations are routinely offered to everyone in the UK for free. Some examples are tetanus, measles, mumps and rubella. Some vaccines such as the influenza vaccine are offered to people in high risk groups such as older people or children. Prophylactic drugs are used as a preventative measure against disease. One example is medication taken to prevent malaria before, during and after travel. National Health Initiatives aim to prevent the spread of disease or promote good hygiene. The Catch it Kill it Bin it campaign encourages the public to adopt good hand hygiene practices.

Secondary procedures such as screening and microbiological examinations help protect service users and patients. Screening is a process of identifying people who appear healthy, but may be at risk of a disease. In pregnancy, women are commonly screened for HIV, hepatitis B, syphilis and rubella susceptibility. As part of infection control measures in hospital, patients are routinely screened for MRSA. Microbiological examinations involve the testing of blood and tissue samples (such as a swab of a wound) to identify outbreaks of infection so measures can be put in place to minimise and prevent risk. The screening process also helps to identify possible infections.

Activity C P7

In your work placement, discuss with members of staff the roles and responsibilities that each worker has in preventing and controlling infection. Why is each member of staff important?

Distinction activity C D3

Evaluate how procedures and workers' roles and responsibilities, in a named health or social care organisation, successfully prevent and control the transmission of infection.

Check your understanding

1 Name two policies and procedures commonly found in settings.
2 Name two individuals who may be involved in infection control and their role.
3 Describe the importance of hand hygiene.
4 State the three steps of the decontamination process.
5 Describe one primary and one secondary method of protecting service users.

Case scenario

Infection control

Florence has been admitted to a hospital ward with tuberculosis (TB). She is nursed in isolation in a negative pressure room. Each member of staff or visitor that comes to see Florence has to wear an apron, gloves and a mask. Florence is confused and frightened at her diagnosis. Some staff are reluctant to enter Florence's room as it takes them longer due to the PPE and are concerned they may catch TB.

How might Florence feel about staff coming in to her room with masks, gloves and gowns?

Why do you think some staff may be reluctant to help Florence?

How can Florence be reassured?

Think about it

Despite evidence about hand hygiene, it is an area commonly missed or carried out ineffectively by many people. Why do you think this may happen?

Further reading

Nursing Times

Royal Marsden clinical nursing procedures

Brooker C. & Nichol, M. (2006) Alexander's Nursing Practice, Churchill Livingstone, London

Weston D. (2013) Fundamentals of Infection Prevention and Control, Wiley-Blackwell

Wilson J. (2006) Infection Control in Clinical Practice, Bailliere Tindall

Useful websites

NHS Database of Conditions and Treatments: www.nhs.uk/Conditions/Pages/hub.aspx

Health and Safety Executive: www.hse.gov.uk

Food Standards Agency: www.food.gov.uk

12 Supporting individuals with additional needs

About this unit

Some people are born with conditions that mean they will need lifelong support for daily living. Others are born with conditions that mean with the right support they can go on to live independently. Yet others through illness lose their independence and require support either on a long term or short term basis. It is important that we support all those with additional needs to lead as independent a life as possible, not just because care is expensive for the rest of society, but because it is an individual's right to make choices about their life. In this unit we will look at some of the reasons why a person may require support and how we can help them overcome problems in daily living. We will look at current practice and recent changes in state provision for children with additional needs and for adults with additional needs and how person centred care is put into practice.

Learning aims

The aims of this unit are to:

A Examine reasons why individuals may experience additional needs.

B Examine how to overcome the challenges to daily living faced by people with additional needs.

C Investigate current practice with respect to provision for individuals with additional needs.

How will I be assessed?

For learning aim A it is recommended by the awarding body that learners write a report that demonstrates a clear understanding of how additional needs are determined and diagnosed, with examples of the additional needs that individuals can experience.

For learning aims B and C it is recommended by the awarding body that learners write a report that demonstrates current practices and procedures for providing care for children and adults with additional needs, including the support given to overcome challenges to daily living.

How will I be graded?

Pass	Merit	Distinction
Learning aim A: Examine reasons why individuals may experience additional needs.		
A P1 Explain diagnostic procedures to determine additional needs for one child and one adult with different additional needs.	**A M1** Assess the requirements of one child and one adult with different additional needs.	**A D1** Evaluate the significance to the individuals, their families and society of a diagnosis of additional needs.

How will I be graded?

Pass	Merit	Distinction
Learning aim B: Examine how to overcome the challenges to daily living faced by individuals with additional needs		**B C D2** Justify the support and adaptations provided for two individuals with different additional needs to help them overcome challenges to daily living, with reference to statutory provision.
B P2 Explain how disability can be viewed as a social construct.	**B M2** Assess the impact of challenges to daily living that may be experienced by one child and one adult with different additional needs, and how effectively these challenges are overcome.	**B C D3** Evaluate the impact of providing support for two individuals diagnosed with different additional needs in improving their well-being and life chances.
B P3 Describe how health or social care workers can help one child and one adult with different additional needs overcome challenges to daily living.		
Learning aim C: Investigate current practice with respect to provision for individuals with additional needs.		
C P4 Explain the benefits of adaptations and support provided to one child and one adult with different additional needs.	**C M3** Analyse how the provision and support provided for one child and one adult with different additional needs have benefited them.	
C P5 Explain the impact of statutory provision on the support provided for one child and one adult with different additional needs.	**C M4** Analyse how statutory provision has impacted on current practice in caring for one child and one adult with different additional needs.	

A Examine reasons why individuals may experience additional needs **A P1**, **A M1**, **A D1**

Additional needs are wider than special educational needs. Additional needs may be long- or short-term and may be caused by the learning environment, family circumstances, disability and health, social and emotional factors. Additional support may be needed from health, social work or voluntary organisations as well as from education.

Special educational needs (SEN) affect a person's ability to learn. Special educational needs may be related to social behaviour for example, some children with autism find it difficult to make friends. Children may have dyslexia which affects their ability to read and write, or they may have Attention Deficit Hyperactivity Disorder and

short attention spans. They may have physical impairments, for example, some children with cerebral palsy have problems walking. They may also have problems understanding things.

Diagnosing or determining additional needs

Diagnosis of additional needs is usually done through neonatal screening programmes, the Healthy Child Programme, or through a specialist health and developmental assessment. CCGs, NHS Trusts, and NHS Foundation Trusts must inform the appropriate local authority if they identify a child under compulsory school age as having, or probably having, a disability or SEN (Section 23 of the Children and Families Act 2014). Under the Children and Families Act 2014, social services have a duty to assess children in need, including children with disabilities to identify the child's specific education and healthcare needs and draw up a plan for meeting these needs. MENCAP, the charity supporting people with learning disabilities, distinguishes between a learning disability, which may interfere with learning and everyday life, and a learning difficulty. MENCAP classify dyslexia as a learning difficulty because it does not affect intellect. Some very intelligent people are dyslexic. Similarly mental health problems such as depression do not reduce intellect but may cause learning difficulties.

Definitions of learning disability used to be based on intelligence tests, but it is now recognised that a holistic approach is needed. Under the Equality Act 2010, which does not apply in Northern Ireland, a physical or mental impairment that has a 'substantial' and 'long-term' negative effect on a person's ability to do normal daily activities is a disability. 'Substantial' in this case means having a major impact on a person's ability to do something such as getting dressed. 'Long term' is more than twelve months. Some conditions such as arthritis and epilepsy fluctuate but people are still classified as disabled between episodes because the condition is likely to recur. Some conditions are progressive, getting worse over time. People with HIV infection, cancer or multiple sclerosis are classified as disabled from the time they are diagnosed.

Definitions of mild, moderate, severe and profound learning disabilities

Learning disabilities affect intellect. According to the British Institute of Learning Disabilities:

People with a *mild* learning disability have an IQ of 50 to 70 and are usually able to hold a conversation and communicate most of their needs and wishes. People with mild learning disabilities often go undiagnosed and lead independent lives.

People with a *moderate* learning disability have an IQ of 35 to 50 and are likely to have some language skills that mean they can communicate about their day to day needs and wishes. They may need some help with their everyday lives.

People with a *severe* learning disability have an IQ of between 20 and 35; they may often use basic words and gestures to communicate their needs. Many need a high level of support with everyday activities. They may have medical problems and need help with mobility.

People with *profound* intellectual and multiple disabilities may have the highest levels of care needs in our communities. They have a profound intellectual disability (an IQ of less than 20) and they may have other disabilities such as visual, hearing or movement impairments, or they may have autism or epilepsy.

In general, the greater the degree of learning disability, the more support is required for everyday living.

Diagnostic procedures, tools and standards used to diagnose a disability

At 10 – 14 weeks of pregnancy, all women are offered a blood test and ultrasound scan to screen for Down's syndrome. From April 2016 screening for Down's syndrome (Trisomy 21 or T21), Edwards' syndrome (Trisomy 18 or T18), and Patau's syndrome (Trisomy 13 or T13) will be part of a combined test.

From weeks 14 – 20 of pregnancy a quadruple test for Down's syndrome is available and mid pregnancy scans are offered for Patau's and Edwards' syndromes, to check for physical abnormalities.

In addition to regular check-ups and ultrasound scans, two further tests are available:

- Amniocentesis, where a small amount of amniotic fluid surrounding the baby is drawn off, tests for a number of genetic conditions such as Down's syndrome. The test is usually recommended for women over 35 who are at an increased risk during pregnancy because of their age or because they already have a child with a disability, or have a family history of disabilities.
- Chorionic Villus Sampling (CVS), where a small amount of the placenta is tested, can be offered earlier than amniocentesis.

Within the first 72 hours of birth babies are screened for heart defects, eye problems, developmental dysplasia of the hip (DDH) which means the hip joint is unstable, and baby boys are checked for undescended testicles. This is part of the Newborn and Infant Physical Examination (NIPE) screening programme.

At five to eight days midwives carry out a blood spot (heel prick) test, which screens for diseases such as cystic fibrosis, sickle cell disease, congenital hypothyroidism which can cause learning disabilities, and inherited metabolic disorders which if untreated can cause brain damage. These inherited metabolic disorders are:

- phenylketonuria (PKU)
- medium-chain acyl-CoA dehydrogenase deficiency (MCADD)
- maple syrup urine disease (MSUD)
- isovaleric acidaemia (IVA)
- glutaric aciduria type 1 (GA1)
- homocystinuria (pyridoxine unresponsive) (HCU).

A hearing test is done using an automated otoacoustic emission (AOAE) test. A soft-tipped earpiece is placed in the baby's ear, gentle clicking sounds played and when the inner part of the ear responds, it is picked up by screening equipment. If results are not satisfactory the test may be repeated or the automated auditory brainstem response (AABR) test may be used. Three small sensors are placed on the baby's head and neck, soft headphones placed over the baby's ears and gentle clicking sounds are played. Sensors detect the response. Screening for hearing impairments at this early stage allows for early intervention. If results are not satisfactory, the baby will be referred to an audiologist (a hearing specialist).

As the child grows, there may be a delay in achieving milestones such as crawling, walking or speaking. A child with cerebral palsy may only start to show problems when they begin walking. Parents may be told that a child has 'global development delay' which just means the child needs more time to achieve milestones. Regular checks are important to discover the nature of the delay.

Professional background, qualifications and experience of those undertaking the diagnosis and assessment

Midwives are trained to recognise obvious disabilities such as Down's syndrome and will then call a specialist doctor, a paediatrician who may make the diagnosis. In less obvious cases it may be later when the health visitor checks a baby's progress that concerns are raised. A baby who fails to respond to sounds in a hearing test, who cannot sit independently because of poor muscle control or who shows no response to social interaction will give rise for concern and will be monitored closely. Health visitors and the GP will monitor the development of the child until school age and liaise with the Special Educational Needs Co-ordinator (SENCO), educational psychologist and speech and language therapist as required. Educational psychologists assess the learning needs of children.

Parameters used to describe the diagnosed condition

The diagnosis of conditions tends to follow a medical model, based on signs and symptoms and treatment. If focuses on the disease, not the person. Disorders are classified by type, cause, severity, stability and prognosis.

According to the National Information Centre for Metabolic Diseases, inherited metabolic diseases are rare, genetic inherited diseases caused by a problem with a specific metabolic pathway in the body. Untreated they can cause brain damage and result in learning disabilities.

Down's syndrome

Down's syndrome is a type of genetic disorder that occurs as a result of an extra chromosome and in most cases is not inherited. There are three types of Down's syndrome – trisomy 21, translocation and mosaicism. Only translocation may be due to inherited factors. Down's syndrome is caused by changes in chromosomes during foetal development. Children with Down's syndrome have almond shaped eyes and have poor muscle tone. They may have heart conditions and problems with the digestive system, hearing and vision. With good healthcare, someone with Down's syndrome can live to around 60.

Disease type	Causation	Severity	Stability Over Time	Prognosis
Phenylketonuria (PKU)	Inherited genetic condition where protein is not metabolised.	If untreated can cause behavioural difficulties, eczema, vomiting, tremors and severe learning difficulties.	Controlled by low-protein diet and regular blood tests to monitor blood levels of phenylalanine.	If treatment is started within the first three weeks of life, severe learning difficulties are avoided.
Medium-chain acyl-CoA dehydrogenase deficiency (MCADD)	Inherited genetic condition where there are problems breaking down fatty acids for energy. Toxins build up in the body. Glucose released from the liver is used, causing a drop in blood sugar.	If untreated can cause coma, brain damage and liver failure.	Controlled by having regular meals and a diet plan devised by a dietician.	With early diagnosis and correct treatment, most children live healthy lives.
Maple syrup urine disease (MSUD)	Inherited genetic condition where the body cannot process certain amino acids. Urine smells sweet.	Without treatment, severe and life-threatening symptoms develop, including seizures (fits), coma, brain damage and developmental delay.	Controlled by low-protein diet and regular blood tests to monitor blood levels.	Eventually they may need a liver transplant.
Isovaleric acidaemia (IVA)	Inherited genetic condition where the body cannot process the amino acid leucine.	Without treatment, symptoms can develop including seizures (fits), coma, brain damage and developmental delay.	Treatment includes a special diet, advice and sometimes medication.	With early diagnosis and correct treatment, most children live healthy lives.
Glutaric aciduria type 1 (GA1)	Inherited genetic condition where the body cannot process certain amino acids.	Without treatment, symptoms develop, including seizures (fits), coma, and brain damage affecting muscle movement causing problems with walking, talking and swallowing. Some have a larger-than-average head (macrocephaly). There may be bleeding around the brain in the back of the eyes (retinal haemorrhage).	Treatment includes a special diet, advice and medication.	With early diagnosis and correct treatment, most children live healthy lives.

→

Disease type	Causation	Severity	Stability Over Time	Prognosis
Homocystinuria (HCU)	inherited genetic condition where the body cannot process the amino acid methionine.	Symptoms show after the first year of life. Without treatment symptoms include: vision problems, weak bones, joint problems, blood clots and strokes, brain damage, and delayed development.	Treatment may include vitamin B6 (pyridoxine), a special diet, advice and medication.	With early diagnosis and correct treatment, most children live healthy lives.
Cystic fibrosis	Inherited genetic condition.	Symptoms at birth – 10% of babies with cystic fibrosis are born with meconium ileus, a serious bowel obstruction. Mucus blocks the lungs making people with CF prone to chest infections. Mucus blocks the pancreas and liver ducts, resulting in damage to these organs. Diabetes, arthritis and infertility may also develop.	As yet there is no cure for cystic fibrosis. Treatment focuses on symptoms – nebulisers and physiotherapy to clear the lungs, long term antibiotics to prevent infection, a diet high in nutrients and supplemented with pancreatic enzymes to aid digestion.	Shorter life expectancy – currently people with CF may live on average about 50 years.

Table 12.1 Metabolic diseases

Activity

Shazia is expecting her first baby and is very happy. She has been to see her GP and is booked in for a scan and a blood test. Who might be involved in her care and what qualifications might they have? What is the blood test screening for?

Cognitive and learning needs

Cognitive is another word for thinking. Cognitive skills are intellectual or thinking skills. Cognitive needs may be lifelong, starting from birth, or they may develop later in life.

Learning difficulties

Learning difficulties do not relate to intellectual abilities. People with learning difficulties often are very able, but learn in a different way to the methods used in schools. Dyslexia is a specific learning difficulty with reading, writing and spelling and affects between 1 in 10 and 1 in 20 people. Dyspraxia or developmental co-ordination disorder (DCD), affects physical co-ordination. Children with dyspraxia are often called clumsy. They may struggle with tasks such as tying shoe laces, or games where throwing and catching is involved. Attention deficit hyperactivity disorder (ADHD) is a group of symptoms affecting behaviour. They include short attention spans, hyperactivity and impulsiveness.

Autism-spectrum disorders

Autism-spectrum disorders cover a wide range of conditions that share the triad of impairment of social interaction, social communication and social imagination. Autism is considered a spectrum disorder, with individuals experiencing varying degrees of the conditions. By itself, autism is not a learning disability, in fact some people with autism learn very well. Autism is considered a developmental disorder and affects social interaction. Asperger's syndrome, one of the best known types of autism, often affects people who are very intelligent. They tend to be very logical and struggle with processing language, for example, socially we may ask 'How are you?' but do not expect a detailed response. Someone with Asperger's might assume the person asking the question really wants to know. People with Asperger's syndrome may appear rude because they do not understand the unwritten social rules in situations. Pervasive developmental disorder not otherwise specified (PDD-NOS), is similar to atypical autism and is used when a person's behaviour does not fit all the criteria for typical autism. Childhood disintegrative disorder (Heller's syndrome) is a rare condition where children develop normally until at least two years of age, but then lose social, communication and other skills.

Inherited conditions

This means certain conditions can be passed on through the genes of parents. Some genetic traits are dominant, others are recessive. Just because one parent has cystic fibrosis does not mean that all their children will have cystic fibrosis. Only one type of Down's syndrome is linked to heredity as explained earlier. Huntington's disease is an inherited condition that progressively damages nerve cells in the brain. It affects movement, perception, awareness, thinking, judgement and behaviour and is a form of dementia.

Dementia

Dementia is an umbrella term that encompasses many different types of brain disorder. It is a syndrome (a group of related symptoms) associated with an ongoing decline of the brain and its functions. Memory loss, thinking speed, language and judgement can be affected. Most types of dementia are not inherited however according to Professor Nick Fox, in the case of fronto-temporal dementias, 30 to 50 per cent of

cases are inherited. Most cases of Alzheimer's disease are not inherited.

Needs of older people

The needs of older people vary with individuals. Some older people climb mountains, play in jazz bands, and travel the world. Others find they have memory loss, perhaps take longer to think things through, and are generally slower. Life-long learning is thought to help maintain brain function and independence. Many older people take up learning a new language or learn to play a musical instrument to keep their brain active. Others find a busy social life keeps them alert.

Activity

Shazia's brother, Mo has autism. He lives at home with their parents and spends a lot of time on his computer. Since leaving college he has found it hard to get a job. Mo's parents want him to get a job, get married and have a family so he will not be alone when anything happens to them.

What are the emotional, physical, social, intellectual and financial impacts of Mo's condition on him and on the family?

Physical and health needs

Needs of older people

Needs of older people vary with their health. Some people have arthritis, and have limited mobility. Obesity is linked to late onset diabetes and cardiovascular disease, and these factors can limit a person's ability to remain independent. Someone with arthritis may struggle with everyday activities while they await a knee replacement. Someone who neglects their health may find they have eyesight problems caused by diabetes, or because of cardiovascular disease they find it difficult to walk far.

Health needs

Health needs affect the amount of support required from others. A child with cystic fibrosis may require physiotherapy to help loosen the mucus clogging their airways. Children with sickle cell disorders, may need the support of a multidisciplinary team to maintain their health. Someone who has a stroke may require physical support to learn to walk and talk again. Mental illnesses pose a variety of challenges. Someone may have an eating disorder and require support to regain a healthy eating pattern. Someone else may be depressed and feel life is not worth living. Each person is an individual with their own unique needs.

Sensory disabilities

Sensory disabilities acquired later in life may affect people psychologically and they may need time to adjust to accepting their deafness and hearing or visual impairment. A baby born without sight accepts the world and learns to adapt, with no regrets for what they never had.

Accidents

Accidents can change health needs. A soldier who is fighting fit may step on a mine and have his legs blown off. Adjusting to life with paraplegia, or loss of other limbs requires physical and psychological support.

Infectious diseases

Infectious diseases can lead to individuals having additional needs. Meningitis, an infectious disease that affects the brain can cause permanent vision or hearing loss, memory loss and problems with balance.

Problems during pregnancy and birth

Problems during pregnancy and birth can lead to individuals having additional needs, for example, if the mother is exposed to rubella infection in the first three months of pregnancy it can result in deafblindness for the unborn baby. A prolonged and difficult labour may cause the baby to be starved of oxygen during birth and this can cause permanent brain damage.

Social and emotional needs

In addition to cognitive and learning needs and physical and health needs, people also have social and emotional needs. These latter needs may be related to long-term conditions or may stem from other causes.

Activity

Shazia and Mo's parents Mr and Mrs Khan are both nearly 70, and Mr Khan is diabetic. His wife has arthritis and finds it difficult to move around. As a side effect of his diabetes, Mr Khan's eyesight is very poor.

If Mr Khan's diabetes is not controlled, what is the prognosis? What is the prognosis for Mrs Khan with her arthritis? How might this affect each of them individually in terms of physical needs? How might it affect the family?

Needs generated from family circumstances

In our society, we assume that families provide love and care, but this is not always so. According to the NSPCC, there were 56,231 children in the UK on child protection registers or the subject of child protection plans on 31 March 2014 (source: Child protection register and plan statistics for all UK nations for 2014). Children such as these need social and emotional support to understand what is happening. *Looked-after* children who are under the care of children's services need to feel loved and safe. Children whose parents have died need extra support to adjust to their new lives especially if they have no other relatives. Children who are bullied at school and then refuse to go to school also need support.

Needs generated by being elderly

Just because someone grows old does not necessarily mean they need additional support. Many older people lead busy and fulfilled lives, but not all do. As people live longer and experience the loss of loved ones, they face their own mortality and for some who have a fear of dying, this can be a time troubled by increasing isolation. Even if they have family close by, they may be isolated as many families are busy with work and child care and cannot often visit elderly parents. Many older people do not want to be seen to be needy. As costs increase, their income may be insufficient and they economise by cutting down on heating.

Needs affected by the learning environment

Some children and young people have additional needs which are influenced by the learning environment. A child with noise sensitivity will find it difficult to learn in a noisy classroom. A child with ADHD will be easily distracted, while one with hearing loss may struggle to hear what the teacher is saying.

Activity

Very sadly, Mr Khan died, leaving Mrs Khan alone to look after Mo in the family home. Mo has difficulty in empathising because of his autism and Mrs Khan found his apparent coldness difficult to deal with while she was coping with her own problems. What social and emotional needs might she have at this time? How would this impact on her physical needs? How might this impact on the family?

Distinction activity A D1

Remind yourself of the definition of the command word 'evaluate'.

Evaluate the significance to the individuals, their families and society of a diagnosis of additional needs.

Check your understanding

1   What is the difference between mild, moderate, severe and profound learning disabilities?
2   What is the difference between learning disability and learning difficulty?
3   Give an example of cognitive and learning needs.
4   Give an example of physical and health needs.
5   Give an example of social and emotional needs.
6   What needs might a child have if they are taken into the care of the local authority?

B Examine how to overcome the challenges to daily living faced by people with additional needs

B P2 , B P3 , B M2 , B C D2 , B C D3

Definitions of disability

Models of disability

There are two main models of disability (Table 12.2). The two case scenarios help to explain the difference between the models.

Medical model	Social model
The medical model looks at what is 'wrong' with the person. Disability is a problem belonging to the individual – It is their problem.	Disability is caused by the way society is organised, rather than by a person's impairment or difference.
They should get 'fixed' to fit in with the rest of society.	People are unique individuals and have a contribution to make whatever their ability.
People with disabilities need caring for - they are dependent.	People with disabilities can be independent given the right support.

Table 12.2 Two models of disability

Case scenario

Social model

Jack, a 16-year-old with cerebral palsy, uses a wheelchair. He wants to train as a teaching assistant. The medical model would say that Jack should stay at home and live on benefits as no school or college would accept him. The social model of disability looks at the person. Jack is intelligent, capable of organising his care needs. He just needs a chance. He gets a place at college. The old building does not have a lift so classes are timetabled on the ground floor. He gets a placement at a local school, where there is a ramp and wheelchair access. Jack successfully passes his course and gets a job as a teaching assistant. The medical model disempowers him; the social model empowers him.

Case scenario

Medical model

Rajiv had a motor cycle accident and broke his back. He lives in a small ground floor flat near his parents. He is very active in local politics and also gives talks to societies about what it is like to live with a disability. One evening he gives a talk to the local college but at 8.30pm he has to leave because the carer organised by social services comes to help him to bed at 9.00pm. He does not want to go to bed at 9.00pm but this is the time the carer has been allocated and he has no say in the matter. If he is late back, he has to stay in his wheel chair all night. This is the medical model of disability – assuming he needs to be cared for and assuming he does not have a valuable part to play in society. Things changed when personalisation of care was introduced. He now has his own personal budget which he uses to employ a personal assistant who comes at 11.00 pm to help him to bed. Personalisation of care assesses the needs of the individual, not the needs of the system, and empowers people to make decisions about their own care needs.

Understanding of disability and dependency as social constructs

Social constructs are ideas constructed or made by a society, for example, in the period up to the 1940s women were not expected to work after marriage. The social construct said that women should stay at home and keep house. It was only during the Second World War when women had to take on jobs traditionally done by men that things changed. Women took on jobs such as ploughing a field, driving a truck, being an air raid warden. After the war, women did not want to return to being just a housewife; they wanted careers and the social construct of what was expected of a woman changed forever, at least in this society.

Similarly, the social construct of disability has changed. Once people felt pity for those with a disability, expected them to stay at home and be dependent on others for everything. People with disabilities were treated like children. As a result of campaigning and through several people with disability challenging assumptions, the social construct of disability has been transformed.

Tom Shakespeare a sociologist, academic and disability rights campaigner has achondroplasia. He worked with the World Health Organisation to raise the profile of disability rights. In his book, *Disability Rights and Wrongs Revisited*, published in 2013, he says it is time to move away from these two opposing models of disability and look at a more complex view of disability.

Definitions

Disability

Under the Equality Act 2010, disability is a physical or mental impairment that has a 'substantial' and 'long-term' negative effect on a person's ability to do normal daily activities.

Disablement

The act of becoming disabled to the extent that full wages cannot be earned. Industrial Injuries Disablement benefit may be claimed by those made ill or disabled from an accident or disease caused by work or while on an approved employment training scheme or course.

Discrimination

The Equality and Human Rights Commission and the Equality Act 2010 define four types of discrimination:

- **Direct discrimination** – treating one person worse than another because of a protected characteristic.

- **Indirect discrimination** – an example of this would be if an organisation put a rule or a policy, or a way of doing things in place which has a worse impact on someone with a protected characteristic than someone without one.

- **Harassment** – treating someone in a way that violates their dignity, or creates a hostile, degrading, humiliating or offensive environment.

- **Victimisation** – treating someone unfairly if they are taking action under the Equality Act (like making a complaint of discrimination), or supporting someone else who is doing so.

Impairment

An injury, illness, or congenital condition that causes or is likely to cause a loss or difference of physiological or psychological function.

Activity

Benjy, who we met in Unit 2 'Working in health and social care', has Down's syndrome. Using a medical model, describe his care needs. Now using a social model of disability, describe his care needs. Discuss the difference with your friends.

Minimising environmental and social challenges

How society's infrastructure should support equality for people with additional needs

Improving infrastructure helps everyone, not just people with disabilities. Improving access to public buildings and public transport helps wheelchair users but also helps parents with small children in buggies. Removing barriers such as steps, and introducing level or sloped access means everyone can move around a building easily.

Minimising barriers, for example providing information in large print means everyone can read information more easily, not just those with visual impairments.

Improving access to employment benefits all of society. Adaptations to the work environment, such as providing a desk at the right height for a wheelchair user, or providing communication aids such as voice activated software not only helps someone gain employment but reduces the amount of benefits paid out from taxes. Many of the adaptations used by people with disabilities are part of everyday life for all. Voice activated software is on most smartphones and is used by many.

Inclusion is increasing. SCOPE, the national charity supporting people with disabilities, lists leisure activities and sports organisation that range from amateur to Paralympic level. The internet is one of the greatest developments in inclusivity. Professor Stephen Hawking uses the internet and technology for social networking and for his work as a world famous scientist.

Daily living activities have changed for many people, not just for those with disabilities. Shopping can be ordered online and delivered, whether by a busy working mother or by someone with disabilities. Home and personal care services can now meet individual needs, thanks to the personal budget for those with disabilities, which can be used to employ a personal assistant. The Motability Scheme enables disabled people to use their government-funded mobility allowance to lease a new car, scooter or powered wheelchair and the Blue Badge scheme makes parking easier.

Activity

Benjy wants to volunteer at the local charity shop. To get there he needs to travel by bus. What help is available to help him do this? He has to read the health and safety policy – how can this be made easier for him? He gets tired easily because of his heart problem and cannot stand for long periods.

What adaptations could be made for him in the workplace?

At Christmas the volunteers organise a party for people in the local care home. How could Benjy get involved?

Carl his support worker has shown him how to cook, but Benjy likes to do his own shopping. What support might there be to help him with this?

Minimising personal challenges

Health and social care workers can minimise some of the challenges to daily living for people with additional needs.

Physical challenges such as dressing and washing are easier if clothes are chosen with ease in mind. Elasticated waists for trousers and skirts make dressing easier. A light warm fleece rather than a bulky knitted jacket does the job better, is easier to put on and take off, and easier to wash and dry. Showers are much safer than baths, and some are large enough for a wheeled shower chair to be used. Nonslip mats under plates help at meal times and non-slip adhesive strips turn normal cutlery into usable cutlery for those with poor grip. Easy grip garden tools can be used for indoor or outdoor gardening to maintain activity. Gel ball hand exercisers help develop and maintain strength in the hands and fingers, especially following stroke. Indoor exercise equipment can help with balance, or for those who prefer swimming, the poolside dipper can help a person into the water.

Intellectual challenges are much easier to meet if the individual is motivated. Free online taster courses such as Futurelearn are offered by universities in this country. YouTube offers many opportunities to learn new things, whether it is how to bake a cake, or how to use a smartphone. It can help people maintain friendships across distances, or join an online club.

Emotional challenges can be harder to overcome. The Internet is one way to reduce social isolation but not everyone is happy using a computer. For older people organisations such as University of the Third Age offers interest groups in the local area.

Language groups, book groups, lunch clubs are just some of the types of activities that can be offered. Sometimes depression prevents people joining groups, and at times counselling is needed to help the individual progress. Specialist counselling such as Cruse for those who have been bereaved can help. Dependency sometimes is a habit. A child with disabilities might have parents who are over-protective and encourage dependency rather than gaining independence. Health and care workers can help people with disabilities gain independence by enabling them and helping them do things rather than taking over and doing things for them. A person with learning disabilities can with support learn to cook, wash up and make their own bed and do their own laundry.

Social challenges are closely linked to emotional challenges. If someone feels good about themselves they are more likely to go out, meet others, make friends and have successful personal relationships. Care workers can help by supporting those with disabilities make the first step towards getting out and about.

Figure 12.1 Bereavement counselling

Mrs Khan has recently lost her husband. She has arthritis and cares for her son who has Asperger's syndrome. As she approaches her 70th birthday she becomes increasingly depressed. It is painful to get dressed and difficult to maintain her personal hygiene. Her family help as much as they can but Shazia her daughter is expecting a baby in a few weeks' time and cannot do much.

What support could help Mrs Khan?

Attitudes of others

In Unit 2 'Working in health and social care', we saw how when Benjy was waiting in outpatients, another person tried to take his turn and Amina the nurse would not allow this. She was aware of the negative attitudes the other person had in trying to deny Benjy his rights, and she responded appropriately. We saw Carl supporting Benjy to manage his own money and choose his own food. Both Amina and Carl challenged the stereotyping and judgemental assumptions shown by others and would not allow Benjy to be marginalised, labelled or disempowered. Unit 2 explains more about counteracting discrimination. We saw Amina the nurse helping a lady with visual impairments find the correct room for the doctor. Failure to make adjustments or modifications is discrimination and should be challenged.

Activity

Mo, Shazia's brother, rarely goes out. When he used to go to college, he found people on the bus would move away when he tried to talk to them, and the kids hanging round the corner shop used to call him names. What support would he need to enable him to go out and try to find a job?

Distinction activity B C D2

What are the procedures and what help is currently available to overcome challenges to daily living faced by:

1 A person with Down's syndrome?
2 A person with Asperger's syndrome?
3 An elderly person with arthritis who has recently been bereaved?

Remind yourself of the command word 'justify'.

Justify the support and adaptations provided for two individuals with different additional needs to help them overcome challenges to daily living, with reference to statutory provision.

Check your understanding

1 What is the difference between a medical model of disability and a social model of disability?
2 Explain what is meant by a social construct and give an example.
3 Define disability.
4 Give an example of how to minimise:
   (a) Environmental barriers to employment.
   (b) Social barriers to inclusion.
5 Give examples of how to minimise four personal challenges.
6 Explain how health and care workers can challenge discrimination.

C Investigate current practice with respect to provision for individuals with additional needs

C P4 , C P5 , C M3 , C M4 , B C D2 ,

B C D3

Professionals involved in supporting individuals with additional needs

In Unit 2 'Working in health and social care', we looked at the roles of occupational therapists and social workers. In Unit 5 'Meeting individual care and support needs', we looked at the roles of speech and language therapists, special needs teachers and psychologists involved in Harry's care. Community learning disability nurses focus on enabling people to reach their full potential in all aspects of their lives. Physiotherapists help and treat people with physical problems caused by illness, injury, disability or ageing. Psychiatrists are medically qualified doctors who deal with mental illness and the interaction between physical and mental illness.

The Single Assessment Process (SAP), introduced in the National Service Framework for Older People (2001), Standard 2: person centred care, aims to ensure that the NHS and social care services treat older people as individuals and enable them to make choices about their own care needs. The Single Assessment Process is a person centred health and social care framework, which includes entry into the system, holistic assessment, care planning, care delivery and review. SAP aims to assess older people's needs thoroughly and accurately, without duplication by different agencies and share the information appropriately between health and social care agencies.

How information is shared between health and social care agencies is crucial in joint working. Electronic SAP (e-SAP) is being introduced: NHS Connecting for Health and the Electronic Social Care Records Implementation Board jointly oversee a project to develop a national framework for e-SAP. The Single Assessment Process is used for older people, people with learning disabilities and in some places for everyone over 18 years of age.

The White Paper, 'Our Health, Our Care, Our Say' (January 2006) proposes a Common Assessment Framework for Adults based on the Care Programme Approach for Mental Health, the Single Assessment Process for Older People, and Person Centred Planning for People with Learning Disabilities. It states in particular that 'SAP provides a generic framework that could be applied more widely'. The Common Assessment Framework will support seamless delivery of services across health and social care; avoid duplication; offer a proportionate assessment according to an individual's level of need; offer person-centred needs assessment that leads into a personalised care plan; and is more transparent about the process.

In 'Living Well in Later Life: A Review of Progress Against the National Service Framework for Older People' - produced by the Healthcare Commission, the Audit Commission and the Commission for Social Care Inspection (March 2006) the SAP was identified as an important way of providing person centred care. SAP is useful for individuals with serious illnesses, physical disability, learning disability, mental health conditions, frailty due to old age.

Activity

Choose three professional roles involved with supporting people with additional needs and find out the training required for each.

Support and adaptations for individuals with additional needs

Equipment and adaptations

Earlier in the unit we looked at mobility aids and in Unit 5 'Meeting individual care and support needs', we explored communication aids, such as British Sign Language, Makaton and hearing aids.

Daily living adaptations mentioned earlier in this unit are just a few of the adaptations available as technologies develop. Computing technology and the internet have done much to equalise the situation for people with disabilities.

Therapies

Occupational therapy helps identify strengths and difficulties a person has in everyday life, and helps them work out practical solutions to everyday activities such as washing, dressing and getting mobile. The aim is to help the person maintain, regain or improve independence by using different techniques, changing their environment and using new equipment.

Art therapy uses art to help people express their feelings. Music therapy does much the same thing. Both work closely with psychotherapists and support people with mental health issues.

Speech therapy helps children who have speech delay, perhaps due to hearing problems. It also helps those recovering from a stroke when speech has been affected.

Physiotherapists may use hydrotherapy to help people mobilise after an operation or they may use manual therapies such as massage, acupuncture, ultrasound and even Transcutaneous electrical nerve stimulation (TENS) which is a method of pain relief involving the use of a mild electrical current.

Short- and long-term support

Support may be short-term, for example helping an older person walk after a knee replacement, or long-term, for example, a child with cerebral palsy may need long-term support of various kinds to help them develop their potential.

Activity

What support and adaptations might help an older person who has difficulty mobilising because of arthritis?

Financial support for individuals with additional needs

Welfare rights

The 2010 to 2015 government policy on welfare reform has introduced changes to welfare. In April 2013, Personal Independence Payment (PIP) began replacing Disability Living Allowance (DLA) for claimants of working age although they do not have to be in work to get this benefit. Personal Independence Payments (PIP) are for people aged between 16 and 64 who because of a long-term illness or disability may need help with daily activities or getting around. Daily activities include:

- preparing or eating food
- washing, bathing and using the toilet
- dressing and undressing
- reading and communicating
- managing medicines or treatments
- making decisions about money
- engaging with other people.

Claimants have a face-to-face consultation with an independent health professional. The assessment looks at an individual's ability to complete ten daily living activities and two mobility activities. Rates may be paid at basic rate or enhanced rate depending on the level of disability.

State Pension

The age at which this can be claimed is gradually increasing and rules of eligibility are changing. The government is planning to gradually raise the state pension age to 67 by 2028. For those aged 55 now, they will have to have ten years of National Insurance contributions in order to claim State Pension. The pension is taxable.

Pension Credit tops up the pension for those on low incomes. The age at which this can be claimed is gradually being increased.

Housing benefit

Housing benefit helps pay the rent for tenants on a low income. It also covers some service charges like lifts and communal laundry facilities. Housing Benefit may be reduced for those in council or social housing with a spare bedroom.

Council Tax Support

Council Tax Support replaced Council Tax Benefit in 2013, and each local authority now runs their own Council Tax Support schemes so what help they get depends where a person lives and their individual circumstances.

Health benefits

Everyone aged over 60 gets free prescriptions and eye tests but people who receive the following benefits may also be entitled to health benefits such as free NHS prescriptions and eye test, a voucher towards the cost of glasses or contact lenses, help with travel costs to receive NHS treatment and free NHS wigs and fabric supports:

- the Guarantee Credit part of Pension Credit
- Income Support
- income-based Jobseeker's Allowance
- income-related Employment and Support Allowance
- Working Tax Credit or Child Tax Credit (in some circumstances)
- Universal Credit.

Support for people at work

Disability Employment Advisers based at some local Jobcentres advise people with disabilities which companies are disability friendly, and they help them address any needs they have for literacy and numeracy. These posts are being phased out and replaced by general work advisors.

The Work Choice programme (not available in Northern Ireland) is a voluntary scheme to help people with disabilities find and keep a job. The programme is tailored to suit the individual and can include:

- training and developing skills
- building confidence
- interview coaching.

In order to apply people need to be of working age, need support in work as well as to find a job, must be able to work at least 16 hours a week after Work Entry Support and have a recognised disability that means it is hard to get or keep a job.

Transport support

The Blue Badge scheme, discussed earlier in the unit, gives exemption from some parking restrictions and access to designated parking spaces.

Shopmobility

This provides community transport services for people who have difficulty using public transport. These include door-to-door transport and trips to shopping centres. Northern Ireland has a separate scheme. Local schemes help people shop in town centres by lending wheelchairs and scooters.

Accessible buses and taxis have helped not only those with mobility issues, but everyone move more easily. The Taxi Card scheme operated locally helps people with mobility difficulties travel independently with an approved taxi company at a discounted price. Members have a card which is credited with a set amount of money every year – they use this to help pay towards each journey they make. Dial a Ride and Ring and Ride operate 7 days a week and into the night to provide a safe, reliable door to door service for those who cannot use normal buses.

Support for carers

The Care Act 2014, which came into force in 2015, sets out carers' legal rights to assessment and support, looking at the impact that caring has on the carer. The Carer's Allowance is the main state benefit for carers.

To be eligible, a carer must:

- be aged 16 or over
- spend at least 35 hours a week caring for someone
- be resident in England, Scotland or Wales for at least two of the last three years
- normally live in England, Scotland or Wales, or live abroad as a member of the armed forces
- not be in full-time education or studying for more than 21 hours a week
- earn less than £110 a week.

The Carer's Allowance cannot be claimed if the carer is receiving the State Pension.

The person being cared for must receive one of these benefits because they need help with personal care. They are:

- Personal Independence Payment daily living component.
- Disability Living Allowance (DLA) at either the middle or high rate of the care component.
- Any level of Attendance Allowance (AA).
- Constant Attendance Allowance of the normal maximum rate, which is paid with a War Disablement Pension or Industrial Injuries Disablement Benefit.
- Armed Forces Independence Payment.

Activity

What financial support might be available for a 70-year-old with mobility problems?

What support might be available for someone with Asperger's who wants to get a job?

Statutory provision for children with additional needs

Common Assessment Framework (CAF)

The Common Assessment Framework (CAF) for Children in Need and Their Families is an assessment framework shared across all practitioners involved with assessing the needs of children. It is a standardised way of assessing a child's additional needs and deciding how those needs should be met. It can be used by practitioners across children's services. It takes into account the role of parents, carers and environmental factors. The CAF helps to improve integrated working by promoting co-ordinated service provision.

The Common Assessment Framework may be used with the 'Team Around the Child' approach and the Single Assessment Process (SAP) may be used with the 'Team Around the Citizen' approach to promote inter-agency working between health, social care, education, youth justice and other relevant agencies. Where a child or young person has additional needs requiring a multi-agency response, a relevant practitioner from those supporting the child is identified as the lead professional to act as single point of contact for the child or family, co-ordinate delivery of the actions, reduce overlap and inconsistency in the services received, support the child and family if more specialist assessments need to be carried out and support the child through key transition points or where necessary, ensure a careful and planned handover to another lead professional.

The involvement of key professionals such as GPs, social workers, occupational therapists, educational psychologists, community mental health nurses, family and others, carers, advocates, interpreters and translators can be more effective if there is a Single Assessment Process or Common Assessment Framework where information is shared. Once needs have been identified and the desired outcomes specified, a support plan is put in place.

The local offer

The Children and Families Act 2014 says that from 1 September 2014, local authorities must publish a 'local offer' setting out what support is available to families with children who have disabilities or SEN. The local offer from health, colleges, schools and early years providers should explain how families can request personal budgets, make complaints and access specialist help. Families with EHC plans will be offered personal budgets. Local authorities have a duty to identify all children in their area who have SEN or disabilities.

Education, Health and Care Plans replace SEN statements

They are described in Unit 6. Education, health and care (EHC) plans will be reviewed regularly and cover people up to the age of 25 years old.

Codes of practice, legislation and policies relating to provision for children with additional needs

The Special Educational Needs and Disability code of practice (SEND): 0–25 years came into force on 1 September 2014. It is statutory guidance, which means it must be followed. The code includes guidance relating to disabled children and young people as well as those with Special Educational Needs (SEN). It focuses on children, young people and parents participating in decision-making and focuses on improving outcomes for children and young people. There is guidance on joint planning and commissioning of services to ensure co-operation between education, health and social care, and guidance on the Local Offer of support for children and young people with SEN or disabilities. School Action and School Action Plus are phased out in favour of a graduated approach to SEN support, and for children and young people with complex needs, statements and Learning Difficulty Assessments (LDAs) are replaced by the 0–25 Education, Health and Care plan (EHC plan).

The SEND code of practice relates to:

- Part 3 of the Children and Families Act 2014
- The Special Educational Needs and Disability Regulations 2014
- The Special Educational Needs (Personal Budgets) Regulations 2014
- The Special Educational Needs and Disability (Detained Persons) Regulations 2015
- The Children and Families Act 2014 (Transitional and Saving Provisions)(No 2) Order 2014.

Policies relating to the local offer have been introduced in each local authority, and each school and college has a policy relating to SEN. In addition, every local authority has a family information service (FIS), which must provide information about local services for all families with children (up to the age of 25, if the child has a disability).

Activity

What provision must local authorities make for children with additional needs?

Statutory provision for adults with additional needs

Codes of practice, legislation and policies relating to provision for adults with additional needs

The Care Act is designed to work in partnership with the Children and Families Act 2014, which applies to 0–25 year old children and young people with SEN and Disabilities. The Children and Families Act 2014 relates to the needs of children and young people up to the age of 25; the Care Act 2014 deals with the needs of adults requiring support. The transition from childhood to adulthood should be a smooth process for those with special needs. The Education, Health and Care plan which extends to the age of 25, allows for an assessment of needs when appropriate for the child and the SEND code is in force for that period. Transition arrangements should be co-ordinated between health, education and social care.

Adults with additional needs are protected by provisions in the Equality Act 2010 which protect them against discrimination in employment, education, in access to goods, services and facilities and when buying and renting land or property. The UN Convention on Disability Rights has been agreed by the UK.

Care and support statutory guidance issued under the Care Act 2014

The following is a summary of the Care and Support Statutory Guidance issued under the Care Act 2014, summarised according to units of the guidance.

The guidance sets out the duties of local authorities to promote well-being, which the guidance says includes

- personal dignity (including treatment of the individual with respect)
- physical and mental health and emotional well-being
- protection from abuse and neglect
- control by the individual over day-to-day life (including over care and support provided and the way it is provided)

- participation in work, education, training or recreation
- social and economic well-being
- domestic, family and personal
- suitability of living accommodation
- the individual's contribution to society.

The well-being principle must be considered in everything. Local authorities have a duty to provide information and focus on preventing further needs arising where possible. They must put the individual at the heart of the process, take their wishes into account and also protect them from abuse while empowering them to become as independent as possible.

Section 2 of the Care Act deals with preventing, reducing or delaying needs.

Primary prevention incudes interventions and advice that:

- provide universal access to good quality information
- support safer neighbourhoods
- promote healthy and active lifestyles (e.g. exercise classes)
- reduce loneliness or isolation (e.g. befriending schemes or community activities such as the case study below)
- encourage early discussions in families or groups about potential changes in the future, e.g. conversations about potential care arrangements or suitable accommodation should a family member become ill or disabled.

Secondary prevention or early intervention is aimed at reducing harm, for example helping someone with a learning disability with moderate needs manage their money. Tertiary prevention is aimed at delaying the effects of disability, for those with established, progressive or complex health conditions such as dementia. The focus is on supporting people to regain skills and manage or reduce need where possible.

Intermediate care is offered in four ways, as crisis response providing short-term care (up to 48 hours); as home-based intermediate care by health professionals such as nurses and therapists;

as bed-based intermediate care for example, in a community hospital; and, re-ablement to help people live independently provided in the person's own home by care and support professionals.

Adults and carers are entitled to an assessment of needs. Sections 9 to 13 of the Care Act 2014; the Care and Support (Assessment) Regulations 2014; and the Care and Support (Eligibility Criteria) Regulations 2014 set out national eligibility criteria for access to adult care and support, and for access to carer support. Independent advocates may be used if the individual requires support in expressing their needs and has no family member able to support them. Once an assessment of needs has been completed, the local authority determines eligibility. Even if a person is not eligible, they must be given information to help them arrange their own care. Eligibility criteria were set out in Unit 2.

Independent advocacy must be offered by local authorities under Sections 67 and 68 of the Care Act 2014 and the Care and Support (Independent Advocacy) Regulations 2014.

Sections 14, 17 and 69 and 70 of the Care Act 2014; the Care and Support (Charging and Assessment of Resources) Regulations 2014; and the Care and Support and Aftercare (Choice of Accommodation) Regulations 2014 deal with charging and financial assessments and are based on the idea that people should only be required to pay what they can afford. Intermediate care, including re-ablement, must be provided free of charge for up to six weeks, aids must be provided free of charge. Care which the local authority must provide and health care is not charged for.

Sections 34 to 36 of the Care Act 2014; and the Care and Support (Deferred Payment Agreements) Regulations 2014 relate to deferral of payments, so that people should not be forced to sell their home in their lifetime to pay for their care. They can 'defer' or delay paying the costs of care and support until a later date.

Sections 24 and 25 of the Care Act 2014 explain the care and support plan for individuals and the support plan in the case of carers. The plan 'belongs' to the person; the local authority ensures production and signing-off to ensure the plan meets the identified needs. The personal budget may be taken as a direct payment where the individual wishes to purchase their own care, or may be administered by the local authority on behalf of the individual, according to the individual's wishes. Local authorities must inform the individual of the responsibilities involved in managing a direct payment and being an employer.

Sections 42 to 46 of the Care Act 2014 concern safeguarding, how and when to report concerns and the establishment of Adult Safeguarding Boards. Local authority statutory adult safeguarding duties apply equally to all adults with care and support needs whether or not the needs are being met, and regardless of the adult's mental capacity, and the setting, (except for prisons and approved premises). Unit 17 details safeguarding procedures.

Sections 3, 6, 7, 22, 23, 74 and Schedule 3 of the Care Act 2014; the Care and Support (Provision of Health Services) Regulations 2014; and the Care and Support (Discharge of Hospital Patients) Regulations 2014 relate to integration of services, co-operation and partnerships, especially where social services, the NHS, housing, welfare and employment are concerned.

Sections 58 to 66 of the Care Act; and The Care and Support (Children's Carers) Regulations 2014 are concerned with the transition to adult care and support.

Section 76 of the Care Act 2014 relates to care and support for adults in prison, approved premises and bail accommodation and those released from custody.

Section 79 of the Care Act 2014 concerns delegation of local authority functions and the ultimate responsibility that the local authority has for services delivered under contract to them.

Sections 39 to 41 of the Care Act 2014; the Care and Support (Ordinary Residence) (Specified Accommodation) Regulations 2014; and the Care and Support (Disputes Between Local Authorities) Regulations 2014 clarify responsibilities. The local authority is required to meet needs for an adult who is 'ordinarily resident' in their area (or is present there but has no settled residence.).

Social Care Act 2012 which came into force on 1 April 2013, creating health and well-being boards, clinical commissioning groups and Public Health England and NHS England. Health watch was set up to listen to people, influence those with power and empower and inform people. They are the consumer champion calling for the public to be allowed more involvement in planning. Health and well-being boards have a statutory duty to involve local people in the preparation of Joint Strategic Needs Assessments and the development of joint health and well-being strategies.

Activity

How is person-centred care brought into the assessment and planning of care?

Distinction activity B C D2 D3

Evaluate the impact of providing support for two individuals diagnosed with different additional needs in improving their well-being and life chances.

Check your understanding

1   What is the role of the following in supporting people with additional needs?
    - Community learning disabilities nurse.
    - Physiotherapist.
    - Psychologist.
2   Which modern communication aids might help a child with communication problems?
3   What therapies might help someone recovering from stroke to walk and regain speech?
4   What has replaced Disability Living Allowance?
5   What is the Work Choice programme?
6   Who can get carer's allowance?
7   What is an Education and Health Care Plan and who is it for?
8   What is a personal health budget and who can apply for one?
9   What is person-centred care?

Case scenario

Jamie is five years old and has global developmental delay. He has no concept of risk and his parents have to be watchful all the time. A Health visitor, a GP, social worker and occupational therapist are involved in supporting Jamie. His mum had to stop work to care for him, but they get direct payments to help with support. They chose a school where he settled in well and they have a good relationship with the SENCO who worked with them to develop Jamie's Education, Health and Care Plan.

They also got information about local events from their local authority children's services Family Information Service Plus, a free service for parents of a child or young person (aged 0 to 19 years) with a disability. They meet up with other families once a month at the local cinema where relaxed screenings of children's films have low lighting and reduced sound aimed at children and young people with a learning disability.

Think about it

Mr W, aged 53, had a heart condition and Down's syndrome. In 2011, his medical notes had a Do Not Resuscitate (DNR) order if his heart or breathing stopped because he had Down's syndrome.

East Kent Hospitals University NHS Foundation Trust has admitted that his human rights were breached for having a DNR order on his records.

(Source: Mencap)

What does this case imply about attitudes to people with learning disabilities?

Further reading

Shakespeare T., (2013) *Disability Rights and Wrongs Revisited*, Routledge

Useful websites

Living with Dementia magazine, published by Alzheimer's Society: www.alzheimers.org.uk

British Institute of Learning Disabilities: www.bild.org.uk

Children Living with Inherited Metabolic Diseases and The National Information Centre for Metabolic Diseases: www.climb.org.uk

Care Quality Commission – Fundamental standards: www.cqc.org.uk

Down's Syndrome Association provides support for those with Down's syndrome: www.downs-syndrome.org.uk

Personal health budgets: see www.england.nhs.uk

Free online courses: www.futurelearn.com

International evidence on impact of funding linked to additional needs on participation and attainment by 16-19 year olds, research report December 2015. Children with special educational needs (SEN). Special educational needs in England: January 2015; SEND code of practice: 0–25 years: Definition of disability under Equality Act 2010. Equality Act 2010 Guidance on matters to be taken into account in determining questions relating to the definition of disability. Care and Support Statutory Guidance Issued under the Care Act 2014 Department of Health. National service framework: mental health. See www.gov.uk

Consumer champion: www.healthwatch.co.uk

Murray, R., (2015) Making change possible, A Transformation Fund for the NHS Case study 2: The National Service Framework for Mental Health in England, Kings Fund: www.kingsfund.org.uk

Equity and Excellence: Liberating the NHS (Department for Health, 2010) and later developments: www.kingsfund.org.uk/healthactprezi

Childhood disintegrative disorder: see www.mayoclinic.org

MENCAP – the voice of learning disability: www.mencap.org.uk

Newborn hearing test: see www.nhs.uk

Learning disabilities: coping with a diagnosis; children with a learning disability: see www.nhs.uk/Livewell

Statistics on child abuse. How many children are abused or neglected in the UK: see www.nspcc.org.uk

Social model of disability: see www.scope.org.uk

A national partnership including central and local government, the NHS, the provider sector, people with care and support needs, carers and family members set up to promote personalisation in care: www.thinklocalactpersonal.org.uk

14 Physiological disorders and their care

About this unit

It is essential that health and social care workers understand and recognise specific signs and are aware of correct diagnosis and the various treatment plans which are available. It is important to understand that not all diseases and disorders have classic recognition signs and some may take longer to diagnose than others. As health and social care workers, learners will be introduced to individualised treatment plans, support services and appreciate the importance of person-centred care planning. This unit will support your learning from Unit 3 (Anatomy and Physiology). It will highlight links with body systems and the diseases, disorders and treatment plans which are associated with them.

Learning aims

The aims of this unit are to:

A Investigate the causes and effects of physiological disorders.

B Examine the investigation and diagnosis of physiological disorders.

C Examine treatment and support for service users with physiological disorders.

D Develop a treatment plan for service users with physiological disorders to meet their needs.

How will I be assessed?

Learning aims: A, B and C (A.P1, B.P2, C.P3, C.P4, A.M1, B.M2, C.M3, A.D1, BC.D2). It is recommended by the awarding body that learners write a report on the impact of two different physiological disorders on the health and well-being of service users and the potential benefits of different investigations and treatment options for service users diagnosed with physiological disorders.

Learning aim: D (D.P5, D.P6, D.P7, D.M4, D.D3). It is recommended by the awarding body that learners put together a treatment plan to meet the needs of a selected service user with a physiological disorder.

How will I be graded?

Pass	Merit	Distinction
Learning aim A: Investigate the causes and effects of physiological disorders.		
A P1 Explain the causes, signs and symptoms of different types of physiological disorder on service users.	**A M1** Analyse the changes in body systems and functions resulting from different types of physiological disorder on service users.	**A D1** Evaluate the impact of physiological disorders on the health and well-being of service users.
Learning aim B: Examine the investigation and diagnosis of physiological disorders.		**B C D2** Justify the potential benefits of different investigations and treatment options for service users diagnosed with physiological disorders.
B P2 Compare investigative and diagnostic procedures for different physiological disorders.	**B M2** Assess the importance of specific procedures in confirming the diagnosis of physiological disorders.	
Learning aim C: Examine treatment and support for service users with physiological disorders.		
C P3 Explain the treatment and support available for service users with different physiological disorders. **C P4** Compare the types of carers and care settings for service users with different physiological disorders.	**C M3** Assess the provision of treatment, support and types of care for service users with different physiological disorders.	

How will I be graded?

Pass	Merit	Distinction
Learning aim D: Develop a treatment plan for service users with physiological disorders to meet their needs.		
D P5 Assess care needs of a selected service user with a physiological disorder. **D P6** Plan treatment to meet the needs of a selected service user with a physiological disorder. **D P7** Explain how the plan would improve the health and well-being of a selected service user.	**D M4** Plan treatment to meet the needs of a selected service user with a physiological disorder, reviewing as appropriate to improve outcomes.	**D D3** Justify the recommendations in the plan in relation to the needs of advantages and disadvantages of treatment options.

A Investigate the causes and effects of physiological disorders
(**A P1** , **A M1** , **A D1**)

Types of physiological disorders and effects on body systems and functions

The term physiology relates to how the body functions in normal conditions. When we study disorders, we are looking at how a disease or disorder has affected the normal working pattern of that system or organ. The signs and symptoms, and then diagnosis will help us to understand the disease process. See Table 14.1 below.

Key terms

Physiological disorders: diseases or disorders that affect the normal functioning of body systems and organs.

Endocrine: disorders affecting the endocrine system (the glands throughout the body that secrete hormones); for example diabetes.

Nervous: disorders affecting the nervous system, for example Parkinson's disease.

Musculo-skeletal: disorders affecting the muscles and skeleton, such as osteoporosis.

Respiratory: disorders affecting the respiratory system such as asthma.

Circulatory: disorders affecting the circulatory system (the system by which blood is transported around the body), for example leukaemia.

Cancer: cells in the body reproduce in an uncontrolled way, affecting the function of organs and systems; for example, bowel cancer occurs in and affects the bowel; however, cancer cells may then spread throughout the body.

Physiological disorder	Brief description and effects	Main body system involved
Asthma	This is a very common respiratory condition often found in children but if long term (chronic) it can be responsible for COPD, particularly if not controlled. Asthma is an inflammatory disorder that affects the airways; it is triggered by infections, exercise, drug allergies, chemical and smoke fumes, emotions and animal allergies. In asthma, the muscle layer of the bronchi are irritated by the inflammation. This causes the muscle to tighten, which causes narrowing of the bronchi and therefore difficulty in breathing, wheezing and coughing. As asthma is an inflammatory condition, it causes mucus to be produced, which inhibits the gaseous exchange, making breathing difficult. Occasionally older adults may be told they have emphysema when in fact they are suffering from asthma, or it could be genetically linked so therefore an inherited condition.	Respiratory
Chronic Obstructive Pulmonary Disease (COPD)	This is a collective respiratory disorder which includes the conditions chronic bronchitis, emphysema and chronic asthma. It affects the respiratory systems, making breathing difficult. As it is a 'chronic' or long-term disease, it usually affects people over the age of 40. It is responsible for over 30,000 deaths a year in England and Wales. COPD is usually caused by smoking. Other causes can be occupational exposure to dusts, indoor pollutants or air pollutants, or inherited causes (for example, there is an inherited lack of protein alpha-1-antitrypsin that results in emphysema). COPD is also caused by lung damage caused by infection (chronic), smoke or pollutants and it damages the elastic structure supporting the air sacs (alveoli) in the lungs. Alveoli are grape-like structures where gaseous exchange takes place. This is reduced to a sac structure in emphysema; the result is reduced surface area, therefore reduced carbon dioxide exchange, so breathlessness occurs.	Respiratory
Coronary heart disease	The arteries that supply the heart and cardiac muscle are called coronary arteries. When they are affected the result is coronary heart disease (CHD). The heart requires oxygenated blood to function properly and this is supplied via the coronary arteries. If these are restricted by atherosclerosis or blocked by a clot (thrombosis), then angina or heart attack (acute myocardial infarction) can result. If the blockage occurs on the left side of the heart muscle, it can affect delivery of oxygenated blood to the body. If it is on the right side of the heart muscle, it can affect blood getting the lungs to replenish oxygen supply.	Circulatory

Physiological disorder	Brief description and effects	Main body system involved
Leukaemia	There are a number of different types of leukaemia. It is a cancer of the blood cells and is named according to the type of white blood cell affected and whether it is chronic or acute. Acute leukaemias come on suddenly, often within days or weeks, progress quickly and need to be treated urgently. Chronic leukaemias develop more slowly, often over many months or years. Each disease presents differently and so has different treatment. Effects on body systems and functions: Reduced levels of white blood cells will cause the body to be more susceptible to catching infections. Also, in cases of anaemia the service user may suffer from breathlessness, fatigue and bleeding as the clotting factor is insufficient. The four main types of leukaemia are: • chronic myeloid (CML) • acute myeloid (AML) • chronic lymphocytic (CLL) • acute lymphoblastic (ALL).	Circulatory
Cancer • Breast • Liver • Bowel • Prostate • Melanoma	Cancer can be described as malignancies. They occur when cells in the body reproduce in an uncontrolled way; this interrupts the normal functioning of that organ and causes problems. Cancer cells can also spread throughout the body, growing and developing, causing wide-spread damage. Prostate cancer is covered in Unit 3.	Various (e.g. breast and prostate cancers affect the reproductive system)

Table 14.1 Physiological disorders

> ## Activity
>
> Watch this two-minute video produced by The Royal College of Physicians, which will inform you about how people may feel when facing an illness or disease that may dramatically affect their lives.
>
> www.youtube.com/watch?v=2j0kbeY_PEI&feature=player_embedded

Impact of disorders on service users' physical, mental, social and emotional health

Individuals will deal with diseases in many different ways and their coping strategies may also be very different. It is the role of the care worker to recognise and deal with these many and varying aspects of care. For example, a person who has just been diagnosed with a life threatening illness may experience anxiety, depression and require support from mental health experts. However, others may feel empowered by such a diagnosis and be defiant, outgoing and strong in their approach to the news.

We should understand that illnesses and their signs and symptoms do not always follow what is laid out in the text books so it is important to act upon the service user's history which will lead to a confirmed diagnosis and appropriate treatment pathway. A holistic approach to care requires us to meet the needs of the individual and deliver person-centred care.

Causes of physiological disorders
Inherited traits

Genetics are the patterns of development that we inherit from our parents and cannot be changed.

Activity

Think about the last time you went to the GP, either with a family member or yourself. What did you describe to the GP? What was a sign and what was a symptom?

Study the list below and with a partner discuss if it is a sign or a symptom.

- headache
- feeling sick
- abdominal pain
- facial rash
- high blood pressure
- lump in the breast
- high temperature.

Activity A P1   A M1   A D1

Disorders pamphlet

From the list of physiological disorders select two disorders to research and begin to formulate your information. Use text books, journals (e.g. *Nursing Times*) specific societies such as The British Heart Foundation; Diabetes UK. Patient UK and NHS choices are invaluable sites. This task requires careful, accurate and detailed research.

Your two chosen disorders should differ in their nature to provide a broad understanding of physiological disorders.

In your pamphlet, explain the causes, signs and symptoms of these different types of physiological disorder on service users. You may like to include pictures or diagrams to enhance your explanations.

Analyse the changes in body systems and functions resulting from different types of physiological disorder on service users. This could include:

- What system is affected?
- What changes have occurred to that system?
- What changes have occurred to the overall bodily functions?
- What influences have played a part in the course of the disorder, for example, inheritance, lifestyle choices, employment, diet or environmental factors?

Remind yourself of the command word 'evaluate'. As a conclusion to this part of the assessment evaluate how the disorder has affected the health and well-being of the service user. Has the disorder influenced the lifestyle, occupation, diet of the service user for example?

Check your understanding

1. What is the difference between Type 1 and Type 2 diabetes?
2. How is Parkinson's disease characterised?
3. Explain the term 'inherited'?
4. What is the difference between a sign and a symptom?
5. What substance accumulates in coronary arteries that causes them to block/narrow?
6. What dietary deficiencies causes rickets?

B Examine the investigation and diagnosis of physiological disorders B P2 , B M2 , B C D2

Investigative procedures for physiological disorders

It is important to establish what is called a 'baseline set of observations' to give to the doctors or supervisors in the care setting. This gives information to professionals to be able to treat and diagnose service users and to follow improvement or decline of their condition. The observations will then be taken at regular intervals to show a pattern of measurements. We must remember that not all service users are the same. Many factors will alter readings and these have to be taken into account when taking observations from service users.

Some measurements taken in order to diagnose a specific disorder may include temperature, pulse and respirations.

Blood pressure

Blood pressure is the force exerted by the blood on the vessel walls. Again this is a measurement to monitor the cardiovascular system. Blood pressure can vary over the body depending on where the pressure is taken. It is usually measured in the arm with a machine and an inflatable cuff. Nowadays these are very often battery operated and will display the pulse rate as well (older styles tend to be manually operated).

- A normal blood pressure reading for an adult can range between 110/60 mmhg–140/90mmhg (millimetres of mercury).

- A high blood pressure or hypertension is usually described as having a blood pressure of 140/90mmHg or above for a constant period of time.

- High blood pressure often causes no symptoms or immediate problems, but it is a major risk factor for developing a serious cardiovascular disease, such as a stroke or heart disease.

- In high blood pressure, your heart has to work harder to pump blood around your body. This can weaken it and over time can lead to life threatening conditions, the increased pressure can damage the walls of arteries, which can result in a blockage or cause the artery to split (haemorrhage). Both of these situations can cause a stroke.

Body temperature

The temperature of the body needs to be kept fairly stable as dramatic changes can seriously affect the body's systems. Body temperature monitors how effectively the homeostatic mechanisms are controlled in your body. Body temperature is measured in °C.

There are different ways to measure a temperature as well as different places on the body where temperature can be taken:

- tympanic thermometers – placed in the ear
- liquid crystal display (LCD) strip thermometers – placed on the forehead

- digital thermometers – placed in the mouth or under the arm.

The normal temperature for an adult is 36–37.2°C.

Investigations as appropriate for each individual

Medical history

Personal history of the individual should be considered and inform future care planning. This could include any medications or procedures which have been tried in the past and may have been unsuccessful. Current medication being taken should also be noted. It could also include family history, for example diseases and disorders which may be genetic or familial. Personal information, such as marital status, living arrangements and support networks, will all be important when planning for individual needs. Other personal information will also be required about lifestyle which may impact on the disease or disorder, for example, smoking, alcohol consumption and exercise patterns. It may also include information about bowel and bladder habits.

After the medical history has been taken a clinical physical examination can be done to give a picture of general health. This will include blood pressure, temperature and pulse rate, it will also include observation including skin colour, texture and level of consciousness. The examination should include a general look at the body including a palpation of specific areas of concern.

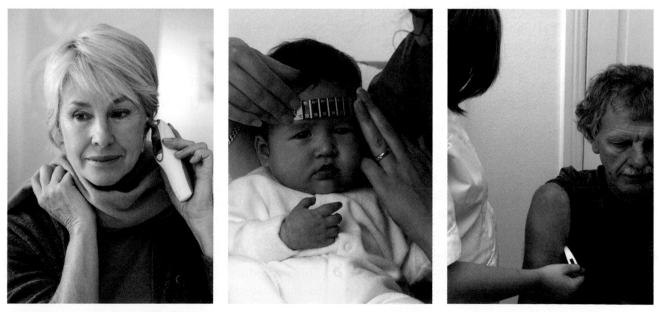

Figure 14.3 Three methods of temperature taking

Blood tests

These are very common medical investigations and can provide a wide range of details in order for diagnosis to be made.

A blood test may highlight infections, assess general health and test particular organ function.

It is important to remember that some tests are not conclusive by themselves so are used with other investigations to show the full medical picture of the service user.

Blood tests are usually performed by taking blood with a needle and syringe from a vein in the arm, with young children veins that may be more accessible are on the hand. Some blood tests can be taken using a finger prick for example blood sugar levels can be quickly checked this way, a heel prick is used to check for PKU (phenylketonuria) in the new born.

- **Full blood count (FBC)** – this is a test which looks at the whole blood picture and can determine factors like haemoglobin levels which would highlight anaemia, it will also look closely at the white cell picture and show if the body is fighting an infection, or has clotting problems. When this sample is taken, if requested, blood group and type can also be checked, this may be necessary if the service user is having surgery and may need to be matched for a blood transfusion.

- **Electrolyte tests** – this blood test checks the levels of minerals in the blood and can show if organs such as the kidneys and liver are functioning effectively. This can also highlight metabolic disorders.

- **Glucose tests** – this is taken to diagnose or monitor service users with diabetes. A specific glucose test called Glucose tolerance test (GTT) can be taken to observe how well the body deals with glucose, this requires the person to fast for a period of time and blood samples are taken at regular intervals after drinking a specific amount of glucose.

- **Blood gases** – this test checks the balance of oxygen and carbon dioxide levels and blood acidity levels in the blood stream, this would be used to diagnose problems with the respiratory system for example chronic obstructive pulmonary disorder (COPD).

- **Genetic tests** – this will be used to confirm a genetic disorder is responsible for the service users condition. For example, sickle cell anaemia, cystic fibrosis or haemophilia, this looks at the DNA in the blood. Genetic screening can also be done by blood sample to check for genetic conditions usually in pregnancy, this gives a likelihood of genetic conditions occurring in the new born for example Down's syndrome.

- **Blood cholesterol** – cholesterol is a blood lipid and high levels can lead to high blood pressure, coronary heart disease, heart attack and stroke. If high levels are diagnosed then lifestyle changes and medication can rectify the situation over a period of time.

- **Blood cultures** – these are usually taken when a service user is displaying signs and symptoms of severe infection (septicaemia) and diagnosis may not be obvious or treatment may not be effective. The blood sample is introduced to nutrition in laboratory conditions and any bacteria present will grow, identification of the bacteria can be done and specific treatment can be given, for example with antibiotics.

Other specific blood tests may be taken, for example in suspected heart attack, cardiac enzymes levels in the blood can confirm the diagnosis. Specific hormone levels can be checked to confirm endocrine disorders, pregnancy and menopause.

Diagnostic procedures for physiological disorders

Procedures for diagnosis which are used by professionals are to ensure correct identification and treatment of specific diseases. These may begin as a broad test, for example a blood test and then be narrowed down to reach a definite diagnosis, for example a biopsy.

Lumbar puncture

This procedure removes some cerebrospinal fluid to diagnose or confirm conditions like meningitis or haemorrhage (bleeding) around the brain. It is carried out under strict hygiene conditions and a needle is inserted into the lower spine to draw some of the fluid to allow testing. This route can also be used to give medication like antibiotics or chemotherapy.

Biopsy

This is removal and examination of a piece of tissue to analyse disease. A biopsy will confirm the presence or absence of a disease and will allow decisions to be made about further medical or surgical procedures to take place.

Difficulties in diagnosis and importance of recognising non-specific or confusing symptoms

As mentioned earlier, signs and symptoms are clues that lead to the eventual diagnosis, but some signs and symptoms can be very general and the diagnosis cannot be pinpointed immediately. As health professionals investigate the service user's condition, difficulties may arise in giving a conclusive diagnosis, especially when some signs and symptoms point to a variety of conditions. It may take time and a second opinion to confirm definite disorders or diseases so it is important to be aware that a service user may be under investigation for some time until a definite diagnosis can be confirmed.

When carrying out your investigations, study the signs and symptoms which lead to the diagnosis, but also assess what other conditions it may point towards.

Difficulties arise when the service user's signs and symptoms are not 'classic' or 'typical' so this may not lead to the correct diagnosis immediately. A variety of tests, re-tests or second opinions may be required until correct diagnosis has been reached.

For example:

- After a blood test, a low haemoglobin level may indicate anaemia but could also be a sign of internal bleeding or nutrition disorders which prevent the absorption of iron such as inflammatory bowel disorders or stomach ulcers.

- High blood pressure may indicate stress or if associated with obesity may point towards coronary heart disease.

- Haematuria (blood in urine) may indicate a urine infection damage or injury to the bladder or kidneys or tumour in the renal tract.

- Following a chest x-ray, a shaded area of lung tissue could indicate an infection or a benign or malignant tumour.

- Myalgic encephalomyelitis (ME), also known as Chronic Fatigue Syndrome (CFS), can manifest with many different signs and symptoms ranging from muscle swelling, tenderness and pain, to tiredness and fatigue. Sleeping problems, concentration and cognition trouble will also be noted. ME is said to be a recognised loose list of vague and non-specific problems which are shared with other illnesses, so diagnostic confusion can frequently occur.

Distinction activity B P2   B M2   B C D2

Disorders pamphlet

You now need to add more information to your pamphlet about the investigations that have been carried out in order to confirm the diagnosis of your two chosen disorders.

Compare investigative and diagnostic procedures for different physiological disorders.

- What referral methods have been used and why?
- Which investigations have taken place, for example medical history, blood tests, and x-ray and give reasons?
- Where have these investigations taken place and why?

First, assess the importance of specific procedures in confirming the diagnosis of physiological disorders. Then, remind yourself of the command word 'justify'. Justify the potential benefits of different investigations and treatment options for a service user diagnosed with physiological disorders. Include an assessment and justification of these investigations which will underline the importance and benefits of them in order to confirm a diagnosis. For example a biopsy is highly important in the correct, accurate and quick diagnosis of a malignant tumour.

Further reading

Waugh, A and Grant, A. (2014) *Ross and Wilson Anatomy and Physiology in Health and Illness*, Churchill Livingstone

'Fundamentals of Anatomy and Physiology for Student Nurses', Wiley-Blackwell; 1 Pap/Psc edition (4 Mar. 2011)

Norris, M and Rae Siegfried, D. (2011) *Anatomy & Physiology For Dummies*, Wiley

Useful websites

Diabetes UK: www.diabetes.org.uk

Age UK: www.ageuk.org.uk

Parkinson's UK: www.parkinsons.org.uk

Alzheimer's Society: www.alzheimers.org.uk

National Rheumatoid Arthritis Society: www.nras.org.uk

National Osteoporosis Society: www.nos.org.uk

British Heart Foundation: www.bhf.org.uk

Cancer Research: www.cancerresearchuk.org

NHS Smokefree: www.nhs.uk/smokefree#AIiClg8eUjlmXK45.97

Health and social care assessments: http://webarchive.nationalarchives.gov.uk/20121015000000/http://www.direct.gov.uk/en/DisabledPeople/HealthAndSupport/ArrangingHealthAndSocialCare/DG_4000436

Carer's Allowance: www.carersuk.org/Information/Financialhelp/CarersAllowance

NICE pathways: http://pathways.nice.org.uk

17 Caring for individuals with dementia

About this unit

As we live longer, we experience disorders that previous generations did not live to develop. One such disorder is dementia, which is progressive and causes problems with memory, problem solving, language and thinking. The Alzheimer's Society estimates that by 2025 over a million people will live with dementia. Family are often the first carers for those with dementia but as the disorder develops caring for them becomes an increasing part of the work of health and social care professionals.

In this unit we look at the different types of dementia, and some of the causes and symptoms that we know about. We look at how the early and later stages of the disorder may affect people and we see how the disorder affects people differently. We look at the role of person-centred care and how thoughtful design of environments and person-centred care can help to maintain independence for as long as possible.

Learning aims

The aims of this unit are to:

A Examine the types, causes and symptoms of dementia.

B Examine the effects of dementia on people who have the condition.

C Investigate the concept of person-centred care for people who have dementia to maintain quality of life and well-being.

How will I be assessed?

For learning aims A and B, it is recommended by the awarding body that learners write a report that examines the types, causes and symptoms of dementia, and the progressive effects on mental and physical health, quality of life and well-being of people who have the condition.

For learning aim C, it is recommended by the awarding body that learners write a report based on a case study of an individual who has dementia that justifies the impact and benefits of person-centred care on the individual, and evaluates how current practice in dementia care meets the individual's needs.

How will I be graded?

Pass	Merit	Distinction
Learning aim A: Examine the types, causes and symptoms of dementia.		**A B D1** Evaluate the importance of understanding how different types of dementia can have a progressive effect on all aspects of a person's health and well-being.
A P1 Explain the causes of three different types of dementia. **A P2** Explain the symptoms of three different types of dementia.	**A M1** Analyse how the different types of dementia might be identified by their symptoms.	
Learning aim B: Examine the effects of dementia on people who have the condition.		
B P3 Explain the effects of three different types of dementia on the mental and physical health of individuals who have the condition. **B P4** Discuss the effects of three different types of dementia on the quality of life and well-being of people who have the condition.	**B M2** Assess how the different types of dementia can have progressive effects on a person's mental and physical health and their quality of life and well-being.	

especially of more recent memories, withdrawal from interests and activities, becoming lost in familiar places and mood swings are typical of the middle to later stages of dementia. Communication difficulties increase.

Vascular dementia

Vascular dementia symptoms may be of gradual onset or may occur suddenly depending on the underlying cause. In the early stages, common symptoms include:

- problems with planning, organising and problem solving (e.g. problems handling money)
- difficulties following a sequence of actions (e.g. making a cup of tea)
- slower speed of thought
- problems concentrating, even on familiar tasks.

Other symptoms of vascular dementia include general forgetfulness, problems recalling recent events, problems with speech and with seeing objects in three dimensions. They may experience mood swings, become depressed or lose interest in things. Symptoms get worse, often in sudden steps, as more strokes occur. In the later stages, there may be confusion, disorientation and increased problems with reasoning and communication. More memories are lost, and behaviours may change. Irritability, agitation, aggressive and socially inappropriate behaviour may be accompanied by disturbed sleep, delusions and hallucinations. As the condition progresses, the person may become less aware of what is happening.

Symptoms of subcortical vascular dementia include early loss of bladder control, mild weakness on one side resulting in an unsteady walk and a tendency to fall. People with this form of dementia may develop clumsiness, lack facial expression and struggle saying words.

Dementia with Lewy bodies (DLB)

Dementia with Lewy bodies (DLB) varies according to where the brain is damaged. The base of the brain governs movement. The symptoms of DLB and Parkinson's disease dementia become more similar as the conditions progress and they are grouped as Lewy body dementias. The main feature of Parkinson's disease involves movement – tremors, stiffness, difficulty swallowing and a shuffling gait. There may be fainting and falls. Lewy bodies deposited in the outer layers of the brain in DLB affect mental abilities, producing cognitive symptoms such as slowness of thought. Difficulties with decision making and organisational tasks, and sleep disturbances develop later.

Frontotemporal dementia (FTD)

Frontotemporal dementia (FTD) symptoms vary according to the part of the lobes affected, but usually involve behaviour and /or language changes. This type of dementia is most commonly seen in early onset dementia.

There are three types of frontotemporal dementia:

- *Behavioural variant frontotemporal dementia* causes a loss of inhibitions and impulsive, easily distractible behaviour. People with this type of dementia may lose motivation, show less interest in others and appear selfish. They may have compulsive behaviours, lose social manners, and binge on 'junk' foods, alcohol or cigarettes.
- *Progressive non-fluent aphasia* results in speech problems with slow, hesitant speech, grammatical errors leaving out words. They may have difficulty understanding complex sentences but may understand single words.
- *Semantic dementia* results in a loss of words and understanding of the purpose of objects. A person with semantic dementia may have trouble finding the right word. They may ask the meaning of familiar words and have difficulty recognising familiar people or common objects.

Memory, visuospatial skills, planning and organising are unaffected in the early stages but as symptoms progress behavioural and language problems develop until symptoms in the later stages are similar to those of the later stages of Alzheimer's disease.

We have covered other common symptoms including confusion and forgetfulness, behaviour changes and mood swings, anxiety, loss of bowel and bladder control, difficulties with communication.

Activity A P2

Using at least two sources, explain the symptoms of the three different types of dementia that you researched in the previous activity.

Activity

How might changes in behaviour, language, memory or visual perception indicate the type of dementia a person experiences? Give three examples of different types of dementia, their symptoms and explain the link between symptoms and type of dementia.

Check your understanding

1 Why is 'dementia' sometimes called 'an umbrella term'?
2 Explain the difference between Alzheimer's disease, vascular dementia, dementia with Lewy bodies and frontotemporal dementia.
3 Why may frontotemporal dementia cause changes in behaviour and language?
4 Which type of dementia may suddenly get worse and why?
5 Which type of dementia is most common?

B Examine the effects of dementia on people who have the condition

B P3 , B P4 , B M2 , A B D1

In the early stages of dementia, a person may feel anxious and depressed as they come to terms with their diagnosis. Dementia is a progressive disorder, which means symptoms get worse, sometimes in sudden steps and sometimes gradually over a period of time. The effects of dementia vary according to the part of the brain affected.

Effects of dementia on mental and physical health

Reasoning and communication

Communication is affected early in frontotemporal dementia, as the left temporal lobe of the brain controls language. The first signs are being unable to find the right word for something or name for someone. People with progressive non-fluent aphasia may have hesitant speech and leave out words in sentences. In the later stages, there may be loss of language (aphasia). Those with semantic dementia may retain vocabulary, knowing the word but lose the meaning, so may ask 'What is shoe?' or 'What is bath?'

Information processing

Information processing problems may be experienced by people with frontotemporal dementia as they struggle to express themselves. In the early stages of Alzheimer's people may have difficulty grasping new ideas and may have problems with visual perception. In the early stages of vascular dementia, people may take longer to process ideas, and may have problems planning and ordering activities, for example, they may forget to boil the water for a cup of tea, or may forget to light the gas after turning it on. They may have problems making decisions.

Sleeplessness and restlessness

Sleeplessness and restlessness is typical of later stages of many types of dementia. If people are mobile, they may search for old friends and family and become aggressive if a carer explains they are not there. People may be restless because of pain which they cannot express. They may be delusional or have hallucinations which cause them to be restless.

Behaviour

Behaviour is affected by the frontal part of the brain, and behaviour changes such as irritability, mood swings and aggression may be early symptoms of frontotemporal dementia. In the later stages behaviour may become inappropriate such as undressing in public, or may become compulsive, for example, compulsive eating.

Movement

Many people with dementia with Lewy bodies have problems with movement. There may be slowness, stiffness and tremor, problems with balance, falls and fainting. Symptoms may fluctuate and be less pronounced on some days. In later stages of Alzheimer's and in the later stages of many types of dementia the person may shuffle assessed as lacking capacity at that particular time for that particular decision according to the Mental Capacity Act, but sometimes they need help to access information, to explore their options and to have their voice heard. They may need someone to speak out to promote their rights. An advocate should be independent of social services and the NHS and should not be a relative or friend as they may have a conflict of interest when providing support.

The Mental Capacity Act 2005

The Mental Capacity Act 2005 introduced Independent Mental Capacity Advocates (IMCAs) to support people who cannot make or understand decisions. The IMCA must represent the best interests of the person. They do not make decisions but may represent the views of the person who can no longer articulate their views and has no one such as a relative or carer to express their views. An IMCA is a statutory service, provided by law, and the IMCA must be instructed, and consulted, for people who lack capacity and have nobody else to support them (other than paid staff). They must be consulted if NHS treatment is being considered, and must be consulted if an NHS body or local authority wishes to arrange accommodation (or a change of accommodation) in hospital or a care home and (a) the person will stay in hospital longer than 28 days or (b) they will stay in the care home for more than eight weeks. According to the NHS website, an IMCA may support someone who lacks capacity during care reviews, when there is no one else to support them. An IMCA must represent such a person in adult protection cases, whether or not family, friends or others are involved.

'Quality statement 9' from the National Institute for Health and Care Excellence (NICE) says that

> 'When significant decisions are being made concerning the current and future care of someone with dementia, it is important that they can access independent advocacy services if they are not fully able to present their own views.'

Despite this and the legal duty to provide such advocacy, there is a shortage of IMCAs.

Activity C P5

Explain how person-centred care can be applied to one individual who has one type of dementia? Base your response on one person you may be aware of or one case study mentioned in this section.

Explain how the type of dementia they have influences the care they may require. If basing your answer on a real person, ensure confidentiality by calling them Mr/Mrs/Ms X and **do not identify them**.

Safeguarding people who have dementia

Protection versus independence and rights

Care must recognise the vulnerability and safety needs of individuals who have dementia. It must balance protection versus independence and rights. It is easy to be so protective that the person's independence is reduced and they may be deprived of their rights. It used to be the case that people with dementia were kept indoors all the time in care homes, to protect them from danger, and prevent them from wandering away and getting lost. They were deprived of liberty in order to protect them. This is illegal under the Deprivation of Liberty safeguards, part of the Mental Capacity Act 2005 which applies to England and Wales which says that staff can only deprive someone of their liberty in a safe and correct way, and that this is only done when it is in the best interests of the person and there is no other way to look after them. There is an application process to deprive someone of their liberty.

Staff training should be targeted on managing the balance between safety and independence, for example, training should be given on the Mental Capacity Act and Deprivation of Liberty Safeguards. There is a free online course from the Open University, Designing space for dementia care, which considers how the environment can be adapted to enable someone with dementia to find their way around. Some residential accommodation has different coloured doors for each resident's room so the resident can find their own way back to their room independently. Some residential care homes have courtyard sensory gardens where residents can sit in the fresh air and enjoy the garden.

Technologies that alert staff but respect a person's dignity and privacy, such as portable alarms which the individual can press for help, or sensors which turn a light on if a person gets up in the night all help maintain independence.

Safe, enabling and empowering environments

Safe, enabling and empowering environments will have safe non-slip flooring and grab rails, and differentiate between the colour of walls and doors. Music may be used for reminiscence sessions, or an individual may have their own favourites on an MP3 player or tablet device. Singing has been found to benefit people with dementia as it helps those with language difficulties remember words.

Awareness of cultural and religious differences

Safeguarding includes having an awareness of cultural and religious differences. Someone who has dementia and previously had strong faith may feel more secure with religious items in their room. A Catholic might like their Bible and a rosary, while someone who is Hindu might like a statue of their favourite deity. Having familiar objects around contributes to emotional security and can help calm a person.

Awareness of representation and advocacy

Safeguarding includes having an awareness of representation and advocacy. Advocacy has been explained earlier, but someone in the early stages of dementia may wish to give lasting power of attorney (LPA) to someone to administer their affairs when they are no longer able to do so for themselves. LPAs must be over 18 years old. There are two types – for financial and property affairs (this LPA cannot be a bankrupt), and an LPA for health and welfare. This applies in England and Wales, but Northern Ireland has Enduring Power of Attorney. Creating a LPA is straightforward but the power must be registered with the Office of the Public Guardian in order to become valid.

> **Activity C P6**
>
> Explain why a flexible approach is needed when planning care for one individual who has one type of dementia.
>
> Use the example from the previous activity as a starting point for this activity. Look at the individual (you may have to explain a little more about their background) and then look at the effect of the type of dementia they have.

Assessment of needs, protection and safety

Health and social care workers can help to manage everyday care after diagnosis in a variety of ways, although it must be remembered that many people in the early stages of dementia are cared for in their own homes by family members with occasional support from health and care professionals.

Communication and behaviour needs

A speech and language therapist may support someone with frontotemporal dementia by making the most of remaining language skills and helping the person develop other ways of communicating, for example, by signs or gestures. They may advise on any swallowing difficulties the person may experience.

Behaviour changes

Behaviour changes are sometimes more embarrassing for the carer than for the person with frontotemporal dementia. Where behaviour changes cause no harm, they may be accepted. In public, behaviours may cause more difficulties. Help cards available from the Alzheimer's Society can be used to explain to the public about the symptoms of dementia.

Sometimes diversion can help avert unwanted behaviours, but it is important to recognise the triggers for such behaviour. It may be that the individual is trying to communicate something, for example, taking their clothes off might mean they are too hot. Taking them out for a walk in a sheltered garden might help them cool down and distract them from undressing. Restlessness may indicate that a person needs the toilet.

Repetitive behaviours may link back to an activity the person used to do when they were younger.

Regular routines that include physical exercise will benefit the individual.

Aids and assistive technologies

Aids and assistive technologies can help people with dementia remain independent for longer. Practical aids such as an extended grabber can help someone retrieve dropped objects and avoid falls. Pagers/alarms that alert others if the person falls can bring assistance quickly.

Diet

It is important to maintain the person's usual lifestyle as much as possible. Awareness of food preferences, together with a little creative thinking, means that an individual can still enjoy their usual food even though they have difficulty swallowing. Soft, moist foods are easier to swallow than hard dry foods, and a spoon may be needed if co-ordination is a problem. A thick soup with soft vegetables provides nutrition and is easy to manage. Finger foods such as sandwiches are easier for people with co-ordination problems, but again the nutritional value should be considered. White bread may cause constipation, whereas a soft oat bread will prevent it.

Water should be available and offered frequently to prevent dehydration.

Just because it is there does not mean it will be consumed. A person with dementia may need to be reminded and helped to eat and drink.

Pill boxes

Pill boxes labelled with the day of the week to help the person to know when to take medication may be helpful. Some pill boxes automatically sound an alarm and dispense medication, sounding the alarm until pills have been taken from the dispenser. Other dispensers send a message to a carer if medication has not been taken or the battery is low. Alarms should be used with caution as they may confuse a person with dementia.

Personal care routines

Personal care routines can be made safer and independence maintained in personal hygiene if there are grab rails and a walk-in shower with a shower stool, rather than a bath. This will help maintain privacy as the individual may then be able to shower with minimal assistance. A raised toilet seat may be helpful for some people with stiffness.

Figure 17.2 Practical aids such as raised toilet seats and bathroom grab rails can help service users to maintain their independence

Ensuring protection and limiting vulnerability

Ensuring protection and limiting vulnerability can be difficult, especially when a person has fluctuating needs. Alarms can be fitted on doors to alert others if the person goes out. The person with dementia may carry a mobile phone with location enabled so they may be traced if they wander too far and get lost. They may have a phone with pre-set contacts to call for help, but these depend on the phone being charged. Routines for daily living such as always having their tablets before breakfast or doing their shopping on a certain day, or attending a lunch club every Wednesday can help a person with dementia retain some independence. Unfortunately people with dementia are vulnerable when financial transactions are concerned.

Local shopkeepers who know them may be very helpful, but increasingly older people and those with dementia are the victims of fraud. They may be tricked into giving card details and cards to criminals. Appointing someone with Lasting Power of Attorney may help to safeguard people with dementia.

Maintaining a safe, enabling environment

Maintaining a safe, enabling environment includes monitoring services such as gas and hot water.

There are automated shut-off devices which can turn off the gas supply or turn off a cooker if the gas has been left on but these services involve a cost. Similarly, water shut off devices are available and plugs that open if water is above a certain level, or change colour if water is too hot. These prevent floods and scalds. Home hygiene may be difficult for a person with dementia, and it may be easier to have someone call in to help with vacuuming and dusting if money allows, otherwise cordless cleaners are safer than those with trailing flexes which are trip hazards.

Loose mats and rugs are also trip hazards and should be removed. Patterned carpet and shiny floors surfaces can confuse those with perceptual difficulties. Plain carpet is better.

The room layout and décor can help or hinder a person with dementia. Mirrors can confuse a person with dementia. They may think it is another person in the room. In the kitchen, cupboard doors which all look the same, and with concealed openers are confusing for those with perceptual difficulties. If cupboard doors cannot be taken off, labels with a photo of the contents will help them locate items. Open shelving with blunt hooks for hanging things are a good alternative. Colour contrast helps a person distinguish between areas for dining and areas for cooking.

The Dementia Services Development Centre (DSDC) is an international centre of knowledge and expertise based at Stirling University and offers ideas for dementia friendly design. It has an online virtual care home designed for people with dementia, showing how colour, lighting and design can aid independence.

Food safety is an issue for many people, not just those with dementia. A relative or carer can help them check expiry dates and ensure food is used in rotation, perhaps by staying and preparing a meal with them. Some fridges have glass doors which help the person with dementia to see what is inside.

Figure 17.3 A hospital corridor decorated to help dementia patients with an easy to see handrail and a sign to the sitting room with a picture of an armchair

Activity C M3

Explain how person-centered care is important to maintain the dignity, rights and entitlements of one individual who has dementia. Base your answer on one case study from a previous activity such as that at the end of the previous section.

Health and well-being

Care for people with dementia should take a holistic approach to health and well-being, focusing on them as an individual. Health and well-being includes physical, spiritual, emotional, social and intellectual aspects of a person's care.

Safe handling and administration of medication has been mentioned earlier in learning aim C.

Diet and nutrition

Diet and nutrition requirements vary depending on the individual. Some people with frontotemporal dementia may over eat while those with Alzheimer's may forget to eat. Everyone needs an adequate fluid intake, especially of water, to prevent dehydration. A person with dry lips and a dry tongue will find eating difficult. Too much tea and coffee may cause bladder problems whereas water hydrates without side effects. Someone with dementia may require encouragement to drink. Just because a glass of water is at their elbow does not mean they see it or associate it with quenching thirst. Healthy snacks, such as fruit should be available, although some people with diabetes or other health problems may need to maintain portion control. Care should be individualised according to the person's needs.

Complementary therapies

Complementary therapies such as massage and aromatherapy may help some people with dementia by calming their agitation and helping them relax. Plug-in room scents are a safe alternative to scented candles but consideration should be given to those with breathing problems. Fresh air may be better than artificial scents.

Activities

Activities such as reminiscence work may help some people with dementia as early memories are retained longer than recent ones. Photographs of people or familiar places, may help them remember and aid communication. Exercise such as digging in the garden or mowing the grass using a push mower helps them retain links to former interests and helps their circulation and digestion.

Sensory stimulation

Sensory stimulation, for example, playing their favourite music quietly may help an individual recall past experiences. Light strings and coloured lights can be relaxing and cheerful especially in dark winter days.

The important factor is to see the person as an individual, find out what they like and what they don't like, what their needs are, and plan care to support their needs and maintain the skills they have.

Activity C D2

Justify the impact and benefits of holistic person-centred care on one individual who has dementia.

What impact does holistic care have on them? Base your answer on one case study from the previous activities and consider social, physical, intellectual, emotional and spiritual aspects of care.

Responsive and flexible care provision to maintain quality of life and well-being

Health and social care workers must continuously reflect on and review support so that relevant care is maintained, and happiness and enjoyment in life is preserved for a person who has dementia.

They do this by using the *care planning cycle* of assessment, planning, monitoring and reviewing outcomes, including regular reviews and forward planning to address fluctuating abilities and changing needs, bearing in mind the needs of carers too. Care should be reviewed within the first three months and then when the person's condition changes. They must be reviewed annually even if there is no change.

Involving the person in their own care planning

Involving the person in their own care planning as much as possible while they are able to participate ensures that the care that is planned meets their needs. If there is no information about their previous interests and preferences, carers may be able to help.

Involving family and friends in care planning

Involving family and friends in care planning or the person who has LPA in care planning helps to represent the person's best interests when they are no longer able to express their views.

Care planning should focus on maintaining the person's current strengths and abilities, while being aware that these may change either gradually or suddenly. Their ability to remember a tune and sing may persist even though they may have lost words for speech and cannot take part in a conversation.

Activities and exercise

Individualising activities and exercise, will increase the chance that the person engages with it. Sensory stimulation in the form of lights may help some, but may confuse others. Dance is good exercise for those who have no problems with balance, but may be difficult for someone with Parkinson's dementia. They may benefit from gentle yoga where they can sit or lie down. Reminiscence activities must be adapted to suit the individual's known preferences. Some people have happy memories, others do not. Reminiscence may help a person but it may also distress them if it reminds them of difficult times in their lives, such as being separated from parents during the war. Activities should be based around individual needs. A keen gardener who has dementia may still like to plant bulbs and take cuttings. In the later stages they may like to look at

flowers. A pianist with early stage dementia might like to play the piano but in the later stages may gain pleasure from listening to piano music.

Activity C D3

Choose one individual with dementia from your own work experience observation. Remember to maintain confidentiality when basing your answer on a real person. How far does current practice (what is really done) meet their social, physical, intellectual, emotional and spiritual needs?

Evaluate how current practice in dementia care meets the needs of an individual with dementia, through managing its effects and maintaining health and well-being.

Are there any areas of care that are overlooked or areas of care that could be improved?

Activity

Look at some inspection reports on the Care Quality Commission website for dementia care services that require improvement. What factors may result in care being less than adequate?

Check your understanding

1 What are the principles of person-centred care? Give an example for each principle.
2 Give three examples of how the physical environment may be made safer for someone with dementia.
3 Give an example of how too much protection may disempower a person with dementia.
4 How may a person in the early stages of dementia be helped to manage their own medication?
5 How may complementary therapies help someone with dementia?
6 Why is it necessary to review care plans for a person with dementia?

How will I be graded?

Pass	Merit	Distinction
Learning aim B: Examine factors that may impact on children's growth and development.		**B C D2** Justify approaches to assessment used for the early recognition and support for children with differing needs. **B C D3** Evaluate the extent to which professionals help children to meet their developmental milestones through the application of the theories of growth and development and use of assessment methods.
B P3 Discuss the influence of factors on children's growth and development.	**B M3** Assess how one area of development affected by factors may impact on other areas of development.	
Learning aim C: Explore how assessment is used to identify children's stages of growth and development and their support needs		
C P4 Explain methods used for the assessment of children's growth and development from birth to eight years. **C P5** Plan for and observe children to identify their stages of development.	**C M4** Effectively plan and implement appropriate methods of assessment to identify the children's stages of development. **C M5** Assess the methods of observation selected for the assessment of each child's growth and development.	

A Understand patterns, principles and theories that contribute to an understanding of growth and development in children from birth to eight years A P1 , A P2 , A M1 , A M2 , A D1

Patterns of growth and development

Definition of growth and development

Growth is an increase in size, height and weight. Growth is regulated by pituitary growth hormone. There are two main types of restricted growth, proportionate short stature (PSS) which is a general lack of growth, where the trunk and limbs are in proportion and disproportionate short stature (DSS) where the limbs are out of proportion with other parts of the body. The tallest man living is Sultan Kösen (born in 1982) who measured 251 cm (8 ft 3 in) in Ankara, Turkey, on 08 February 2011.

Development is concerned with gaining new skills. A child may grow into an adult, but may not develop skills. If they have brain damage they may never learn to communicate, to walk or care for themselves.

Growth and development do not necessarily go together. A person may develop skills yet have restricted growth perhaps because of achondroplasia (dwarfism). Dr Tom Shakespeare is a very well respected disability rights campaigner and academic who has achondroplasia. Someone with restricted growth, and someone with excessive growth, does not automatically have problems with intellect.

Developmental milestones for children between birth and eight years and areas and aspects of development

Children are individuals and develop at different rates so any developmental charts must be regarded as indicative, not fixed. They develop physical, intellectual, communication and social skills while developing emotionally, and vary in the rate at which they develop in each area. Unit 1 'Human lifespan development' explains physical development between birth and eight years, including fine and gross motor development, locomotion, balance, co-ordination and hand–eye co-ordination. The same unit also explains social and emotional development during the same period and into adulthood.

Developmental milestones

Theories:

Piaget: 0–2 years sensori-motor stage

Bowlby: bonding with primary care giver

Freud: 0–18 months oral stage

Erikson: birth to one year – trust versus mistrust.

Age	Physical	Intellectual/cognitive	Speech, language and communication	Social/emotional
2 months	Can hold head up and begins to push up when lying on tummy Smoother movements with arms and legs	Pays attention to faces Follows things with eyes and recognises people at a distance Cries if bored	Coos, makes gurgling sounds Turns head toward sounds	Smiles Tries to focus when looking at parent
4 months	Holds head steady Pushes down on legs when feet are on a hard surface Starts to roll over from tummy to back Holds and shakes a toy, reaches for toys Brings hands to mouth When lying on stomach, pushes up to elbows	Responds to affection Reaches for toy with one hand Hands and eyes co-ordinate to reach a toy. Follows moving things with eyes from side to side Recognises familiar people	Babbles with expression and copies sounds Different cries for hunger, pain, or being tired	Smiles spontaneously Likes to play with people and might cry when playing stops Copies some movements and facial expressions, like smiling or frowning Watches faces closely
6 months	Rolls over in both directions (front to back, back to front) Begins to sit without support Supports weight on legs and might bounce Rocks back and forth, sometimes crawling backward before moving forward Teething starts	Explores the world by taste – putting everything in mouth Curious about things and tries to get things that are out of reach Passes things from one hand to the other (hand to hand co-ordination)	Responds to sounds by making sounds, taking turns with parent, babbling Responds to own name Makes sounds to show joy and displeasure Begins to say consonant sounds: mama, baba	Recognises familiar faces, knows if someone is a stranger Likes to play with others, especially parents Responds to other people's emotions and often seems happy Looks at self in a mirror

Bandura

Bandura's social learning theory says human behaviour is a result of continuous interaction between cognitive, behavioural and environmental influences.

The stages of social learning are:

- Attention, recognising a behaviour. For example, Child A watches an adult comfort another crying child.
- Retention, including rehearsal of the behaviour. Child A imagines what they would say or do in that situation.
- Motor Reproduction. Child A tries it out and uses self-observation and feedback to check how it went
- Motivation – if praised by an adult for comforting another child, Child A feels a sense of achievement.

You can imagine how this sequence would go if a child heard an adult swear.

Emotional and social development

John Bowlby

John Bowlby's attachment theory suggested that babies are pre-programmed to bond with those who care for them and this gives them a secure base from which to explore the world. Failure to bond at this stage can make it difficult for them to form close relationships later in life. Robertson and Bowlby believe that short term separation from an attachment figure leads to distress and formulated the PDD model of protest, despair and detachment. The primary care giver's behaviour towards the child affects the child's internal working model of themselves. A child who is positive and loved will feel secure. One who is unloved and rejected will develop avoidant behaviour.

Three main features of the internal working model are:

1. a model of others as being trustworthy or not
2. a model of the self as valuable or worthless
3. a model of the self as effective or not when interacting with others.

Rutter

Rutter rejected Bowlby's first theory that the primary bond has to be with the mother, and pointed out that some babies form this bond with others. Rutter also pointed out the difference between never having established a bond (privation) and the loss or damage to a bond (deprivation). Rutter suggested that privation was much more harmful resulting in clinging attention-seeking behaviour and indiscriminate friendliness at first, then later on anti-social behaviour, inability to form lasting relationships or feel guilt. There may also be issues with language, intellectual development and physical growth.

Erikson

Erikson's theory of life stages is widely used in health and social care. This is a psychodynamic theory which looks at how emotional and motivational forces affect behaviour.

Erikson described eight stages of development as explained in the following table.

Stage	Age	
Trust vs. Mistrust	Birth to 1 year	The baby learns to trust the world about them if someone responds to their cry. If the child is neglected, the child will be frustrated, withdrawn, suspicious, and will lack self-confidence.
Autonomy vs. Shame and Doubt	2 to 3 years	The child needs a supportive atmosphere so it can develop a sense of self-control without a loss of self-esteem. If a child does not trust the world, or is labelled as naughty, they will experience shame and doubt. A child opens a cupboard and pulls out glasses. A carer who says the child is naughty will instil shame and doubt. A carer who encourages exploration also encourages independence and autonomy. Of course the carer must make sure the environment is safe for the child by removing breakable objects.

→

Stage	Age	
Initiative vs. Guilt	4 to 5 years	The child develops a sense of responsibility which increases initiative during this period. If the child is made to feel too anxious then they will feel guilty.
Industry vs. Inferiority	6 years to puberty	The child starts school and learns about the world through books and technology. The child learns from every aspect of the environment and is eager to learn. Success and mastery bring a feeling of achievement and encourage further industry. Failure at this stage makes them feel inferior.
Identity vs. Role Confusion	adolescence	The child emerges as an adolescent and forges a new identity or remains confused about their role, sometimes acting childishly.
Intimacy vs. Isolation	young adulthood	The young person either remains isolated or enters a close and intimate relationship
Generativity vs. Stagnation	adulthood	This creative and nurturing phase encourages the younger generation in developing and leading useful lives too. An unfulfilled life is stagnant.
Integrity vs. Despair	older age	This is when the individual looks back and evaluates their life. Some feel they have had a good life and have few regrets. They experience integrity. Some people feel bitter and betrayed by lack of life chances. They are full of regrets and may despair.

Table 18.3 Erikson's stages of development

Sigmund Freud (1856–1939)

Sigmund Freud developed the psychodynamic perspective which emphasises the importance of the unconscious mind, and of early experiences.

Feud suggested there are three parts to our mind:

1 The 'id' (fully unconscious) contains drives and basic instincts. A baby passes urine without thinking about it.

2 The 'ego' (mostly conscious) deals with external reality so the child learns the rules of society, for example, to use the toilet.

3 The 'super ego' (partly conscious) is the conscience or the internal moral judge so a child who knows where the toilet is and how to use it, but has an 'accident', may feel ashamed.

Freud said that early experiences shape us. He described the following stages of development:

- Oral (birth to 18 months) – In this stage, the baby puts everything to the mouth.

- Anal (18 months to 3 1/2). During this phase the child learns to control bowels and gains pleasure from this.

- Phallic (3 1/2 years to 6 years) – In this phase, children are working out what it means to be a girl or boy. Freud said that children fall in love with the parent of the opposite sex. Boys love their mothers – the Oedipus complex. Girls love their fathers most at this stage. This is the Electra complex.

- Latency (6 years to puberty) is a period of calm in a child's life.

- The genital phase (puberty to adulthood) is a period of creativity when work and love are both balanced. The person is psychologically well-adjusted and balanced. The child grows into the adult, and no longer is 'in love' with the opposite sex parent but may identify with their values: a girl loved her father because he was kind. As an adult, she will adopt this as her own value and try to be kind.

Check your understanding

1 What stages did Piaget identify in a child's development?

2 What did Vygotsky mean by the 'zone of proximal development'?

3 Why did Skinner say punishment does not work?

4 What methods did Skinner use to encourage a desired behaviour?

5 What is social learning?

6 Explain Bowlby's idea of the internal working model.

7 What does Rutter say about the effects of privation and of deprivation?

8 Erikson's stages include Autonomy vs. Shame and Doubt. Explain this with an example.

9 How may an understanding of Kohlberg's theory of moral development help in childcare?

10 What is the Language Acquisition Device?

B Examine factors that may impact on children's growth and development B P3, B M3, B C D2 B C D3

Factors

Factors impacting on growth and development may be:

- Personal factors, such as health, disability, and genetic inheritance are explained earlier in the unit. Cystic fibrosis limits what a child can do, affects the ability to absorb nutrients from food, and limits life expectancy. Hearing impairment may affects language development. Down's syndrome is associated with heart defects. On the other hand, a healthy child born when due has a sound start in life.

- Prenatal factors impact on growth and development. A lack of antenatal care (care during pregnancy) may mean problems go undetected. Gestational diabetes which happens in some pregnancies, may cause the baby to grow much bigger than expected, causing problems in a normal delivery. Genetic disease may go undetected if the mother does not attend for antenatal screening. A mother who has extreme morning sickness (hyperemesis gravidarum) and is untreated may have a smaller baby, as may a woman who smokes during pregnancy. Smoking narrows blood vessels and restricts the flow of nutrients to the baby. Alcohol is best avoided during pregnancy because alcohol passes through the placenta directly to the baby. A mother who drinks more than 6 units a day may have a baby with Foetal Alcohol syndrome, which is a combination of poor growth, facial abnormalities and learning and behavioural problems. There is an increased risk of miscarriage if a mother drinks alcohol in the first three months of pregnancy. Antenatal screening enables problems to be detected early. Mothers and their babies can benefit from advice about healthy eating and healthy lifestyles.

- Socio-economic factors such as poverty affect growth and development. If parents do not offer a balanced diet and instead offer chips, sugary drinks and sweets as a cheap means of feeding children, the children will have tooth decay and are likely to be overweight. Access to health and education services is fairly widespread but some parents may not fully understand the dangers of a diet high in sugar. Culture too plays a part. Some parents believe 'a fat baby' is a healthy baby and start solid foods before 6 months, giving cereals and starchy foods which result in the baby drinking less milk and having less of the protein and calcium that they need for strong bones and teeth. Parents who have an adequate income and are able to access and use information about a healthy diet give their babies a head start in life.

- Environmental factors, such as damp and overcrowded housing increase the risk of a baby having chest infections. Tuberculosis rates have increased over the last twenty years and some strains of tuberculosis are drug resistant. Tuberculosis is spread more easily in overcrowded conditions.

Atmospheric pollution, poor air quality, especially in large cities, has been linked to increase risk of premature birth, low birth weight, birth defects and increased risk of diabetes and heart disease in adulthood. In contrast, a baby born where air quality is good, and raised in a home where there is clean water and adequate heating will have a better chance of a healthy life.

- Emotional factors affect babies and children. The Bucharest Early Intervention Project, a collaboration between Tulane University, University of Maryland, and Boston Children's Hospital began in 2000, to examine the effects of early institutionalization on brain and behaviour development. They followed children from infancy to age twelve, and found the results of neglect can include significant cognitive delays, increased risk for psychological disorders, and stunted physical growth.

- When there is domestic abuse, parents may interact less with the child, and the abused parent may be depressed and withdrawn. A child may be neglected, and speech may be delayed. Inconsistent parenting may cause the child to be anxious, and withdrawn or over-controlling as they try to manage the situation. They may have problems at school and have low self-esteem. The positive impact of high-quality foster care as an intervention for children who have been placed in institutions has been shown during this study. Poor attachment in the first years of life may affect the child both emotionally and physically for many years, which is why it is important to provide high-quality foster care as soon as possible if adoption is not available when babies are taken into care.

- Transitions are changes in circumstances. Some personal transitions or changes such as starting school happen to all children, they may be anxious and unsettled until they adjust to the new situation. In 'School starting age: the evidence', Cambridge researcher David Whitebread suggests that children learn better from play activities than they do from being instructed and starting formal instruction later would help children develop intellectual and emotional 'self-regulation' by giving them more time for physical, constructional and social play.

- Some transitions that children may experience are not shared by all. Family breakdown affects children. A child may feel a sense of loss, losing a parent, a home, a way of life. They may feel different, frightened that the other parent may leave too, and they will be alone. They may be angry, feel rejected and insecure and feel that is it their fault. They may be angry with one or both parents and torn between parents. As a result of these emotions children may regress to earlier behaviour, bedwetting, 'being clingy, having nightmares, and being worried or disobedient.

Activity B P3

Consider the factors identified in the previous section. Discuss the influence of factors on children's growth. You may wish to base your answer on the children mentioned in previous activities.

The impact of factors on growth and development

Factors may affect growth and development positively or negatively, and their effects may be short term or long term.

Negative impacts may include failure to grow and thrive and delayed development. Positive impacts may be enhanced development.

Impacting on one area of development may affect other areas, so a child who feels loved, valued and emotionally secure will grow physically, and one who is neglected may fail to thrive physically and have delayed intellectual development.

Some factors may be counterbalanced by other factors. Sure Start and free nursery places for children in poverty help to counteract the effect of a poor environment. In the Bucharest previously undetected problems such as hearing problems may delay language development. Early detection and intervention can reduce the impact of problems.

At ages 2 to 3, an early years practitioner or health visitor will check:

- Communication and language
- Physical development
- Personal, social and emotional development.

These are recorded and shared with parents. Early detection of problems such as autism may allow for early support and interventions.

At 2½ years old, the child is screened for:

- general development, movement, speech, social skills and behaviour, hearing and vision
- growth, healthy eating and keeping active
- managing behaviour and encouraging good sleeping habits
- tooth brushing and going to the dentist
- safety
- vaccinations.

Early detection of health and development problems and parenting skills allow early interventions and extra support if required. Problems with hearing and vision may become apparent at this stage. This allows treatment to start, thus reducing developmental delay.

At between 4 and 5 years old, as part of the National Child Measurement Programme, a health screening is carried out including the child's height, weight, vision and hearing (if required). This screening is to monitor for childhood obesity and also to detect underweight children who may need extra support.

The Early Years Foundation Stage Profile
In the final term of the year in which the child reaches age five, and no later than 30 June in that term, the Early Years Foundation Stage Profile must be completed for each child. Summative assessment at this stage gives a baseline to measure further progress and monitor the effectiveness of any interventions.

Growth monitoring

One way of assessing a child's growth is by measuring and recording their growth, i.e. their height and weight and comparing it to what is expected of a child of the same sex and age. The Royal College of Paediatrics and Child Health publish growth charts for school age years, plus charts for childhood and puberty close monitoring and Down's syndrome, as well as for body mass index based on World Health Organisation (WHO) Child Growth Standards. Such charts enable monitoring of growth and referral to specialists if there is a variation from the expected range.

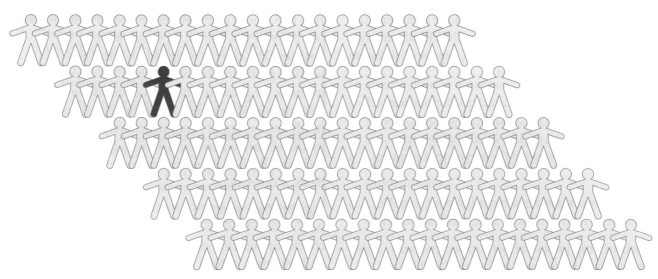

Figure 18.3

If a child's weight is on the 25th centile, this means that if you lined up 100 children of the same age in order from the lightest to the heaviest, your child would be number 25 and there would be 75 children heavier (see Figure 18.3).

Curved centile lines on the charts show the average weight or height gain for children. (Centile refers to results out of 100.)

Figure 18.4 shows part of a centile chart for the weight of boys aged 1 to 4 years.

It's normal for a child's weight or height to be anywhere within the top and bottom centile lines on the charts. The centile lines show roughly how healthy children are expected to grow. Measurements may go up or down by one centile line, but if they went up or down by

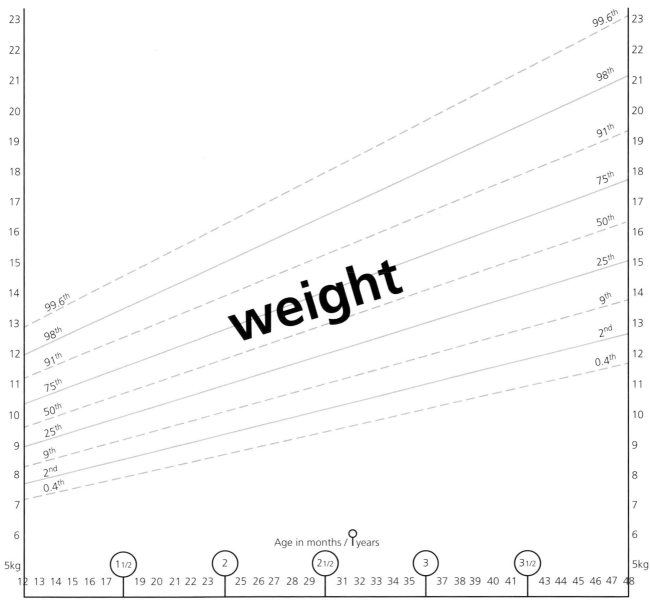

Figure 18.4

Literacy	
Reading	Children read and understand simple sentences. They use phonic knowledge to decode regular words and read them aloud accurately. They also read some common irregular words. They demonstrate understanding when talking with others about what they have read.
Writing	Children use their phonic knowledge to write words in ways which match their spoken sounds. They also write some irregular common words. They write simple sentences which can be read by themselves and others. Some words are spelt correctly and others are phonetically plausible.
Mathematics	
Numbers	Children count reliably with numbers from 1 to 20, place them in order and say which number is one more or one less than a given number. Using quantities and objects, they add and subtract two single-digit numbers and count on or back to find the answer. They solve problems, including doubling, halving and sharing
Shape, space and measures	Children use everyday language to talk about size, weight, capacity, position, distance, time and money to compare quantities and objects and to solve problems. They recognise, create and describe patterns. They explore characteristics of everyday objects and shapes and use mathematical language to describe them.
Understanding the world	
People and communities	Children talk about past and present events in their own lives and in the lives of family members. They know that other children don't always enjoy the same things, and are sensitive to this. They know about similarities and differences between themselves and others, and among families, communities and traditions.
The world	Children know about similarities and differences in relation to places, objects, materials and living things. They talk about the features of their own immediate environment and how environments might vary from one another. They make observations of animals and plants and explain why some things occur, and talk about changes.
Technology	Children recognise that a range of technology is used in places such as homes and schools. They select and use technology for particular purposes.
Expressive arts and design	
Exploring and using media and materials	Children sing songs, make music and dance, and experiment with ways of changing them. They safely use and explore a variety of materials, tools and techniques, experimenting with colour, design, texture, form and function.
Being imaginative	Children use what they have learnt about media and materials in original ways, thinking about uses and purposes. They represent their own ideas, thoughts and feelings through design and technology, art, music, dance, role-play and stories.

Table 18.6 The Early Learning Goals: specific areas

Source: EYFS Framework, www.gov.uk/government/uploads/system/uploads/attachment_data/file/335504/EYFS_framework_from_1_September_2014__with_clarification_note.pdf

Child's name:	Age:			Date:
Understanding	Understand position words, 'in' 'on' 'under', e.g. 'put teddy under the chair'.			
	Answer 'who' 'what' 'where' questions about a story.			
Speaking	Talk about ownership, e.g. 'My teddy' 'Sam's car'			
	Use simple pronouns correctly such as 'I', 'me', 'you'.			
	Talk about what s/he has been doing.			
Listening and attention	Stop and listen to an adult who has called their name and then refocus on their original activity.			
	Attend to an adult's choice of activity for a short period of time.			
Interaction	Include another child in their play and talk to them as they do so, e.g. give a child a cup to drink from			
	Seek out others to share experiences, e.g. by saying 'watch me'.			

Table 18.7 Assessment checklist for a four-year-old

A time-sample observation sheet may be used to track a child's activities, for example, Table 18.8 shows Onur is involved with a variety of activities and plays with different children, which is what one might expect of a 3 to 4 year old.

9.00	Playing with cars alone
9.10	Playing football outside with J, S, and B
9.20	Still playing football with J, S, and B
9.40	Indoors – painting
9.50	In Home corner – being daddy, cooking food for T, W and G
10.00	Still in home corner, playing with T, W and G

Table 18.8 Onur's morning: time-sample observation sheet

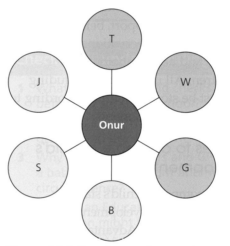

Figure 18.5 Onur's morning: sociogram

If the time-sample observation sheet had shown Onur sitting by himself engaged in solitary play or looking at a picture book for this hour, Onur might need help to make friends and staff could support him by involving him in a group activity.

A sociogram might be used to monitor social skills. Onur's morning might be recorded in the sociogram in Figure 18.5. This shows who he played with and is colour coded for the different activities, but it does not show for how long he played with each set of friends.

Other methods of assessment may include recording what a child does for a period of time usually by writing down everything they do. Film or sound digital recordings may be made with

parental permission but must be stored securely. Children whose parents have not given permission must not be recorded.

Areas of development are described earlier in the unit. The Early Years Foundation Stage Profile assessment gives a base line for teachers in Year 1 and further assessments may be designed to focus on areas of development where needs have been identified. There are several considerations to be taken into account when assessing children.

Timing and environmental considerations are extremely important. A tired child, or one who is unwell should not be observed in order to assess them as this would give a false picture. Assessors must be aware that their relationship with the

Think about it

The Brooklands Experiment

Until the 1950s, many children with learning disabilities were sent away to live in institutions. In 1957, Professor Tizard took 16 children aged between 4 and 10 years from such an institution and put them into groups of 8 with a housemother. He found that children in family groups made better progress than those in large institutions. This changed the way that people with disabilities are cared for.

Further reading

Arnold, C. (2015) *Doing Your Child Observation Case Study: A Step-by-Step Guide*. Open University Press

Bowlby, J. (1953). *Child Care and The Growth Of Love*. London: Penguin Books

Center on the Developing Child at Harvard University (2012). 'The Science of Neglect: The Persistent Absence of Responsive Care Disrupts the Developing Brain', Working Paper No. 12. Retrieved from www.developingchild.harvard.edu.

Gross, R. (2015) *Psychology: The Science of Mind and Behaviour 7th Edition*, Hodder Education

Harter, S. (2015). *The Construction of the Self, Second Edition*, Developmental and Sociocultural Foundations, New York: Guilford Press

Power, F. C. (2002) 'Kohlberg, Lawrence (1927–1987)', *Encyclopedia of Education*. Retrieved 6 January 2016 from Encyclopedia.com: www.encyclopedia.com/doc/1G2-3403200355.html

Sharma A. and Cockerill, H. (2014) *Mary Sheridan's From Birth to Five Years: Children's Developmental Progress, Fourth Edition*. Routledge

DfE (2014) 'Statutory Framework For The Early Years Foundation Stage: Setting the standards for learning, development and care for children from birth to five'.

Useful websites

Harter's self-perception theory: https://prezi.com/bxoqdqfyzknf/susan-harters-self-perception-profile/

Birth to Five (2009 edition): see http://webarchive.nationalarchives.gov.uk

'School starting age: the evidence': www.bucharestearlyinterventionproject.org   www.cam.ac.uk and www.cdc.gov

Center on the Developing Child at Harvard University (2012) 'The Science of Neglect: The Persistent Absence of Responsive Care Disrupts the Developing Brain', Working Paper No. 12: see www.developingchild.harvard.edu

Statutory framework for the early years foundation stage: Setting the standards for learning, development and care for children from birth to five. Published March 2014, Effective September 2014. EYFS framework from 1 September 2014 with clarification note: see www.foundationyears.org.uk

Parents' Guide to the Early Years Foundation Stage Framework: www.foundationyears.org.uk/files/2015/01/EYFS_Parents_Guide-amended1.pdf

History of the Brooklands experiment: see www.mencap.org.uk

Birth-to-five development timeline: An interactive guide to child development from birth to five years old, including videos and advice to help parents: see www.nhs.uk

Restricted growth: see www.nhs.uk/conditions

Royal College of Paediatrics and Child Health (for growth charts): www.rcpch.ac.uk

'A genius explains' – interview with David Tammet, autistic savant, by R. Johnson, 12 February 2005: www.theguardian.com/theguardian/2005/feb/12/weekend7.weekend2

19 Nutritional health

About this unit

The nutritional health unit will allow you to investigate sources and functions of nutrition. It allows research into factors which may affect nutritional health, for example medical conditions, allergies and intolerances, religion and culture. During this unit you will develop skills in planning and preparing tailored nutritional meals to meet the needs of specific individuals.

Nutritional health is a key concept which should be at the heart of all workers in the health and social care sectors. Good nutrition can influence lifestyle choices and eating habits and so avoid conditions like obesity, diabetes and heart disease.

Learning aims

The aims of this unit are to:

A Understand concepts of nutritional health and characteristics of essential nutrients.

B Examine factors affecting dietary intake and nutritional health.

C Plan nutrition to improve individuals' nutritional health.

How will I be assessed?

For learning aims A and B it is recommended by the awarding body that learners produce a report relating dietary intake and essential nutrients to two individuals with differing needs, considering the factors influencing their nutritional health.

For learning aim C it is recommended by the awarding body that learners produce plans to improve the nutritional health of two individuals with differing needs, showing the application of concepts of realistic situations.

How will I be graded?

Pass	Merit	Distinction
Learning aim A: Understand concepts of nutritional health and characteristics of essential nutrients		**A B D1** Evaluate the role of nutritional health in maintaining the selected individuals' health and well-being, and the impact of influencing factors.
A P1 Explain how the concepts of nutritional health contribute to health and well-being. **A P1** Explain the sources of essential nutrients and their functions in the body.	**A M1** Assess the impact of dietary intake and dietary deficiencies on nutritional health.	
Learning aim B: Examine factors affecting dietary intake and nutritional health		
B P3 Explain the health, socioeconomic and cultural factors that can influence the nutritional health of the selected individuals. **B P4** Compare the dietary intake of the selected individuals with their nutritional requirements.	**B M2** Assess how the dietary intake and nutritional health of the selected individuals are influenced by their dietary habits and lifestyle choices.	

How will I be graded?

Pass	Merit	Distinction
Learning aim C: Plan nutrition to improve individuals' nutritional health		
C P5 Produce clear plans to improve the nutritional health of two individuals with different dietary needs. **C P6** Explain how the recommendations will improve the nutritional health of the selected individuals.	**C M3** Produce professionally presented plans to improve the nutritional health of two individuals with different dietary needs. **C M4** Analyse how the recommendations will improve the nutritional health of the selected individuals.	**C D2** Justify the recommendations in the plans in relation to the needs and situations of the selected individuals. **C D3** Evaluate the importance of planning nutritional health for selected individuals to ensure their dietary needs are met, and that influencing factors are taken into account.

A Understand concepts of nutritional health and characteristics of essential nutrients A P1 , A P2 , A M1 , A B D1

Concepts of nutritional health

Healthy eating and a balanced diet

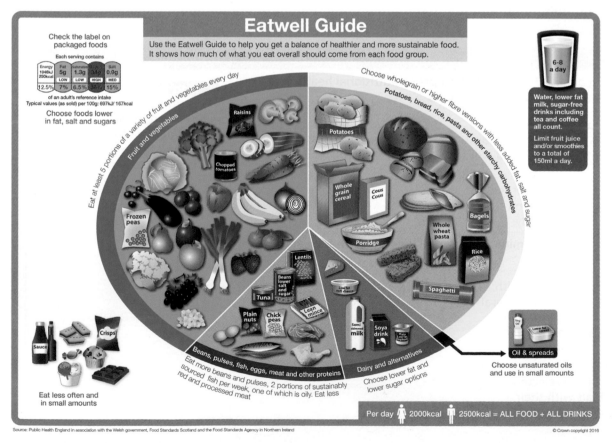

Figure 19.1 The Eatwell Guide

The Eatwell Guide is a pictorial representation of recommended daily food groups which also includes drinks and snacks.

It suggests that you may not get it right at every meal but a good balance over the week or day is something to aim for.

The guide is based on the five food groups.

- Bread, rice, potatoes, pasta and other starchy foods.
- Fruit and vegetables.
- Milk and dairy foods.
- Meat, fish, eggs, beans and other non-dairy sources of protein.
- Foods and drinks high in fat and/or sugar.

The Eatwell Guide encourages you to choose different foods from the first four groups every day, to help ensure you obtain the wide range of nutrients your body needs to remain healthy and function properly.

Choosing a variety of foods from within each group will add to the range of nutrients you consume.

Foods in the fifth group – foods and drinks high in fat and/or sugar – are not essential to a healthy diet.

The guide is suitable for most people including people of all ethnic origins and people who are of a healthy weight or overweight. It is also suitable for vegetarians. However, it does not apply to children under two years of age because they have different needs. Anyone under medical supervision or with special dietary needs might want to check with their GP, or a registered dietitian, to be clear about whether or not it is suitable for them.

> ## Think about it
>
> Print off a blank Eatwell Guide plate and consider the food you consumed yesterday, make a prediction about your diet then write or draw it into the plate in the respective sections and then consider
>
> - Is this balanced?
> - What food groups have you omitted to consume?
> - What food groups have you consumed in excess?
> - How could you address this?

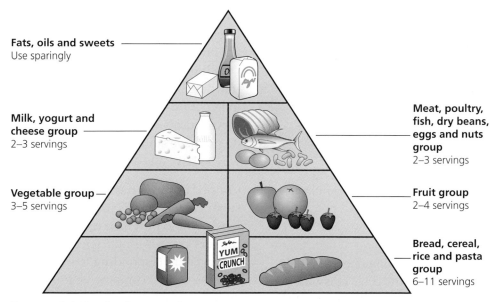

Figure 19.2 The food pyramid

The food pyramid

The food pyramid (see Figure 19.2) is a concept of looking at foods and the amounts that should be eaten. It was developed in the USA based on nutritional requirements.

This has now been further developed with different types of pyramid depending on life stage and activity levels, and has also been adapted for vegetarians. For more information go to www.mypyramid.gov

Malnutrition

Malnutrition is the result of a long period of time with insufficient or excessive amounts of nutrients. This could be from inadequate amounts of specific nutrients or lack of a combination of nutrients, or an excessive intake of high energy foods resulting in health problems.

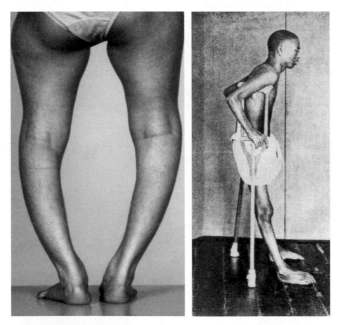

Figure 19.3 A deficiency of vitamin D can lead to rickets (left). The main cause of beriberi (right) is a diet low in thiamine.

Under-nutrition

Under-nutrition results when someone consumes less than is needed for a healthy diet. This can result in the individual becoming ill or more at risk from developing certain conditions. Under-nutrition may be caused when not enough food is provided, or when there is a deficiency of a specific nutrient. It can also be caused if the body is unable to use or absorb nutrients.

Obesity

Weight problems and obesity are usually caused by an energy imbalance. This means that the number of calories consumed is higher than the number of calories used (for example, through movement or exercise). This imbalance may be caused by eating too many calories or by not doing enough exercise. In other words, the intake of calories is higher than those which the body is using up.

Obesity is an increasingly common problem, because many modern lifestyles often promote eating excessive amounts of cheap, high-calorie food and spending a lot of time sitting at desks, on sofas or in cars.

Obesity can also affect quality of life and lead to psychological problems, such as low self-esteem or depression.

It's a common problem, estimated to affect around one in every four adults and around one in every five children aged 10 to 11 in the UK. For more information on this subject go to www.nhs.uk/news/pages/newsarticles.aspx?TopicId=Obesity

Effects of food processing and preparation methods

During preparation and processing, foods may lose some of their nutritional value. Foods that are processed and sealed in cans are heated to a very high temperature and may be said to be less nutritious, but canned foods do not deteriorate for long periods of time so may be convenient to some service users who are unable to get to the shops or do not have storage facilities, it may be a cheaper way to have an easy meal.

Canned or ready meals can have high salt and sugar content so it is important to check the food label prior to purchase or serving particularly if the service user is on a specific diet. Manufacturers however are responding to consumer worries and processed food can now be purchased in natural juices, spring water and with reduced sugar and salt content. The traffic light system for instantly identifying nutritional content will clearly show the food's nutritional value at a glance so the consumer can be aware of nutritional intake for that particular meal.

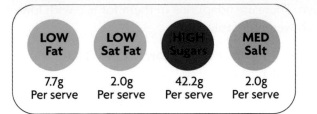

Figure 19.4 Traffic light labelling for food

Current nutritional issues and effects on health

Self-prescribed health supplements

Health or dietary supplements refer to a range of products commonly consumed for the purpose of supplementing the diet and enhancing health. They are usually presented in dosage forms such as capsules, soft gels, tablets and liquids. Some examples of health supplements include vitamins, minerals (e.g. calcium, iron, magnesium) and herbal supplements (e.g. Echinacea, Guarana). These products typically contain ingredients from natural sources. They are not medicinal products meant to prevent, treat, cure or alleviate the symptoms of medical diseases or conditions and are generally considered low-risk.

> **Think about it**
>
> Investigate the following web link to see the benefits and controversy of self-prescribed health supplements:
>
> www.ehow.com/about_4672439_what-dietary-supplement.html

Genetically modified foods

With the help of technology, food and animal characteristics can be changed to enhance specific properties and make food more desirable to the consumer. For example, disease resistance, enhanced nutrient levels, longer shelf life. Some questions have been raised as to whether modified genes in our food may cause adverse effects in humans.

> **Think about it**
>
> Have a look in your local supermarket at some foods with added nutrients. Discuss the advantages and disadvantages of this.
>
> Look at the web link below to investigate this topic further.
>
> www.who.int/foodsafety/publications/biotech/20questions/en/

> **Activity** A P1
>
> **Assignment**
>
> As a health care assistant in a local clinic your manager has asked you to produce some annotated posters for the walls of the waiting area.
>
> The title should be 'Nutritional health for all' and it should highlight areas such as
>
> - the Eatwell Guide
> - the main food groups
> - 5 a day.
>
> Ensure that your poster explains how the concepts of nutritional health contribute to health and well-being.

Nutritional measures and recommended dietary intakes

Balancing energy requirements for protein, fat, carbohydrate (kilocalories and kilojoules)

The rate at which energy is used in the body is called the metabolic rate, so even a person who is resting needs energy to carry out internal activities.

All food contains energy, which is released in the body when the food is completely broken down. Energy in food is measured in a laboratory with a piece of apparatus called a 'bomb calorimeter'

Energy yields of nutrients are as follows

- 1g protein provides 17kj (4kcal)
- 1g carbohydrate provides 16 kJ (3.75 kcal)
- 1g fat provides 37kj (9kcal).

Measuring body mass index (BMI)

BMI looks at the relationship between height and weight and is a good indicator of whether someone is the right weight for their height.

The calculation is as follows:

Body weight (kg) divided by Height $(m)^2$

BMI is measured like this:

- Underweight: below 20
- Normal: 20–25
- Overweight: 25–30
- Obese: 30-40
- Morbidly Obese: 40+

Therefore someone who weighs 65kg and is 1.72m tall would have a BMI of 22 (rounded up) and would be in the normal weight range.

The calculation is as follows:

1.72^2 (i.e. 1.72×1.72) = 2.96

65 divided by 2.96 = 21.9

Activity A M1

Work out the BMI for the following people:

- Jim is 1.70m and weighs 57kg.
- Billy is 1.83m and weighs 121 kg.
- Sian is 1.62m and weighs 45kg.
- Sam is 1.55m and weighs 70kg.

After considering these findings assess the impact that under or over nutrition may have on the health of these individuals.

Some adults who have a lot of muscle may have a BMI above the healthy range. For example, professional rugby players can have an 'obese' BMI result despite having very little body fat.

Using growth charts to monitor weight gain

These are used to plot the average growth of children from birth to the age of 4 years. They have been designed specifically to be used in the personal child health records which all children

have. There are adaptions in them for use with low birth weight infants.

See www.rcpch.ac.uk/Research/UK-WHO-Growth-Charts

This link provides a range of specific charts for children from birth to 18-years-old and also provides a video link showing the use of growth charts by professionals.

Using and interpreting dietary reference values (DRVs)

Dietary reference values (DRVs) were developed by the Department of Health in 1991, to replace recommended daily amounts (RDAs). DRVs are benchmark intakes of energy and nutrients – they can be used for guidance but shouldn't be seen as exact recommendations. They show the amount of energy or an individual nutrient that a group of people of a certain age range (and sometimes sex) needs for good health. Although DRVs are given as daily intakes, people often eat quite different foods from one day to the next and their appetite can change so in practice, the intake of energy and nutrients needs to be averaged over several days. Also DRVs apply only to healthy people. DRV is a general term used to cover:

- Estimated average requirement (EAR) – this is the average amount of energy or a nutrient needed by a group of people
- Reference nutrient intake (RNI) – this is the amount of a nutrient that is enough to meet the dietary needs of about 97 per cent of a group of people
- Lower reference nutrient intake (LRNI) – this is the amount of a nutrient that is enough for a small number of people in a group with the smallest needs – most people will need more than this
- Safe intake – this is used when there isn't enough evidence to set an EAR, RNI or LRNI. The safe intake is the amount judged to be enough for almost everyone, but below a level which could have undesirable effects.

Age	Males		Females	
	MJ	kcal	MJ	kcal
0–3 months	2.28	545	2.16	515
4–6 months	2.89	690	2.69	645
7–9 months	3.44	825	3.20	765
10–12 months	3.85	920	3.61	865
1–3 years	5.15	1230	4.86	1165
4–6 years	7.16	1715	6.46	1545
7–10 years	8.24	1970	7.28	1740
11–14 years	9.27	2220	7.72	1845
15–18 years	11.51	2755	8.83	2110
19–50 years	10.60	2550	8.10	1940
51–59 years	10.60	2550	8.00	1900
60–64 years	9.93	2380	7.99	1900
65–74 years	9.71	2330	7.96	1900
74+ years	8.77	2100	7.61	1810

Table 19.1 Estimated average requirement (EAR) of energy per day, expressed in both MJ and kcal

Nutrient intakes

The tables on the following pages show the number of nutrients sufficient for almost every individual. It tends to be higher than most people need.

Note: Shortly before this book went to press, the Department of Health released revised DRVs and so the tables in this book are out of date. You can find the new DRVs at the British Nutrition Foundation website, www.nutrition.org.uk

Age	Thiamin (mg)	Ribo flavin (mg)	Niacin (nicotinic acid equivalent) (mg)	Vitamin B6 (mg)	Vitamin B12 (µg)	Folate (µg)	Vitamin C (mg)	Vitamin A (µg)	Vitamin D (µg)
0–3m	0.2	0.4	3	0.2	0.3	50	25	350	8.5
4–6m	0.2	0.4	3	0.2	0.3	50	25	350	8.5`
7–9m	0.2	0.4	4	0.3	0.4	50	25	350	7
10–12m	0.3	0.4	5	0.4	0.4	50	25	350	7
1–3y	0.5	0.6	8	0.7	0.5	70	30	400	7
4–6y	0.7	0.8	11	0.9	0.8	100	30	400	–
7–10y	0.7	1.0	12	1.0	1.0	150	30	500	–
Males									
11–14y	0.9	1.2	15	1.2	1.2	200	35	300	–
15–18y	1.1	1.3	18	1.5	1.5	200	40	700	–
19–50y	1.0	1.3	17	1.4	1.5	200	40	700	–
50+y	0.9	1.3	16	1.4	1.5	200	40	700	**

Age	Thiamin (mg)	Ribo flavin (mg)	Niacin (nicotinic acid equivalent) (mg)	Vitamin B6 (mg)	Vitamin B12 (µg)	Folate (µg)	Vitamin C (mg)	Vitamin A (µg)	Vitamin D (µg)
Females									
11–14y	0.7	1.1	12	1.0	1.2	200	35	600	–
15–18y	0.8	1.1	14	1.2	1.5	200	40	600	–
19–50y	0.8	1.1	13	1.2	1.5	200	40	600	–
50+y	0.8	1.1	12	1.2	1.5	200	40	600	**
Pregnancy	+0.1***	+0.3	*	*	*	+100	+10	+10	10
Lactation	+0.2	+0.5	+2	*	+0.5	+60	+30	+350	10

Table 19.2 Daily nutrient intakes for vitamins

*No increments **After age 65, the RNI is 10µg ***For last trimester only

Age	Calcium (mg)	Phosphorus (mg)	Magnesium (mg)	Sodium (mg)	Potassium (mg)	Chloride (mg)	Iron (mg)	Copper (mg)	Selenium (µg)	Iodine (µg)
0–3m	525	400	55	210	800	320	1.7	0.2	10	50
4–6m	525	400	60	280	850	400	4.3	0.3	13	60
7–9m	525	400	75	320	700	500	7.8	0.3	10	60
10–12m	525	400	80	350	700	500	7.8	0.3	10	60
1–3y	350	270	85	500	800	800	6.9	0.4	15	70
4–6y	450	350	120	700	1100	1100	6.1	0.6	20	100
7–10y	550	450	200	1200	2000	1800	8.7	0.7	30	110
Males										
11–14y	1000	775	280	1600	3100	2500	11.3	0.8	45	130
15–18y	1000	775	300	1600	3500	2500	11.3	1.0	70	140
19–50y	700	550	300	1600	3500	2500	8.7	1.2	75	140
50+y	700	550	300	1600	3500	2500	8.7	1.2	75	140
Females										
11–14y	800	625	280	1600	3100	2500	14.8**	0.8	45	130
15–18y	800	625	300	1600	3500	2500	14.8**	1.0	60	140
19–50y	700	550	270	1600	3500	2500	14.8**	1.2	60	140
50+y	700	550	270	1600	3500	2500	8.7	1.2	60	140
Pregnancy	*	*	*	*	*	*	*	*	*	*
Lactation	+550	+440	+50	*	*	*	*	+0.3	+15	*

Table 19.3 Daily nutrient intakes for minerals

*No increments **Insufficient for women with high menstrual losses

Nutrients on food labels

Food manufacturers are not legally obliged to provide nutritional information unless a nutritional claim is made about the product. For those that do provide the information, they must state:

- The energy value in kilojoules and kilocalories
- The amount of protein, carbohydrate and fat in grams.

Stating the amount of sugars, saturated fats, fibre or sodium is optional unless a claim is made about these levels.

Information must always be given as amounts per 100g or 100ml of food. Values per portion can be given as well, as long as the number of portions in the pack is stated.

Typical composition	A serving (340g) provides:	100g provides:
Energy	1625 kJ 388 kcal	478 kJ 114 kcal
Protein	21.8 g	6.4 g
Carbohydrate Of which sugars	42.8 g 6.5 g	12.6 g 1.9 g
Fat Of which saturates	14.3 g 5.4 g	4.2 g 1.6 g
Fibre	3.7 g	1.1 g
Salt	3.1 g	0.9 g

Figure 19.5 Food labelling

Characteristics of essential nutrients

All foods have components, known as nutrients. Nutrients consist of:

- carbohydrates, which are necessary for energy and may be turned into body fat
- fats, which provide energy, protect vital organs and also help the absorption of certain vitamins
- proteins, which are essential for growth and repair of the body
- minerals and vitamins, which regulate the body's processes and some of which are also used for growth and repair.

Water is also essential for health although it is not defined as or considered to be a nutrient. Fibre is also not considered a nutrient as the body does not absorb it, but it is needed for healthy bowels. Sometimes substances are added to food to perform specific functions. These are known as additives. Additives may be used to prevent food spoilage or enhance the texture, flavour or appearance of food.

> ### Key terms
>
> **Macro-nutrient** – these are nutrients required in large quantities for example, carbohydrates, proteins and fats.
>
> **Micro-nutrient** – these are nutrients which are needed in small amounts which include vitamins and minerals.

Figure 19.6 A healthy diet is varied and should include fresh fruit and vegetables, protein and carbohydrates

Nutrients are available to the body through digestion or sunlight. During digestion, nutrients enter the small intestine and pass through into the bloodstream. The liver then controls the distribution around the body. Some nutrients such as vitamin D are obtained through sunlight acting on substances within the skin.

Essential macro-nutrients

Carbohydrates (simple)

Carbohydrates contain the elements of oxygen, hydrogen and carbon. They are essential for the storage and release of energy. Simple carbohydrates are an easily accessible form of energy.

Monosaccharides – these are also known as 'simple sugars' and are soluble in water. There are three types:

1 fructose
2 glucose
3 galactose.

Disaccharides – these are sometimes known as double sugars and are soluble in water. These are two monosaccharides joined together. There are three main types:

1 sucrose
2 lactose
3 maltose.

Sources are:

- fructose: occurs in fruit and vegetables and especially honey
- glucose: found in fruit and plant juices;
- galactose: found in milk
- sucrose: occurs in sugar cane and sugar beet and in some fruits
- lactose: found only in milk
- maltose: this is sometimes known as malt sugar.

When the body does not have enough carbohydrates to produce energy from glucose it begins to burn fat for energy instead. Ketones are acids in the blood that form when fat is used as an energy source.

Over time, the accumulation of acidic ketones causes you to lose minerals vital to normal health functions like fluid balance, nerve transmission and muscle contraction.

Carbohydrates (complex)

This form of carbohydrate is the preferred form of energy – it is slow release and so benefits the body over a longer period of time.

Polysaccharides – poly means many – these are many saccharides joined together (complex). Polysaccharides are insoluble in water and there are a number of types including starch and non-starch polysaccharides. It is found in corn, bread, pasta and rice and is also supplied by traditional staple foods such as cereals, roots and tubers.

When the body does not have enough carbohydrates to produce energy from glucose it begins to burn fat for energy instead. Ketones are acids in the blood that form when fat is used as an energy source.

As with simple carbohydrates, over time, the accumulation of acidic ketones causes you to lose minerals vital to normal health functions like fluid balance, nerve transmission and muscle contraction.

Proteins

Proteins are necessary for the growth and repair of the body and can also be used for energy. Proteins are large molecules made up of smaller units called amino acids. There are 20 amino acids commonly found in plant and animal proteins and there are therefore numerous combinations. Amino acids are often divided into two categories essential or non-essential. When amino acids are linked together they are known as peptides. Longer chains are polypeptides.

Good sources of protein include meat, cheese, fish and dairy products such as milk and eggs. For vegans and vegetarians, peas, beans, lentils, mushrooms, nuts and pulses are good sources.

Insufficient protein in the diet results in the body breaking down its own protein, mainly in the muscle tissue. Muscle wasting occurs leading to serious long-term problems. In extreme cases, often found in areas experiencing famine, *Marasmus* or *Kwashiorkor* occur. These conditions are extremely serious and are often seen in babies who are not getting sufficient nutrients from their mother's breast milk.

Fats and oils

Fats and oils have the same chemical structure but the main difference is that fats are solid at room temperature and oils are liquid. The main functions of fats are as a source of energy, to protect vital organs, to provide insulation, to preserve body heat, as a source of fat-soluble vitamins (A, D, E, K) and to add texture and flavour in food.

Fats are made up of carbon, oxygen and hydrogen. The difference between these and carbohydrates is that fats contain less oxygen. Fats are a mixture of triglycerides. These are a combination of three fatty acids and a unit of glycerol. Saturated fatty acids have atoms with single bonds joined together:

- Unsaturated fats have double bonds:

- Unsaturated fatty acids come in two shapes. They may be 'cis' or 'trans' fatty acids depending on how the atoms are arranged. 'Cis' fats are considered better for health and can be found in unmodified dietary sources such as olive oil.

Sources are:

- Saturated fats – cream, full fat cheese, lard, butter, animal fats, pastry.

- Unsaturated fats – soya, corn oil, fish, olive oils.

Deficiency can lead to reduced amounts of energy and can also lead to fat-soluble vitamin deficiencies.

Essential micro-nutrients

Fat-soluble vitamins

Vitamin A (retinol)

Essential for vision in dim light. It helps with the maintenance of healthy skin and keeps mucous membranes (such as eyes and throat) free from infection, supple and smooth. It also assists in the growth of bones and teeth and helps the body fight infection.

Good sources of vitamin A are animal foods, milk, cheese, eggs, oily fish, fruit and vegetables. In animal products it is known as retinols and plant carotenes (which the body converts to retinol).

A prolonged lack of vitamin A can lead to night blindness. Too much vitamin A can lead to a toxic effect as the liver cannot process it. There is also a link between too much vitamin A and birth defects. As a consequence pregnant women are advised not to take nutritional substances which contain vitamin A.

Vitamin D (cholecalciferol)

Required for bones and teeth - these contain large amount of calcium and phosphorus. Vitamin D helps the absorption of calcium

It is found in fish liver oils, oily fish, eggs and dairy produce and is added to margarine by law. Vitamin D is also found in the UV rays in sunlight. It is then stored in the liver and can be used as required.

People are unlikely to be deficient in vitamin D unless they have limited exposure to the sun. Lack of vitamin D can cause weak bones and teeth, Bones may then bend which can cause rickets in children or osteomalacia in adults. Too much can lead to deposits of calcium in the joints which can damage organs.

Vitamin E (tocopherol)

Major role as an antioxidant. Stored in the body to protect body cells from free radicals (unstable compounds that damage healthy body cells). It also maintains a healthy reproductive system, nerve and muscles

Good sources of vitamin E can be found in vegetable oils, nuts and egg yolk.

As vitamin E is absorbed in the small intestine with dietary fats, anyone who suffers with poor absorption from genetic or intestinal problems may have poor transmission of nerve impulses, muscle weakness and degeneration of the retina that can cause blindness.

Vitamin K

Vitamin K is essential for the blood clotting process.

Widespread in many foods including leafy vegetables such as spinach and cauliflower. It can be produced in the body by bacteria. Babies tend to be given an injection of vitamin K at birth.

Vitamin K deficiencies would be present in a new born if the body does not produce its own natural supplies. This would cause internal bleeding, a condition called Vitamin K deficiency bleeding.

Water-soluble vitamins

Vitamin B_1 (thiamine)

Vitamin B_1 helps release energy from carbohydrates.

Vitamin B_1 can be found in milk, eggs, vegetables and fruit.

A deficiency of vitamin B_1 is a condition called Beri-Beri which includes neurological symptoms, pain and fatigue.

Vitamin B_2 (riboflavin)

Vitamin B_2 helps utilise energy from foods

Vitamin B_2 can be found in milk and milk products.

A lack of vitamin B_2 causes a dry mouth, cracked and ulcerated lips and tongue.

Vitamin B_3 (niacin)

Vitamin B_3 helps utilise food energy.

Vitamin B_3 can be found in cheese, meat (especially chicken).

A deficiency in vitamin B_3 may cause *Pellagra* (the 4Ds – diarrhoea, dermatitis, dementia and death).

Vitamin B_6 (pyridoxine)

Vitamin B_6 is required for the metabolism of amino acids and helps form haemoglobin.

Sources of vitamin B_6 can be found in meat, fish and eggs.

A vitamin B_6 deficiency will lead to anaemia, dermatitis, neuromuscular issues.

Vitamin B_{12} (cyanocobalamin)

Needed by cells that divide rapidly. One example is bone marrow which helps make red blood cells.

It is found in meat (especially liver), milk, eggs, cheese. Does not occur in vegetables.

A vitamin B_{12} deficiency will lead to nerve problems and anaemia.

Vitamin B_9 – folate (folic acid)

Helps vitamin B_{12} produce rapidly dividing cells.

Vitamin B_9 can be found in green vegetables, yeast extract, brown rice, some cereals.

Because folate is crucial in cell division particularly in bone marrow which produces red blood cells a deficiency can cause, megaloblastic anaemia – common in pregnancy.

Vitamin C (ascorbic acid)

Vitamin C aids the absorption of iron and helps build bones and teeth. It helps absorption of vitamin E as an antioxidant and is necessary to build and maintain skin and the digestive system. Vitamin C can help fight infection by protecting immune systems.

Found in fresh fruit, especially citrus fruit, as well as vegetables, fruit juices.

Vitamin C deficiency can include dry and splitting hair; gingivitis (inflammation of the gums) and bleeding gums; rough, dry, scaly skin; decreased wound-healing rate, easy bruising; nosebleeds; and susceptibility to infection. A severe form of vitamin C deficiency is scurvy.

Minerals

Calcium

Calcium has a number of important functions. It helps build strong bones and teeth, it regulates muscle contraction, including the heartbeat and it ensures that blood clots normally.

Good sources of the mineral calcium include milk, cheese and other dairy foods, along with green leafy vegetables.

Too little calcium can cause *rickets* or *osteoporosis*; too much can lead to stomach pain and diarrhoea, or can lead to calcium deposits forming.

Iron

Iron is needed to form haemoglobin which is used to transport oxygen in the blood to all parts of the body. Vitamin C can help the absorption of iron. Pregnant women may need more iron due to the baby's needs and menstruating women may need more iron due to the loss of blood.

Iron is found in foods like liver and other red meat, breakfast cereals, bread and dark green vegetables such as spinach and watercress.

A lack of iron may lead to anaemia. Iron is used to produce red blood cells, which help store and carry oxygen in the blood. If you have fewer red blood cells than is normal, your organs and tissues will not get as much oxygen as they usually would.

Sodium

Sodium is essential to maintain a fluid balance in the body and to help muscle and nerve function.

It is a major part of table salt (sodium chloride).

Found in many processed foods, meat products, pickles, canned foods, cheese and salt added to foods. Too little salt can cause muscle cramps, but too much is a concern as it can lead to high blood pressure and strokes.

Water

Water is important to the body and the body's functions. It makes up the body's fluids, helps the bodily processes which need water, regulates body temperature and helps excretion. Water needs replacing every day and the amount you need depends on activities undertaken – you will need more water if you do more exercise.

Water is readily available as tap water, bottled water, in fruit and vegetables, and the main component of foods such as soups and jellies.

A lack of water can cause tiredness, irritability, reduced concentration, dry skin. Not taking in enough water is linked to urinary tract infections and irritable bowel syndrome.

Fibre

Fibre is made up of a number of complex carbohydrates. There are two types of fibre, soluble and insoluble. There are no calories, vitamins or minerals in fibre and it is not digested when we eat it. When fibre passes through the bowel it absorbs a lot of water and increases the bulk of the waste matter. It also protects against bowel disease such as bowel cancer.

Fibre is only found in the cell walls of plants and is necessary for healthy bowel movements and prevents constipation.

Activity A P2   A B D1

Your manager in the health clinic was very pleased with your annotated posters and would like you to continue the theme of nutrition and produce some bespoke information sheets for the following population groups.

- School children
- Older people
- Pregnant women.

Include the following details:

1 An explanation of the sources of essential nutrients and their functions in the body.
2 Assess the impact of having a deficiency of those nutrients in their diet.
3 Appropriate menu suggestions in order to meet the needs of that diet.

Evaluate the role of nutritional health in maintaining the health and well-being of the selected individuals, and the impact of influencing factors.

Check your understanding

1 How can you use the Eatwell Guide?
2 What does BMI stand for?
3 What is a macro-nutrient? Give an example.
4 What is a micro-nutrient? Give an example.
5 How would a vegan source their protein intake?
6 What deficiency occurs from long-term lack of Vitamin C?

B Examine factors affecting dietary intake and nutritional health B P3   B P4   B M2   A B D1

Dietary needs of individuals

Dietary needs of different service user groups include:

- New-born infants rely on milk for their nutritional needs. Human breast milk contains all the nutrients necessary for an infant and it

Breastfeeding mothers

Women who are breastfeeding require adequate amounts of food containing energy, protein, vitamins and minerals due to the extra demands of the baby. Women should also ensure they drink plenty of fluids and avoid foods and alcohol which may be passed through into the breast milk and so affect the new born infant.

Factors affecting nutritional health

Eating habits, including meal patterns, snacking, personal preference and vegetarian diets

People tend to eat the foods they like and this has implications for their health. For example, if people eat a lot of fatty foods, they are putting themselves at risk of cardiovascular disease. People also tend to follow a specific pattern of eating – this may be cereal for breakfast or a sandwich for lunch. These patterns may vary according to cultures. Finally, the availability of food has a big impact on dietary influences. If food is not available then people cannot buy it. Time is often cited as a factor in the purchase of convenience foods, such as people saying 'I just never have time to cook.' In more rural areas, the distance to larger supermarkets can affect the availability of foods.

Lifestyle

The lifestyle people lead can impact on their health. A person with a very busy occupation may find it easier to buy 'ready meals' rather than cooking every day. People in jobs requiring more activity or those who do a lot of exercise require more energy-dense foods, because they use up more energy. Social eating and peer pressure can also influence the food we eat.

Other values may impact upon the food people eat. For example, some people may choose to buy free-range eggs, or dolphin friendly tuna. Others may choose not to eat any meat and fish (vegetarian) or not to eat any animal products at all (vegan). The way, in which we are socialised, our culture, families and communities, has an impact upon the food we eat and the way in which we eat it. Some families place an importance on sitting down and having a meal together, whereas others may not.

Socioeconomic

Economic factors can affect food production. These include the way food is processed and sold and what is available within local outlets. The cost of food has a significant impact upon purchasing and availability. Also economy impacts on physical access to shopping areas and ability to be able to store food at home for example in freezers, so access to 'buy one, get one free' offers may not be useful.

Cultural

People's beliefs can have an impact on the food that they eat. Jewish people, for example, do not eat shellfish, pork, rabbit or derivatives of these animals and meat and dairy products are not eaten in the same meal.

Activity B P3

Explain the overall health, socio-economic and cultural factors that can influence the nutritional health of the selected individuals.

Education

Health education plays a major role in our dietary habits. We can be persuaded to eat particular brands of foods because of the media and we can also be advised to use or avoid certain foods by education through the media.

Education and nutritional knowledge also play a big part in the choices we make about our food. People who are aware of healthy eating tend to choose healthier foods. This awareness may come from public health campaigns such as the five a day campaigns, through education at school, package labelling or from health professionals.

Think about it

What adverts can you think of that have made you aware of the benefits or drawbacks of a certain food or drink type?

Public health

Public Health England have produced a set of documents which contain guidelines for healthy eating with various settings and groups of people. – see relevant legislation section also in Unit 2.

www.gov.uk/government/publications/healthier-and-more-sustainable-catering-a-toolkit-for-serving-food-to-adults

Food hygiene

Food hygiene is the action taken to ensure food is handled, stored and cooked in a way and under such conditions that as far as possible food contamination is prevented. Everyday people get ill from the food they eat. Bacteria, viruses and parasites found in food can cause food poisoning. Food poisoning can lead to gastroenteritis and dehydration, or potentially even more serious health problems such as blood poisoning (septicaemia) and kidney failure. Food poisoning can be serious in babies, children, older people and pregnant women because these people have a weaker immune system.

Marketing

Information such as television adverts, magazine articles, leaflets, posters and soap opera stories on television, published research articles and news events all have an influence on our food choices, although we sometimes don't realise it. Because many news items are written to draw attention or shock us they become the ones we remember, these may not be the items or opinions which have been researched by experts and based on scientific opinions. They may become newsworthy because they highlight a differing of opinions so experts are seen to contradict each other. Many people regrettably may see this as a reason not to follow sound dietary advice.

Labelling

By law all foods, other than loose foods, should be labelled and show their nutritional content so the consumer can compare products. The recent *traffic light system* has been employed by some manufacturers and supermarkets to assist the consumer with healthy choices. Look at the link below to see the legislation behind food labelling and then search for some recent news articles around this topic.

www.bupa.co.uk/health-information/Directory/F/food-labelling

Health professionals

Most members of the public will ask dietary advice from members of the primary health care team and it is now a recognised part of many health professionals' training that the study of health and nutrition should be included in the curriculum.

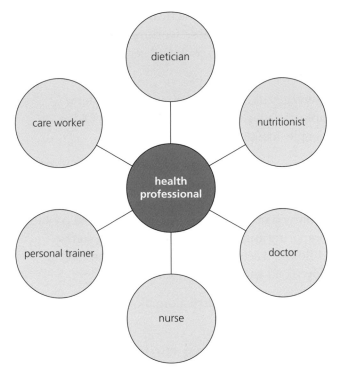

Figure 19.8 Health professionals

Activity

Choose one of the following health professionals: dieticians, public health nutritionists, doctors, nurses, carers, sports nutritionists, health and fitness instructors. What role would they have in promoting good nutritional health?

Relevant legislation

Legislation is set out to cater for and protect vulnerable service users who may be unable to cater adequately for themselves to their age, ability or knowledge of health eating.

Public Health England has prepared various guidelines to enable organisations to meet specific standards. One example is 'Healthier and More Sustainable Catering: A toolkit for serving food to older people in residential care'

This also meets the requirements of the Care Quality Commission (CQC). The toolkit aims to improve the health and well-being of the nation and reduce health inequalities. It contains nutritional guidelines, sample menus, information on food hygiene and cultural/religious and specific needs.

This toolkit contains practical information and useful tips to help those working within residential care settings to buy, cook and serve healthier, more sustainable food.

www.gov.uk/government/uploads/system/ uploads/attachment_data/file/347890/Older_ people_toolkit.pdf

Children's Food Trust is a recognised charity which has produced guidelines for all childcare settings to give advice about getting young children to eat a healthy diet. It provides information about cooking, preparing and serving healthy food to young children. It sets out sample menus, materials to download and practical tools.

www.childrensfoodtrust.org.uk/childrens-food-trust/early-years/

Factors affecting dietary intake

Specific conditions, including diabetes mellitus and coronary heart disease can affect dietary intake.

(See Unit 3 for more on these conditions.)

Irritable bowel syndrome (IBS)

IBS affects a large number of the population and more commonly young adults and his twice as common in women.

IBS is a functional disorder of the bowel so no abnormality is seen in the structure of the bowel, so diagnosis may be quite difficult.

Service users with IBS may suffer abdominal pain, which is spasmodic, wind, bloating, swelling, and a changing stool pattern.

Various research studies showed that a high-fibre diet can, in some cases, make IBS worse, others have come to the opposite conclusion. So, the role of fibre can be confusing! The following link highlights general dietary guidelines: www.patient.co.uk/health/Irritable-Bowel-Syndrome.htm

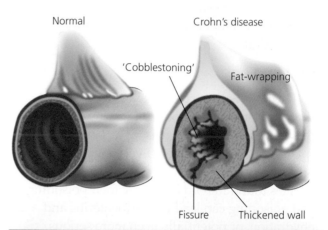

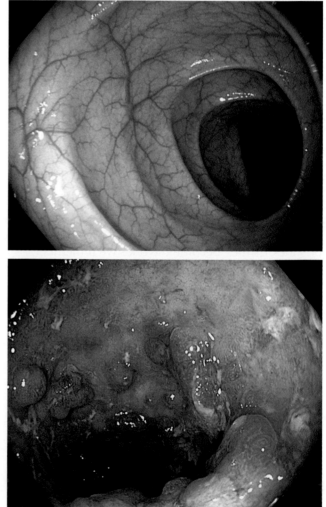

Figure 19.9 Comparison of a healthy colon with that of a patient who has Crohn's disease

Crohn's disease

Crohn's disease causes inflammation in the small intestine, as a result nutrients from food are not absorbed effectively via the villi into the bloodstream, if not corrected the service user will lose weight, become fatigued and may have anaemia. The condition will alter the normal functioning and structure of the small bowel and faeces may contain blood, mucus and undigested food.

Food allergies and intolerances, including coeliac disease and lactose intolerance

Some people are 'intolerant' of certain foods. This may be due to a variety of reasons but not normally an immune reaction. An example is someone who is *lactose intolerant*. Strictly speaking, lactose intolerance is the inability to absorb lactose – the predominant sugar in milk – into the digestive system. If lactose is not absorbed properly, it ferments and this results in abdominal pain, a bloated stomach and diarrhoea. It is treated by avoiding foods with lactose in them, although it is still important to eat products containing calcium in order to avoid a calcium deficiency.

Coeliac disease is discussed in Unit 3, Anatomy and Physiology.

Loss of ability to feed independently, including paralysis and stroke

If service users are unable to feed independently because of a stroke which can cause paralysis or difficulty swallowing, they may have to have supervision with meals or meals which are easy to swallow or it may be necessary to give parenteral feeding.

' "Parenteral feeding" describes the intravenous administration of nutrients. This may be supplemental to oral or tube feeding or it may provide the only source of nutrition as total parenteral nutrition (TPN).'

Source: www.patient.co.uk/doctor/Parenteral-Feeding. html

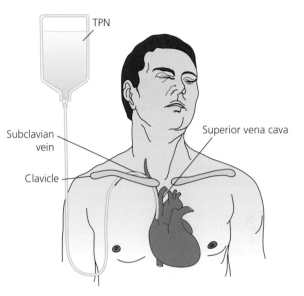

Figure 19.10 Total parenteral nutrition

http://img.tfd.com/MosbyMD/thumb/total_parenteral_nu.jpg

This process is illustrated in Figure 19.10. Other methods of feeding those who cannot feed themselves include:

- Nasogastric tubes (NGT) – see Figure 19.10
- Percutaneous tubes
- Endoscopic gastrostomy (PEG) tubes
- Intravenous infusion (IV)
- Thickened fluids.

Think about it

Think about the long-term effects of excessive amounts of salt and convenience foods for Ronnie – how may Adam be affected from excessive amounts of sugars – consider how Salem will manage his busy lifestyle through his fasting period.

Check your understanding

What main food group could cause tooth decay?

1 Name three foods that should be avoided in pregnancy.
2 Explain what the suggested guidelines for alcohol unit intake are for adults.
3 Explain the difference between diabetes Type 1 and Type 2.

Activity B P3 B P4 B M2

Consider the following case studies.

Case scenario 1

Ronnie is a 78-year-old widower and has just returned home after recovering from a stroke which has left him with a weakness down the right side of his body and difficulty swallowing. He lives alone in a bungalow which is close to local amenities and some close relatives. He prefers eating small meals as his appetite is not what it used to be. He is unsure about food preparation and storage of his food so tends to opt for convenience foods.

Case scenario 2

Adam is 18 years old and is just about to start university life, living away from home for the first time. He has been diabetic (type 1) since the age of 10. He is studying a sport science degree and has secured a part-time job in a local gym. Adam is very partial to the menu from his local take away pizza outlet and diet drinks. He has never budgeted before but is also looking forward to experimenting with new cooking techniques with his friends. He has some awareness of healthy eating and also understands his student loan needs to be used sensibly.

Case scenario 3

Salem is 46 years old and runs his own business. He has an extremely active and busy lifestyle where his meal times can occasionally be very erratic as he travels around the country to attend meetings. He is a Muslim and follows religious festivals and a strict Muslim diet. He lives alone but has very close family members nearby.

Using these three case studies

1 Explain the health, socio-economic and cultural factors which may affect each diet.
2 Choose **two** and compare the diets of both individuals according to their specific requirements.
3 Still with the two individuals in mind assess how their nutritional health can be affected by their dietary habits.

C Plan nutrition to improve individuals' nutritional health

C P5 **C P6** **C M3** **C M4** **C D2** **C D3**

Assessment of nutrient intake

How to record food intake, including meals, snacks, drinks and portion sizes

A record of food intake is necessary to examine the diet of an individual. To analyse this successfully it is essential to gather as much information as possible. This should include types of food eaten, including brands if possible. This is because different brands may contain different nutrients. Cooking methods should also be included - fried chicken for example is much higher in fat than grilled skinless chicken. Portion sizes should be included; you can show the individual a typical portion size and ask them to assess theirs in relation to the example. The individual should also record all drinks they consume, as well as all snacks, all confectionary, and any supplements they may take. How this information is recorded can be tailored to meet the needs of the individual but you could use a table similar to the one below.

- Maintaining nutritional needs, including nutritional assessment score, fluid balance and food charts.

- Sources of nutritional information, including food analysis tables (database or printed), charts relating to portion sizes, information on food packaging (especially for processed foods).

- The diet of the individual can then be examined by using food analysis databases or printed tables. Remember that each food can contain different nutrients. The nutrients obtained from the food can then be compared to the dietary reference values (see earlier in this unit).

Quantitative analysis

This includes energy, protein, fat, iron, vitamin C, fibre intakes.

Each of the foods can then be analysed for their nutritional content, to work out its energy, protein, fat, iron, vitamin C, fibre and the proportion of energy from fat.

Day	Food and drink consumed (Identify food preparation type)	Mark the nutritional groups included in this meal		Activity/inactivity
Breakfast		✔ Carbohydrate ✔ Protein ✔ Fat ✔ Water ✔ Fibre ✔ Calcium	✔ Vitamin A ✔ Vitamin B ✔ Vitamin C ✔ Vitamin D ✔ Iron	
Lunch		✔ Carbohydrate ✔ Protein ✔ Fat ✔ Water ✔ Fibre ✔ Calcium	✔ Vitamin A ✔ Vitamin B ✔ Vitamin C ✔ Vitamin D ✔ Iron	

Day	Food and drink consumed (Identify food preparation type)	Mark the nutritional groups included in this meal		Activity/inactivity
Dinner		✔ Carbohydrate ✔ Protein ✔ Fat ✔ Water ✔ Fibre ✔ Calcium	✔ Vitamin A ✔ Vitamin B ✔ Vitamin C ✔ Vitamin D ✔ Iron	
Snacks		✔ Carbohydrate ✔ Protein ✔ Fat ✔ Water ✔ Fibre ✔ Calcium	✔ Vitamin A ✔ Vitamin B ✔ Vitamin C ✔ Vitamin D ✔ Iron	
Please comment in the box below about RNIs, food groups, 5-a-day and amount of activity taken. This should highlight areas for change.				
Findings from today's food diary:				

Table 19.4 Template for a record of food intake

Example: Weetabix per 100g contains

- Energy 354 kcal/1482kj
- Protein 10.7g
- Fat 2g (20 per cent saturated fat)
- Fibre 8.5g
- Iron 6.0mg
- Vitamin C 0mg

An average serving is 40g, therefore two Weetabix contain the following: energy 141.6 kcal, protein 4.28 kcal, fat 0.8g, fibre 3.4g, iron 2.4mg, vitamin C 0. These can then be compared with the recommended nutritional requirements. A 17-year-old man, for example, needs 11.2mg of iron. Two Weetabix provide 21 per cent of this.

Think about it

Write down the foods you had yesterday and analyse their content using a database or tables. What proportions of nutrients are you getting from your food?

Assessment of analysis, including comparison with recommended intakes (Reference Nutrient Intake or RNI) and general health targets.

This information is discussed earlier in the unit.

Activity C P5 C P6

Using the nutritional analysis charts shown earlier in the unit, collect a three day analysis of two individuals with differing dietary needs.

These individuals can be from the case studies earlier, from your placement or family member.

Please ensure confidentiality and make sure you ask permission if required and do not include personal details.

Produce clear plans to improve the nutritional health of two individuals with different dietary needs.

Explain how the recommendations will improve the nutritional health of the selected individuals.

Nutritional health improvement plan

Good nutrition is essential for health and well-being. A balanced diet consists of a range of nutrients which have different functions within the body. Too few nutrients can lead to deficiencies and too many can also have adverse effects. There are many social, cultural and economic factors which can impact on the food that we eat. In-depth nutritional analysis can be carried out on diets, after which recommendations for improvements can be made, taking into account factors such as an individual's lifestyle choices.

Recommendations for meals, snacks, drinks, portion size, cooking methods

A dietary plan for an individual should take into account the nutritional needs and the amount needed to fuel the body for energy needs. Look back at the start of the unit and consider the life stage of the individual and relate this information to your plan – for example portion sizes and frequency will differ in an infant than in an adult's diet, look at the Eatwell Guide for information about proportion of food groups. Other things to consider are cooking methods, these may require a change for example a meal can be reduced in saturated fats dramatically purely by changing from frying to grilling, so improving someone's diet does not always mean changing the foods they eat.

Recommendations for activity level, daily exercise and energy expenditure

Each individual's lifestyle choices should be taken into account, for example their activity levels, how much they sleep, walk and exercise. Energy requirements are based on the amount that is needed to keep the body going (this is known as the *basal metabolic rate*) and extra energy needed for any physical activity. Depending on the level of activity and the time spent doing it, different amounts of energy are required. Resting, for example, exerts 60–80 kcals per hour while jogging can exert 360 kcal an hour. So if you spend 30 minutes jogging you will need an extra 80 kcal.

Recommendations relating to lifestyle and personal food preferences

You are unlikely to persuade someone to eat something they do not like! So be realistic in your changes and suggestions, you may suggest trying a food for the first time and depending on your individual you can include or eliminate it then from the diet. Choices are also an important part of the plan, if it is going to be realistic: we do not eat the same things each day, so choice allows leeway and so the individual is more likely to stick to the plan. For example, a choice of cereals or toast in the morning will feel better than being prescriptive in only making one suggestion. Economic circumstances – how much money an individual can afford to spend will also need to be taken into account. Social and cultural factors – such as family meal times, religious beliefs, how much time someone has to prepare meals – are also considerations.

Figure 19.11 The amount of exercise people take has an impact on their recommended daily intake of calories. A brisk 40-minute walk burns up between 150 and 220 calories.

How the plan will be monitored

Once you have recorded your two individuals' intake over a controlled period of time (a three-day analysis will give a satisfactory view), consider the above points when formulating a nutritional health plan for them. Include both diet and health needs for a period of **1 month**.

Firstly identify areas for change. This is a starting point, and you may also want to include a starting measurement, for example a BMI if appropriate.

It is important to incorporate all the changes in your plan but with a gentle start. Drastic changes in the first week may not be realistic and so the individual is less likely to adhere to the plan, achieving nothing.

To ensure your plan meets all the desired changes by week 4, put a note in about this in week 1 saying you are working towards this. For example, if one of your individuals needs to increase fluids in their diet, ensure they reach 2 litres a day (adults) by week 4 and in week 1 ensure a definite increase in their fluid intake is suggested.

The design of your plans are your choice, but to ensure they can be monitored and measured remember the acronym SMART:

1 Be **specific**; ensure the individual is aware of the changes you wish to put in place, a discussion and list will help here and will form a starting point for the plan.

2 Ensure it can be **measured**; in the plan include language like – by the end of week 1…, BMI at the start of the process is. By the end of the process we hope it to be …

3 Make it **achievable**; if the plan is too idealistic the individual may make no attempt to change for example going from no exercise to daily visits to the gym could be off putting and unreasonable.

4 Be **realistic**; have you chosen foods that are available, foods that are liked, foods that are affordable.

5 Consider **times**; have you considered working patterns, leisure patterns and if the individual needs to stick to any religious fasting periods or cultural meal times.

Activity

Using the information you have collected prepare plans which will improve the health of your chosen individuals.

Introduce the individual highlighting their individual needs and any influencing factors which are important, for example medical conditions, religious or cultural requirements.

List the findings you intend on improving, then formulate plans to achieve this. This could be separate plans on a weekly basis, showing subtle changes, or one large plan highlighting changes within it.

However you choose to present your plans and report you need to clearly show these points.

- What changes you are addressing.
- The reasons for those changes.
- How these changes will benefit the individual – so tailoring the plans to meet the individual needs
- The importance of those changes, so including long-term health conditions which may be avoided.

Ensure all dietary needs and influencing factors are accounted for.

Distinction Activity C D2 C D3

Remind yourself of the command words 'justify' and 'evaluate'.

Justify the recommendations in the plans in relation to the needs and situations of the selected individuals.

Evaluate the importance of planning nutritional health for selected individuals to ensure their dietary needs are met, and that influencing factors are take into account.

Check your understanding

1 Why is fibre important in the diet?

2 Suggest some cooking methods to change to a healthier diet?

3 How could you suggest a child increases their intake of Vitamin D?

4 Why is it important for a teenage girl to include iron in her diet?

5 What long-term conditions could be avoided if refined sugars are avoided in the diet of a child?

6 What does S.M.A.R.T stand for?

Further reading

Intermediate Nutrition and Health: An Introduction to the Subject of Food, Nutrition and Health, Highfield.co.uk Ltd; 3rd Revised edition (2008)

Essentials of Human Nutrition, Mann, J. and Stewart Truswell (Contributor) Oxford University Press, USA; 4th edition (2012)

Dietary Reference Values of Food Energy and Nutrients for the United Kingdom: Report of the Panel on Dietary Reference Values of the Committee on ... (Reports of Health and Social Subjects) – 9 Jul 1991

Carbs & Cals: Count your Carbs & Calories with over 1,700 Food & Drink Photos! (2013) by Chris Cheyette, Yello Balolia

Fox and Cameron's Food Science, Nutrition & Health, 7th Edition (Hodder Arnold), 2006 by Michael EJ Lean

McCance and Widdowson's The Composition of Foods: Seventh Summary Edition (2014)

Useful websites

The Eatwell Guide: www.food.gov.uk/northern-ireland/nutritionni/eatwell-guide

Children's Food Trust: www.childrensfoodtrust.org.uk/childrens-food-trust/early-years/

Food Standards Agency: www.food.gov.uk

RCPCH growth charts: www.rcpch.ac.uk/Research/UK-WHO-Growth-Charts

NHS: www.nhs.uk/Conditions/Pages/hub.aspx

Patient (medical information and support): http://patient.info/

Public Health England: www.phe.gov.uk

British Nutrition Foundation: www.nutrition.org.uk

Food and Drink Federation: www.fdf.org.uk

Healthier and more sustainable catering toolkit: www.gov.uk/government/publications/healthier-and-more-sustainable-catering-a-toolkit-for-serving-food-to-adults

20 Understanding mental well-being

About this unit

Mental well-being affects us all. If a person lacks mental well-being, no matter how physically healthy they are, they will not be able to make the most of their abilities. According to the UK Faculty of Public Health, the costs of mental health problems in England, including costs for health and social care, loss of output and human cost, were £105 billion in 2009–10. According to the Nuffield Trust, the largest single category of NHS expenditure is mental health, which includes patients with dementia. The personal cost to individuals in terms of quality of life, and the cost to society, make this an important topic. In this unit you will learn about different views of mental well-being and mental health and the factors affecting them. You will learn about mental ill-health classifications, their strengths and limitations and the impact of mental ill-health on individuals and their relationships. In the final section, we look at ways of promoting mental health through legislation, policies, codes of practice, and through assessment and treatment.

Learning aims

The aims of this unit are to:

A Understand different views on the nature of mental well-being and mental health.

B Examine how the main forms of mental ill-health are classified.

C Examine the impact of mental ill-health on individuals and others in their social networks.

D Examine strategies which promote mental well-being and mental health.

How will I be assessed?

For learning aims A and B, it is recommended by the awarding body that learners write a report, using a case study, on the nature of mental health and well-being and the role of current classification systems in improving the diagnosis of two selected mental ill-health conditions and their symptoms.

For learning aims C and D, it is recommended by the awarding body that learners write a report on the importance of promoting, protecting and restoring the mental well-being and mental health of a selected individual diagnosed with a mental ill-health condition.

How will I be graded?

Pass	Merit	Distinction
Learning aim A: Understand different views on the nature of mental well-being and mental health.		A B D1 Evaluate the nature of mental health and well-being and the role of current classification systems in improving the diagnosis of selected mental ill-health conditions and their symptoms.
A P1 Explain factors which influence mental well-being and mental health.	A M1 Analyse factors which influence mental well-being and mental health with reference to a view on the nature of mental well-being and mental health.	
Learning aim B: Examine how the main forms of mental ill-health are classified.		
B P2 Explain the impact of current classification systems on the diagnosis of mental ill-health conditions.	B M2 Analyse the contribution of current classification systems in the diagnosis of selected mental ill-health conditions and their symptoms.	
B P3 Discuss the strengths and limitations of current classification systems in recognising selected mental ill-health conditions and their symptoms.		

How will I be graded?

Pass	Merit	Distinction
Learning aim C: Examine the impact of mental ill-health on individuals and others in their social networks.		**C D D2** Evaluate the importance of promoting, protecting and restoring the mental well-being and mental health of a selected individual diagnosed with a mental ill-health condition
C P4 Explain the impact of mental ill-health on a selected individual. **C P5** Explain how mental ill-health affects a selected individual's relationships with others.	**C M3** Analyse the impact of mental ill-health on a selected individual's relationships within their social networks with reference to factors that may have caused it.	**D D3** Evaluate how accurate diagnosis of mental ill-health conditions leads to correct treatment.
Learning aim D: Examine strategies which promote mental well-being and mental health.		
D P6 Explain strategies that can be applied to promote the mental well-being and mental health of a selected individual diagnosed with a mental ill-health condition.	**D M4** Justify strategies that can be applied to promote the mental well-being and mental health of a selected individual diagnosed with a mental ill-health condition, making reference to relevant legislation, policies and codes of practice.	

A Understand different views on the nature of mental well-being and mental health **A P1** , **A M1** , **A B D1**

Ways in which mental well-being and mental health are understood

According to the World Health Organisation,

> 'Mental health is defined as a state of well-being in which every individual realises his or her own potential, can cope with the normal stresses of life, can work productively and fruitfully, and is able to make a contribution to her or his community.'

This definition equates mental health with positive mental well-being.

Around 1 in 5 of the world's children and adolescents have mental disorders or problems and suicide is the second leading cause of death in 15 to 29 year olds. Mental disorders and substance abuse are major causes of disability worldwide and increase the risk of developing other health problems. Not surprisingly war and natural disasters increase the numbers with mental illness.

Mental well-being, according to the Faculty of Public Health, includes the capacity to:

- realise our abilities, live a life with purpose and meaning, and make a positive contribution to our communities
- form positive relationships with others, and feel connected and supported
- experience peace of mind, contentment, happiness and joy
- cope with life's ups and downs and be confident and resilient

drowsiness, dizziness, a dry mouth, constipation, nausea, vomiting, blurred vision, low blood pressure, uncontrollable movements, such as tics and tremors, seizures, reduced white blood cells which fight infections. In some cases there may be rigidity, muscle spasms, tremors, and restlessness. Long-term use of antipsychotic medications may cause tardive dyskinesia (TD) which is uncontrollable muscle movements of the mouth.

Mood stabilisers can cause side effects which include: itching, rash, excessive thirst and urination as the body attempts to get rid of the drug, tremor, nausea and vomiting, slurred speech, irregular heartbeat and blackouts, seizures, hallucinations, loss of coordination and generalised swelling.

Anticonvulsants may cause similar side effects and may also damage the liver or pancreas and may cause polycystic ovarian syndrome in females.

Lithium, which is prescribed for bipolar disorder, and Clozapine, taken for schizophrenia may have serious side effects therefore it is important that blood is tested regularly to make sure the dose is at the level which causes least side effects.

Children, older adults and pregnant women must be carefully monitored for side effects. Some drugs have not been tested as safe for children or pregnant women. Older people are more likely to have more medications and these may interact with each other.

The outcomes of psychological treatments

Psychological treatments, or psychotherapies, most commonly available in the NHS include:

- Cognitive-behaviour therapy
- Psychodynamic psychotherapy
- Family therapy
- Group therapy
- Various forms of counselling
- Eclectic and integrative approaches.

These are often referred to as the 'talking therapies' because they use talking and listening as the method of helping people manage their health. These treatments are used for people with emotional difficulties, depression, anxiety disorders, obsessive compulsive disorder, post-traumatic stress disorder, and borderline personality disorder and addiction issues.

Treatments vary in how long they last but the general outcome is to help the individual understand the issues affecting their mental health and help them take control of their own life.

Electroconvulsive therapy

The use of electroconvulsive therapy (ECT) is controversial and is no longer widely used. ECT involves sending an electric current through the brain to cause an epileptic fit. No one knows how it works although research has shown that inducing an epileptic fit seems to improve the recovery from severe depression. According to the Royal College of Psychiatrists, ECT should be considered for the rapid treatment of severe depression that is life-threatening, or when other treatments have failed. It may also help people with Parkinson's disease. It should not be used when other treatments are available.

Counselling

Counselling, or talking therapy, is therapy in its own right. In general counselling involves the counsellor using techniques such as open questioning, reflecting and summarising to help the person express their feelings and thoughts so they can better understand their actions and find more positive ways of dealing with situations. The relationship between client and counsellor is key to the effectiveness of the therapy.

Counselling approaches may be based on the following:

- Psychoanalysis, developed by Sigmund Freud and later developed into other forms of analytic psychotherapy by Adler and Jung.
- Humanistic approach based on personal growth and self-development theories such as those of Maslow, in an approach developed by Carl Rogers.

- Behavioural Therapies used for dealing with specific phobias and anxieties.

Counsellors are trained but come from different backgrounds. Clinical and counselling psychologists may be healthcare professionals who specialise in assessing and treating mental health conditions using evidence-based psychological therapies. Psychiatrists are qualified medical doctors with further training in diagnosing and treating mental health conditions. They may not necessarily be counsellors. Psychotherapists are similar to counsellors, but with more extensive training. Cognitive behavioural psychotherapists may come from a variety of professional backgrounds. They are trained in cognitive behaviour therapy and registered and accredited with the British Association for Behavioural and Cognitive Psychotherapies (BABCP).

(Source: NHS)

Cognitive-behaviour therapy

Cognitive-behaviour therapy is a talking therapy that aims to change the way a person thinks and behaves. It does not remove problems but helps the person deal with them in a more effective way. It deals with current problems and focuses on practical solutions. It is mostly used for anxiety and depression. Here is how it works. Mr A has been made redundant after thirty years in the steel industry. He has applied for several jobs and been told he is too old or not qualified enough. He is depressed, anxious about the future and feels life is not worth living. Cognitively he sees himself as a steelworker and his behaviour is focused on trying to get a job in the industry. After starting CBT he begins to see that he has many talents. He can drive, he has a keen interest in gardening and grows organic vegetables in his large garden. CBT helps him see himself as a driver, a gardener, as well as a husband, father and grandfather. CBT helps him change his behaviour. He volunteers as a driver with a local charity and meets new people. He sees opportunities where previously he saw closed doors and starts selling his home grown organic vegetables through the local greengrocer. He may not make as much money as he previously did but he is happy and fulfilled, enjoying life.

Psychodynamic psychotherapy

Psychodynamic psychotherapy is a talking therapy that differs from most other therapies in aiming for deep seated change in personality and emotional development. (Psycho refers to the mind, and dynamic refers to change). Psychodynamic therapy is based on the idea that early life sets patterns of behaviour especially in how we relate to others. The relationship with the therapist is important. By delving back into these early memories we begin to understand why we behave the way we do in relationships and with support can then change current negative behaviours. NICE recommend psychodynamic therapy as a treatment for depression.

Family therapy

Family therapy is a talking therapy offered to the whole family when there are problems such as child and adolescent behaviour problems, separation or divorce, domestic violence, addiction or mental health conditions or illnesses that impact on family relationships. The aim is to help family members understand each other better and improve family relationships.

Group therapy

Group therapy is a talking therapy where a group of up to 12 people with common problems meet together with a therapist to support each other. Group therapy may be used in conjunction with other treatment, for example, when supporting people with addiction issues or may be used without other treatment, for example, when supporting people with depression. Group therapy is based on the idea that someone who has had the same problems can help others with overcoming the problem.

Various forms of counselling

There are several types of counselling a few of which are described here. Person-centred or client-centred counselling focuses on the individual and has three core conditions which the counsellor brings to the situation; empathy or being able to put oneself in another's place, unconditional positive regard where the person is not judged but accepted for themselves, and congruence or honesty and openness. This establishes trust between client

- acting in a professional capacity for, or in relation to, a person who lacks capacity working

- being paid for acts for or in relation to a person who lacks capacity.

Other relevant legislation

Other relevant legislation is as follows:

- The **Human Rights Act 1998** has been explained in Unit 5 'Meeting individual care and support needs'.

- The **Mental Health Act 2007** revised the 1983 Act, but did not replace it. The 2007 Act brought in more protection for the public and made treatment compulsory under the new compulsory community treatment orders (CTOs). It also brought in a single definition of mental disorder: ' "mental disorder" means any disorder or disability of the mind'. The 2007 Act introduced Independent Mental Health Advocates (IMHAs) who could speak on behalf of those who were too ill to speak for themselves. An approved mental health professional (AMHP) is responsible for organising and co-ordinating assessments under the Mental Health Act and can recommend that you are detained in hospital under the Mental Health Act (sectioned) or that you receive a CTO.

- The **Equality Act 2010** has been explained in Unit 7.

Relevant codes of practice are:

- The Code of Practice for the Mental Health Act (1983), Mental Capacity Act (2005) is described above.

- Codes of Practice for health and social care provide guidance for professionals and organisations are described in Unit 2 'Working in health and social care'.

- The Northern Ireland Social Care Council (NISCC) Codes of Practice for Social Care Workers

- Employers of Social Care Workers echo those published by Skills for Care in England which replaced the codes published by the General Social Care Council for England which in 2012 was incorporated into the Health and Care Professions Council.

Mental health impact of policy and practice

A Kings Fund Briefing paper, 'Mental Health under Pressure', highlights the fact that despite various initiatives mental health services are still under resourced and around 40 per cent of mental health trusts experienced reductions in income in 2013/14 and 2014/15. Attempts have been made to increase provision in the community and in anticipation of this, the numbers of beds for mental health inpatients have been reduced. According to the report:

- There is widespread evidence of poor-quality care. Only 14 per cent of patients say that they received appropriate care in a crisis, and there has been an increase in the number of patients who report a poor experience of community mental health care.

- Bed occupancy in inpatient facilities is frequently well above recommended levels, with community services, in particular crisis resolution and home treatment teams, often unable to provide sufficient levels of support to compensate for reductions in beds. This is having a negative impact on safety and quality of care.

- The lack of available beds is leading to high numbers of out-of-area placements for inpatients. Out-of-area placements are costly, have a detrimental impact on the experience of patients and are associated with an increased risk of suicide.

In practical terms staff shortages in the community and in hospitals and insufficient provision for inpatients, especially age-appropriate provision for young people with mental health issues, mean that people who would benefit from hospital admission are sometimes treated in the community or are shipped out to other parts of the country where there are beds. This means that for someone who is mentally ill, and perhaps frightened, they do not have the support for family and friends nearby.

Legislation has attempted to improve the situation for people with mental ill-health but policies and practice have not supported this. Charities such as Rethink and Mind provide a great deal of support but they rely on donations to keep going and they cannot supply the full services that the NHS should be able to offer.

> **Activity**
>
> Legislation is just one of the strategies that can be applied to promote the mental well-being and mental health of a person diagnosed with a mental ill-health condition. How may legislation promote the mental health and well-being of the person you have previously described? In your answer consider legislation on Equality and Human Rights in addition to the Mental Health Acts of 1983, 2007 and the Mental Capacity Act 2005 with its associated code of practice.

Assessment and treatment

Health and well-being boards that include local representatives, the local authority and clinical commissioning groups (CCGs) agree the joint strategic needs assessment (JSNA) for the area. This determines what services are provided locally.

Assessment of need

A mental health care assessment is carried out by a health professional or team, such as a GP, a Community Mental Health Team, a mental health link worker or a community mental health nurse (CMHN) to find out what support or treatment is appropriate. They decide whether to refer the person to another service or whether help can be given directly, for example, the GP might prescribe medication. The person should be reassessed if their needs change.

Carers are also entitled to an assessment of their needs.

The basic process for the assessment of needs, and the criteria for eligibility under national regulations, are the same for mental health as for physiological disorders. These are described in Unit 14, Physiological disorders and their care, including an explanation of financial assessment (means testing).

Care programme approach (CPA) assessment

If someone has a severe mental health problem or is at risk of self-neglect, suicide, self-harm or harm to others, or if they do not co-operate with their treatment plan, or are vulnerable, are misusing drugs or alcohol or are currently or have recently been detained under the Mental Health Act (sectioned) they may be referred by a community mental health team (CMHT) for a care programme approach (CPA) assessment. Someone who relies on the support of a carer, or is a carer and has multiple services such as housing and employment services may also be referred for a CPA. This will entitle the person to a co-ordinator who should fully assess the person's needs, write a care plan that shows how these will be met and review the plan. Care coordinators can be social workers, community psychiatric nurses (CPN) or occupational therapists.

Mental Health Act assessment

In a crisis situation, where there is a risk of harm, a Mental Health Act assessment may be carried out by two doctors and an approved mental health professional (AMHP). This may result in compulsory detention (sectioning) to protect the person from harm. On discharge after compulsory detention, a person is entitled to an assessment under section 117 of the Mental Health Act.

Care and support planning

The process of care and support planning, and the documentation of the plan, are the same for mental health as for physiological disorders. These are described in Unit 14, Physiological disorders and their care.

Inter-agency working

The Single Assessment Process (SAP) is a person-centred health and social care framework, which aims to avoid duplication of work by different agencies and share information appropriately between them. The process is the same for mental health as for physiological disorders. This is described in Unit 14, Physiological disorders and their care.

The role of professionals in the assessment process

Unit 2 looks at the roles of professionals in the assessment process. Often the GP is the first person to contact but they may also work with an approved mental health professional (AMHP), a Community Mental Health Team, a mental health link worker or a community mental health nurse (CMHN), community psychiatric nurses (CPN) or occupational therapists as explained in the previous section.

Benefits of early intervention

The benefits of early intervention are that a person may be helped before they are so ill that they need to be admitted. Early intervention can mean that a parent may be able to look after their children, or a person can keep their job and they can retain something of their day to day life. Early intervention mean that symptoms are more easily controlled which means recovery can be quicker, benefiting not only the individual but also reducing the demand on services.

Agreed ways of working include knowing when to refer a person on for more specialist services, knowing how to work together for example when a person has complex needs and has a Care Programme Approach. They include knowing when and how to share information appropriately between professionals to work in the best interests of the person.

Person-centred approach

A person-centred approach is the only effective way to provide care for a person with mental health issues. There is no point in giving medication to alleviate depression if the problem still remains because the person will only become depressed when they are off medication. A person-centred approach may require a combination of talking therapies and medication, together with a period in hospital but even then this will not work if they return to a situation where they are abused. A person-centred approach to care that considers all the needs of the person is expensive but is the only effective way to prevent a person relapsing.

Approaches to recovery

Approaches to recovery can only be effective if they include:

- empowerment of individuals, enabling them to take an active part in their assessment and care plan
- advocacy, enabling individuals to use advocacy to have their views heard
- self-management, enabling the individual to be as independent as possible
- recognition of individual rights, avoiding unnecessary deprivation of liberty
- Support for individuals to adopt and maintain mentally healthy lifestyles, by providing community support for those no longer requiring hospital admission.

Previous approaches traditionally focused on treating the mental illness in a medical model approach, and disregarded mental well-being. The Dual Axis model of mental health suggests a holistic person-centred approach to care should consider the individual's well-being as well as their illness.

At an individual level, support may be needed to develop resilience, coping skills, self-esteem, self-management, emotional literacy and parenting skills.

At a community level support may be needed to develop a safe environment, provide social support such as housing, to create opportunities for inclusion and participation, and to gain new skills or improve education so that the person can enter the workforce.

On a societal level, addressing and reducing inequality, prejudice and stigma will help to improve well-being for those with mental illness. Social inclusion, a reduction in poverty and better housing will increase the likelihood of greater well-being and will in turn benefit all of society as people with a greater sense of well-being are better equipped to remain independent and self-managing.

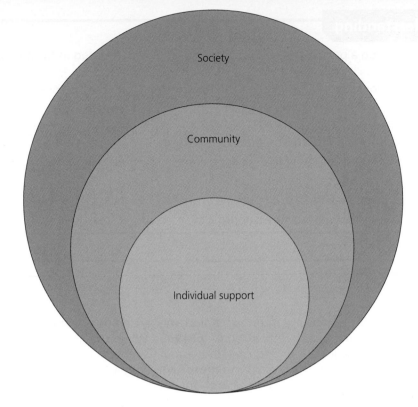

Figure 20.2 Social inclusion, society, inclusion, community

Addressing inequality

Addressing inequality remains one of the biggest challenges in mental health. Inequality of provision, whereby mental health services are underfunded is perhaps the greatest inequality of all, for if people cannot have the treatment they need when they need it, they continue to suffer. According to the Kings Fund report, 'Has the government put mental health on an equal footing with physical health?', published in February 2015, the Health and Social Care Act 2012 laid a legal duty on the NHS to bring 'parity of esteem' between mental and physical health, and the government has pledged to achieve this by 2020. The government launched a new mental health strategy 'No health without mental health' in 2011 and since then has introduced policies such as the Improved Access to Psychological Therapies programme with standard waiting times for this and for early intervention for people experiencing their first bout of psychosis. A further policy, the Crisis Care Concordat, launched in February 2014, created local joint working agreements between the police, social care, mental health and ambulance services. As a result, the number of people with mental health crises detained in police cells has fallen. There is also a national policy to reduce deaths from suicide.

Activity

Give evidence to support the view that relevant legislation, policies and codes of practice promote the mental well-being and mental health of a selected individual diagnosed with a mental ill-health condition. Consider policies such as Improved Access to Psychological Therapies and the Crisis Care Concordat. Base your answer on the person you have studied so far, but remember to maintain confidentiality.

Distinction activity D D3

Evaluate how accurate diagnosis of mental ill-health conditions leads to correct treatment.

Explain your answer using examples to support what you say.

Check your understanding

1 Which Act sets out when a person can be admitted, detained and treated in hospital against their wishes?
2 Which Act says what you can do to plan ahead for a time when you can no longer make decisions for yourself?
3 Which Act introduced Deprivation of Liberty Safeguards (DOLS)?
4 Which Act introduced community treatment orders (CTOs)?
5 Which Act sets out the rights of individuals to be treated fairly and without discrimination?
6 Who may be involved in the assessment process?
7 What types of assessment may be carried out and why?
8 Explain what is meant by a person-centred approach.

Case scenario

Counselling

X has mood swings. When she is high she is restless, full of energy and does not need to sleep. She is an artist and when she is high sometimes paints through the night. When she gets low, she is tired, has no motivation and finds it hard to get out of bed. She does not eat properly, cuts herself off from her friends and family and gets very depressed. She has a part time job teaching art. She lives alone so there is no one to grumble if the place is untidy, and she has gradually isolated herself from her friends so no one comes round to visit. One day things got so bad that she felt life was not worth living. At that point she realised she needed help and made an appointment to see her GP.

Her GP did not have a lot of time but did offer X a choice of treatments – antidepressants or counselling. After the GP explained the risks and benefits of each treatment, X decided to wait and have counselling. She found the counsellor really listened to her and checked back to make sure she had understood what X had said. The counsellor did not judge X or tell her to snap out of it – she just listened and when X was ready to move on helped her explore options.

One of the things the counsellor suggested that helped her regain control was keeping a diary and looking back at the things that gave her a greater sense of well-being. X had always wanted a dog but could not have one when she lived at home with her parents. She got a dog and that helped her get out and meet people. On her regular walks she saw some local volunteers tidying up the local car park and they asked her if she would like to join them every week. After the tidy up they all went for coffee and X found herself getting involved with more local activities. Her sense of well-being improved and although she still had mood swings, they were not as great as before and she could cope with life.

Think about it

Early Intervention in Psychosis (EIP) services are the best way to help young people recover from a first episode of psychosis. They reduce the risk of a young person taking their own life, saving the NHS millions of pounds each year. According to Rethink's report, 'Lost Generation,' early intervention services in England are threatened by funding cuts which could mean many young people with psychosis may not get support.

If you were a government minister where might you get funding from to support this service?

Further reading

Hough M., (2014) *Counselling Skills and Theory 4th Edition*, Hodder Education, London

Rogers C., (2004) *On Becoming a Person*, Constable, London

Sanders P., (2004) *First Steps in Counselling: A Students' Companion for Introductory Courses, 4th Edition,* (Steps in Counselling Series) PCCS Books, Ross on Wye

Useful websites

Promoting Mental Health Improvement, NHS Scotland: www.elearning.healthscotland.com

World Health Organisation's International Statistical Classification of Diseases and Related Health Problems 10th Revision (ICD 10): http://apps.who.int/classifications/icd10

British Association for Counselling and Psychotherapy (BACP) – a professional body and a registered charity that sets standards for therapeutic practice and provides information for therapists, clients of therapy, and the public: www.itsgoodtotalk.org.uk For theoretical approaches, see: www.bacp.co.uk

The British Psychoanalytic Council: www.bpc.org.uk

Concepts of mental and social well-being; The cost of poor mental health: see Faculty of Public Health, www.fph.org.uk

Kirkwood, T., Bond, J., May, C., McKeith, I. and Teh, M. (2008) Foresight Mental Capital and Well-being Project. Mental capital through life: Future challenges. The Government Office for Science, London. Available at: http://webarchive.nationalarchives.gov.uk/20121212135622/http:/www.bis.gov.uk/assets/foresight/docs/mental-capital/mental_capital_through_life.pdf.

Foresight Mental Capital and Well-being Project (2008), Final Project report – Executive summary. The Government Office for Science, London, Mental Capital and Well-being: Making the most of ourselves in the 21st century, Mental capital through life: Future challenges, Improving better access to mental health services by 2020: see www.gov.uk

Mental health under pressure Nov15; Has the government put mental health on an equal footing with physical health? February 2015: see www.kingsfund.org.uk

A charity supporting those with mental health issues: www.mentalhealth.org.uk

Mind, the Mental Health Charity: www.mind.org.uk

Measures of National Well-being – Measuring national well-being, personal well-being in the UK 2014–2015: see www.neighbourhood.statistics.gov.uk and www.ons.gov.uk

Five mental disorders genetic link 02February2013; Conditions: stress, anxiety, depression -talking therapies explained: see www.nhs.uk

The American Psychiatric Association: www.psychiatry.org

The use of ECT: see www.rcpsych.ac.uk

A charity supporting those with mental health issues: www.rethink.org

Murray CJL, Richards MA, Newton JN, *et al*. UK health performance: findings of the Global Burden of Disease Study 2010. The Lancet. Published online March 5 2013: see www.thelancet.com

World Health Organisation definition of mental health: www.who.int/features/factfiles/mental_health/en

Glossary

Anatomy The study of the body's structure and how each part relates to others.

Arteries Usually carry oxygen-rich blood away from the heart (A – Away).

Cancer Cells in the body reproduce in an uncontrolled way, affecting the function of organs and systems; for example, bowel cancer occurs in and affects the bowel; however, cancer cells may then spread throughout the body.

Circulatory system disorders Disorders affecting the circulatory system (the system by which blood is transported around the body), for example leukaemia.

Cytology The study of cells.

Embolism This occurs when a part of the blood clot (thrombosis) breaks off and travels around the body colliding with small vessels, for example in the lungs, causing pain and difficulty in breathing.

Endocrine system disorders Disorders affecting the endocrine system (the glands throughout the body that secrete hormones); for example diabetes.

External respiration Breathing in and breathing out is one respiration.

Genetic disorder A disorder which occurs when mutations are present in the DNA at conception (not always inherited).

Histology The study of tissues.

Inherited disorder A disorder which is passed on from a parent and is present in the genetic makeup.

Jaundice A yellowing of the skin and whites of the eyes caused by a build up of something called bilirubin in the blood, or damage to the liver.

Macro-nutrient These are nutrients required in large quantities, for example, carbohydrates, proteins and fats.

Micro-nutrient These are nutrients required in small amounts, which include vitamins and minerals.

Musculo-skeletal system disorders Disorders affecting the muscles and skeleton, such as osteoporosis.

Nervous system disorders Disorders affecting the nervous system, for example Parkinson's disease.

Peristalis A muscular wave-like movement that moves the food through the digestive system. The gut muscles contract behind the bolus and relax in front of the bolus so that the food can move along the gut.

Physiological disorders Diseases or disorders that affect the normal functioning of body systems and organs.

Physiology The study of how the body works and functions within the organs and alongside other structures.

Puberty The normal stage in adolescence development where secondary sex characteristics occur.

Respiratory system disorders Disorders affecting the respiratory system such as asthma.

Thrombosis A blood clot that disrupts, slows or stops blood flow to major body areas.

Veins Carry de-oxygenated blood back to the heart.

Index